THE OTHER SIDE OF ENGLAND
PART II: NO BREAD, NO WORK, NO HOPE

The Other Side of England

PART II:

NO BREAD, NO WORK, NO HOPE

(Continuing the story of Jem Stebbings)

JOSEPH CANNING

To Carol

By the same author:

Once Upon An Island

Olive's Boys

The Other Side of England: Part I – THE HOMECOMING

Excepting historical characters and historical events, all other
characters and events in this publication are entirely fictitious. Any
resemblance to any person or persons, living or dead, is purely
coincidental.

ISBN: 978-1-4457-3609-9

AUTHOR'S NOTE:

The Other Side of England: PART I

IN PART I, in the aftermath of the Battle of Waterloo, infantryman Jem Stebbings rescues an officer's wife, who has walked from Brussels to search the field of battle for her husband. When later Jem is demobilised, he returns to the small Eastern Counties village of Hamwick Dean, determined to become an independent husbandman on its open-fields and to forget the horrors of war. It is a time of great struggle for all on the land: a massive explosion of the Tambora volcano in the Dutch East Indies has thrown a great cloud of dust into the stratosphere, affecting the whole of Europe: bad summer follows bad summer and harvest after harvest fails. In addition, the controversial Corn Laws of 1815, introduced to protect the British landowners and farmers from Continental competition, have pushed up the price of grain and, consequently, the price of bread. Further, the Speenhamland system of poor relief, whereby the parish makes up the wages of poorly paid agricultural labourers, has led to farmers cutting pay and employing men only when they are needed. Great numbers of the rural poor of England are without work and near to starving, unheeded by an unsympathetic Parliament of landowning gentry.

During this time of great hardship, one of Jem's comrades-in-arms leads a revolt of starving labourers in the nearby market town of Hamwyte and is one of five hanged by the same uncaring authorities. Jem, meanwhile, has married his friend's sister, Mary-Ann, and in time they are blessed with a son, Jed, and a daughter, Thirza. But, as they struggle to farm their land in the village, Jem makes an enemy of the bailiff of the church's Glebe Farm, Joshua Jaikes, who later becomes the new salaried overseer of the poor in the village, responsible for doling out parish relief.

Into the village, too, has come a rich, blustering Yorkshireman named Titus Broake, who takes up residence at Hamwick Hall, the long abandoned manor house of the late squire, and immediately begins buying up land. He then consorts with others to petition Parliament for an Enclosure Bill to end the open-field system of agriculture, so forcing Jem and the other husbandmen off the land they lease and on to parish relief at a time when the relief itself is being cut by those who pay the poor rate.

JOSEPH CANNING

ONE

ON THE LAST DAY of the old year, Jem Stebbings stood in the doorway of his cottage in the small ridge-top village of Hamwick Dean in the northern half of the county, watching the rain teeming down: sometimes it seemed to him as if it had been raining all winter. The December dark had long since closed in and the lane outside was deserted: across the way, though it was still early evening, most of the cottages were already in darkness, as if abandoned: the light of neither oil lamp nor candle showed in their windows, no smoke spiralled up from their chimneys. In those cottages, Jem knew, the families would already have gone to bed in the hope of finding some warmth and comfort huddled under ragged blankets, waiting for the oblivion of sleep to dull their despair.

Behind him, by the light of a flickering dip, his wife, Mary-Ann, was stirring a pottage of chopped turnip, beans and potatoes in a blackened iron-pot set on a small fire, lit a half-hour before for just that purpose. Either side of her, watching their mother, sat two children, ten-year-old Jed and nine-year-old Thirza, huddled on low stools, leaning forward towards the fire's glow, their hands outstretched so as to absorb what they could of its warmth: for, after the cooking was done and the meal eaten, it would be allowed to die out and they, too, would take to their beds.

It would not be much of a supper that evening, but they would eat it without complaint nevertheless, all of it, as they had done for breakfast that morning, the same pottage of turnip, beans and potatoes, and for supper and breakfast the day before and breakfast and supper the day before that, for the past four days, in fact, glad of anything to fill their bellies and assuage the gnawing hunger.

It was three months since Jem and Mary-Ann had sat together in the nave of St. Bartholomew's Church along with the rest of the villagers of Hamwick Dean, listening to the cooper, Elijah Candler, acting as the parish constable, reading out the awards of the three enclosure commissioners as the land of the whole parish had been parcelled and redistributed. On that day, Jem Stebbings, former soldier of the 44th Regiment of Foot, who for four years had marched back and forth across the Iberian Peninsula at the Duke of Wellington's bidding, who had been wounded twice in his service, who had stood with the same Iron Duke at the great battle of Waterloo to defeat the megalomaniac Emperor of the French, Napoleon Bonaparte, and had returned in such hope to his home village to take up a life as an independent husbandman – on that day he had become instead a dispossessed husbandman. The land he had farmed for ten years had been taken from him by enclosure, by the avarice of one man, the new lord of the manor of Hamwick Dean, a Yorkshire incomer by the name of Titus Broake: by the avarice, too, of those who had supported him in his petition to Parliament, three large farmers of the village: Amos Peakman of Goat Lodge Farm, directly to the east of the village, down a lane of the same name: Marcus Howie at Smallponds, situated a mile or so to the southeast of the village: and Joshua Godwin at Milepole Farm, some two miles from the village along the main Maydun-to-Wivencaster coach road.

They and several absentee landowners, amongst them a titled lady, a marchioness, two Members of Parliament, the dean and chapter of an Oxford college and several London gentry, had conspired together to rob the husbandmen and small farmers and other commoners of Hamwick Dean of the inheritance of generations, freedom of the commons and the waste surrounding their villages: the right to graze livestock such as cattle, sheep and horses: the right of pannage, allowing the rooting of pigs: of estovers: the right to take bracken for bedding and fodder and brushwood, furze and gorse for fuel: of turbary, the right to take peat for fuel, too: of piscary, the right to the fish in the streams and ponds: and of soil, the right to take sand, stone and gravel as they required it. Worst of all, they had taken away, too, their right to farm the three great open-fields which lay below the village on the ridge's south-facing slope: by the granting of the petition, the leases on all land in Hamwick Dean had been annulled and the open-fields, the common meadowland and the waste had all been thrown into a general mix, to be parcelled and allotted as the commissioners chose, mostly to landowners far richer than they. In consequence, farms of a hundred and fifty or so acres became farms of several hundred acres and were growing still as those who could afford to pay the price bought up yet more acres, to be fenced and hedged and everafter denied the husbandmen who once had farmed them.

Along with sixty others who had also been husbandmen and small farmers, Jem had lost his independence: from the eight acres, ten roods and eighteen perches which he had farmed before enclosure, albeit glebe land which he had leased from the Church, he had been awarded as compensation for the loss of his common rights a parcel of land no bigger in size than a garden and a small garden at that, five roods and thirty-four perches. In the month following, he had sold all of his small allotment to Marcus Howie at Smallponds because he could not afford to fence or hedge the plot as the commissioners had decreed he must do within six months: then he had driven his five cows to the nearby market town of Hamwyte, walked his horse over to the knackers' yard at the village of Budwick because it was too old to be sold for further work and tossed his plough and his implements into a ditch to rust and to rot. He now was landless, reduced to the status of a serf: from that time on, he would only ever be a day-labourer, paid by the day for his toil, at the beck and call of any master who might wish to employ him.

Fortunately, there was still had a little money in the flour jar from the sale of his small award to Marcus Howie and the sale of his cattle and his horse, but it was dwindling week by week and, as the end of the year approached, they were virtually eking out the pennies and halfpennies. Jem could sense the anxiety in Mary-Ann's eyes every time she went to it: several times, in odd moments, he had caught her staring out of the small window overlooking the lane, her eyes moistening at the corners as the thoughts of what had happened to them overwhelmed her, before she quickly brushed at the tears lest they trickle down her cheeks and give her away.

For his part, with no labour to occupy him and no fields to tend, Jem remained in the cottage for much of the time, idling and brooding upon his misfortune. However, about one thing he was adamant: so long as there was money in the flour jar, he would not seek relief like all the others, as his friends and fellow dispossessed husbandmen, Dick Dollery and Enos Diddams, were doing: he had told Mary-Ann that. The mere thought of having to stand before his enemy, Joshua Jaikes, the overseer of the poor, with his hat in his hand and his head bowed, angered him: it would be a humiliation and Jaikes, he knew, would revel in it. They had clashed too many times in the past: over the land which Jem had acquired and which Jaikes had wanted when first he had set himself up as a husbandman on his return from the wars, over the taking of the host in church one Sunday when Jaikes and he had clashed and the senior churchwarden had been reprimanded by the parson afterwards and, lastly, over Jem's straying cattle when Jaikes had got his cohort, Lemuel Ring, the pinder man, to untie the hurdles in which his cows had been penned overnight and drive them off to the pound as 'found strays.'

No, Jem's pride would not allow him to seek relief so long as there was a single penny in the flour jar. He had seen all the other former husbandmen gathering outside the church door each Friday, whatever the weather, waiting to go into the vestry and to answer the overseer's jibes and questioning before receiving their meagre handout from the poor rate: humiliated, paupers, serfs, joining the line of other unemployed day-labourers of the village.

Of his other friends who had been a part of the same tithing as him and who had been his long-time drinking companions in the bay-windowed parlour of the Wayfarers' – John Romble, the wheelwright, Thomas Judd, now a cordwainer in his own right, William Stubbs, the saddler and harnessmaker, and Nathaniel Newman, the blacksmith – they had managed to struggle on, but their work was greatly reduced. Nathaniel Newman, for instance, found himself with far fewer horses to shoe and far fewer implements to mend or make as a result of so many husbandmen having given up: similarly William Stubbs, Thomas Judd and John Romble no longer had the work they once had. It was the same, too, for the basketmaker William Tulloh, who had laid off his helper, the bricklayer Henry Jacobs, who had laid off his man, the rakemaker, the carpenter and the like.

Enclosure of the three great open-fields of Hamwick Dean twelve years after the fall of Napoleon had ended forever the old village ways: everywhere, there was a deep gloom, made worse by the grimness of the weather. For Jem and the other husbandmen who had farmed their strips on their leased acreages and part acreages, who had grazed their cattle on the commons and staked and penned their sheep and goats on the waste, it had meant the loss of their means of self-sufficiency: through enclosure, they were reduced to a landless poverty which was worse even than that of the peasants of France before their Revolution. The irony was that these were the very men, against whom Jem had fought so long to defeat during his twelve years of soldiering.

Before the French peasants rose up against their own lords and masters, they had existed in an intolerable state of forced labour and abject poverty: a man's whole harvests could be confiscated at the whim of an aristocratic landlord and he and his family left to starve: he could, too, be forced to perform almost any humiliating task demanded of him without redress: the French peasant was, before the Revolution, without exception, the most downtrodden in all of Europe. The revolution had freed them from that subjugation and they now cultivated their own land and lived a life which was as independent as had once been that of the English husbandmen. It was a paradox that the very conquerors of Napoleon and his armies now found themselves more impoverished than those they had defeated, without property, without rights and without power. As well, the safety net of subsistence on which the landless day-labourers, the mere cottagers, the long-time squatters upon the margins of the village, had always relied in lean times – that is, access to the common land and the waste to graze whatever livestock they owned – that was gone and gone forever.

Wearily, Jem closed the door and took his seat at the table as Mary-Ann began spooning out the mash from the iron pot: the fire was already dying.

TWO

FOR MANY, it was a terrible first winter following enclosure: after the endless days of rain during December came several days of hard frosts which extended into the mid-January , to be followed by heavy fall of snow on the night of the fifteenth which lay on the frozen ground for a fortnight. Unhappily, such had been the unfairness of the enclosure awards that some who had not received so much as a single rood or perch in compensation for their lost commonable rights and, therefore, had no land to sell to those who were buying up all that they could, that is, the lord of the manor, Titus Broake, and the three large farmers, Amos Peakman, Marcus Howie or Joshua Godwin – they were thrown into immediate penury and found themselves having to exist for weeks on end on raw onions and little else till the skin on the roofs of their mouths blistered. Yet all around them, stored still in the barns and sheds and mills all over the Hundred, was the harvest of the previous summer, grain, vegetables and fruit, which, despite the violent gales of the August, had been gathered in and now was being shipped daily by barge from the quaysides at Maydun and Wivencaster to the wharves and hards of London or trundled the thirty-eight miles there by carrier for the gratification of the seething, riotous masses and the ungrateful, condescending, overly rich gentry, none of whom gave a care or a thought for the plight of those who had produced it.

Once the snows had gone and the ground had softened, there was some work for the villagers in the early February, fencing the commons, the same commons which for centuries had been the patrimony of the village's poor, but that went solely to the day-labourers who drank in the Carpenters' Arms, the ale house at the lower end of the village's main thoroughfare, The Street, and in that time the landlord, Jack Tickle, did three times the business of Caleb Chapman, the landlord of the Wayfarers' Inn at the top end of The Street. Poor Caleb's place, for so long the preferred hostelry of the indpendent husbandmen, small farmers and tradesmen, as opposed to the landless day-labourers down at the Carpenters' Arms, was empty most evenings and so he brewed less: and the less he brewed the less he sold.

Early in the March, as had been stipulated by the enclosure commissioners, work began on constructing the new route from the Merchant Staplers road across the Reeve's Croft third of the former Third Field and the Partridge lesser fields of Long Field and down between Likely and Milepole woods towards the parish's southern boundary, to join Hall Lane leading to the lord of the manor's enlarged estate. The contractor, who was from Wivencaster, either did not know or did not care about the problems of the village and, when eighty men, youths and boys lined up one morning along The Street for hiring, like a former hiring fair, he simply walked along the line, choosing the thirty youngest and fittest to dig out the new way, while a second team of twenty laid down the sand and gravel: though as there was a surplus of willing labourers, the work was poorly paid at only six shillings a week. Dick Dollery and Enos Diddams were fortunate in that they were amongst the very last half-dozen to be hired to erect the new roadside fences, plant the new quick-growing blackthorn hedgerows and to dig the roadside ditches: and hard labour it was at that, over six days from Monday to Saturday, so that Sundays remained their only day of rest.

Jem stood with them on The Street, but the contractor had noticed his limp and his crooked arm and did not take him up: it was a hard blow as he had counted on getting the work. If the contractor would not take him, where could he find work? He did not expect to get it from those who were in sway to Titus Broake, such as Amos Peakman, Marcus Howie and Joshua Godwin, in view of his stand against them all over enclosure, and so did not bother to tramp to their farms to ask, but returned to the cottage and brooded some more. Poor Mary-Ann almost collapsed with the despair of it when he told her he had failed but Dick Dollery and Enos Diddams had been taken up!

There was nothing else for it! Solely for the sake of Mary-Ann, Jed and Thirza, with no more coins in the bottom of the flour jar, Jem realised that he would have to swallow his pride and go to the vestry to request relief from the poor rate, something which he had never done in the twelve years since his return, which he had vowed he would never do, but which he did on the Friday after his rejection.

In view of the sudden increase in the number of paupers about the place since enclosure and the extra work it all entailed, on the recommendation of a special ,meeting of the vestry and with the approval of the parson, the Reverend Doctor William Wakefield

Petchey, Joshua Jaikes had given up as the full-time bailiff of Glebe Farm after its sale to Titus Broake and had moved with his wife into a cottage on Forge Lane, taking over a second cottage alongside into which he and his cohort Lemuel Ring, transferred by cart all the goods which the vestry was expected to hand out to the poor. Further, the parson, as he was allowed by law, had also appointed Joshua Jaikes as the vestry clerk, paid eleven pounds and six shillings and twopence per annum on top his overseer's salary and now, since the last vestry meeting, an amount, too, of ten pounds and fifteen shillings per annum as the surveyor of the parish's roads: the one-time Glebe Farm bailiff was now becoming a well-to-do man, if a busy one.

The moment Jem walked through the door of the vestry, there was on Joshua Jaikes's face the smirk of a man who was thinking, 'So you have come at last! I have been wondering when you would appear. You have had to swallow your pride, Jem Stebbings, and now you must come begging to me!'

He did not say so aloud, of course, because the curate from Lower Rackstead, Reverend William Waters, was seated with him and Jaikes did not want to alienate him: however, he did not hesitate to extract his revenge for all the humilations he considered he had suffered at Jem's hands in the past, though it was slyly done. First, he granted Jem a paltry two shillings in immediate relief, barely enough for the price of two loaves of Samuel Thorn's poor quality bread, which he could not refuse him since the curate was sympathetic and looking on, though he pleaded lack of immediate funds to hand for not being able to give more and smiled to himself as he said it. Then, with so many already employed on digging the new roads and building fences and planting hedges, Jem was obliged in return to submit himself to the vestry's roundsman system, whereby the able-bodied unemployed worked in rotation, being sent in turn to work for a few days or a week for different farmers who paid a part of the wages and the parish paid the rest.

Jem hoped he would be sent within the village to the enlarged Glebe Farm, which had a new tenant, a man named Henry Cadger, who had come down from the next county just after the Christmas with his wife and family to take Jaikes's place, paying a hundred and forty pounds a year in rent to Titus Broake as the new owner and bent on turning it mostly to arable, keeping only two of the former six meadows and only a half-dozen cows.

Jaikes, however, had other ideas: since Hamwick Dean and the adjoining hamlets of Lower Rackstead and Merchant Staplers were administered by a joint vestry, he sent Jem instead first to Thomas Godbear's place in Merchant Staplers for a week's work, then to Richard Shadwell's place in the same hamlet for a week, then on to John Dicker's and Henry Sweetapple's farms there also for a further week apiece, which meant an hour's daily trudge in drenching spring rain and freezing hail on one day and even a late flurry of snow towards the end of the month which was akin almost to a blizzard. The long walk meant Jem had to rise well before cock crow just to be in the yard at six-thirty, otherwise he could be fined as a slacker and the parish refuse him its part of the relief or, worse, he might even be turned away by the farmer and, in consequence, be declared one of the 'idle poor' – one who could work but would not – and his relief stopped altogether. After that, he was sent for a week in turn to Silas Kempen and James Allen, at Lower Rackstead, and a few days each to Jonathan Hartless, Thomas Crawley and Thomas Templeton, there also, and yet more walking through the early light of dawn, setting off even as the birds were beginning their chorus and not returning till well after dusk. And when he had completed his first 'round,' he was sent on a second and then a third, each time to Merchant Staplers and then to Lower Rackstead so that each day he faced a long walk to begin work and a long walk back afterwards: Joshua Jaikes was repaying him in as spiteful a way as he could devise.

A labourer out of work then could not just take to the roads and wander anywhere and everywhere there was a likelihood of work: his liberty was entirely controlled by the parish officers and the Law of Settlement: for, if a man went into another parish seeking work, he was often told to go back to his own. No one then had a guarantee of employment, let alone a man from one parish going into another.

Since an Act of 1662, any man who left his settled parish to move elsewhere – from Hamwick Dean to Inworth, perhaps, or to Tidwolton or to Dark Leyton, north of Hamwyte, say – then he had to possess a 'settlement certificate,' issued by the overseer of the poor of his home village, which guaranteed that, if he fell into destitution, if he became ill or out of work and a likely drain or claimant on the poor rates of the host parish, then his home parish would pay the cost of bringing him back so that he and his family would not become 'chargeable' on another parish's poor rate.

Nor could anyone expect to get a 'certificate of leave,' as the villagers called it, to go to another parish if the overseer or the parish authorities were minded for him and his family to remain in his settled parish: in the first place, before any certificate was granted, the applicant had to be examined before a Justice of the Peace, showing that he did actually belong to one of the parishes within the Hundred. Even if he complied with that condition and was a labourer, any certificate granted would not exceed the distance of three miles most times so that it was less troublesome bringing him back if that requirement arose: and, if he were a tradesman, artificer, or manufacturer, a certificate might be granted to allow him out of the Hundred, but in no case was that to exceed the distance of twenty miles from the parish to which he belonged.

At that time, to gain settlement in a parish, a person had to be born into it, or to have lived in it for three years or to have been hired within it for a year and a day, the latter ruling inevitably leading to short-term hiring so that settlement could not be obtained. Alternatively, a man seeking settlement could gain it by holding an office in the parish, renting a property in it worth ten pounds per year or paying the same in rent, by marrying into the parish, gaining poor relief in the parish previously or taking up a seven-year apprenticeship with a settled resident, like a wheelwright, a tanner, a maltster, a weaver or a blacksmith and the like. Persons with an estate of their own, of course, were irremovable if residing upon it, however small it might be, though, a hundred years before, as a further control, a Bill had been enacted that no person was to obtain a settlement in any parish by the purchase of any estate or interest of less value than thirty pounds sterling.

Understandably, therefore, parishes were cautious in permitting newcomers to gain settlement within their boundaries: and, even if a man with a certificate were lucky enough to obtain employment in another parish within the limits prescribed, perhaps as an assistant to some tradesman or even in a manufactory, making woollens, silk or leather goods, say, or as an apprentice bricklayer, or wheelwright or such, some would hire him for fifty-one weeks only and that way would defeat his attempt to obtain settlement status for himself and his family.

Even as the allotment of land for Hamwick Dean and the two adjoining hamlets was being apportioned by the commissioners, two of the husbandmen, Aaron Smith and James Harding, as if knowing which way the wind was blowing, had gone to Parson Petchey, as a Justice of the Peace, and had asked for certificates of leave and had moved themselves and their families to Dark Leyton a good seven miles beyond Hamwyte amid the rolling, wooded countryside north of Hamwyte, where they had obtained employment with a large titled landowner. But, come the end of that year, they and their families had been forced to return to Hamwick Dean when they fell into want because they had not worked for the necessary year and a day to gain settlement in their new parish.

Joshua Jaikes was sent to fetch them: when they came into the village, the children's bare feet were red raw and the women and men were exhausted, having walked the whole ten miles back with their goods piled on two rickety wheelbarrows because Joshua Jaikes would not pay for a carrier. He, meanwhile, rode behind them on his new horse the whole way without so much as offering to give one crying child a lift, looking on dispassionately as the older children carried the younger on their backs and the men and their wives struggled up hill and down dale with their loads as best they could. They arrived to find that Titus Broake, their former landlord, had demolished the cottages which they had left since and so they were forced to build their own furze-roofed hovels on a back lane towards Lower Rackstead.

Jaikes, of course, received the usual allowance for having returned paupers: a journey of twenty miles was considered a full day's work, so he was allowed twopence for the use of his pony and trap and so on in proportion per mile. His only regret was that they had not gone to a more distant village, for had the distance been more than the twenty miles, or had he been obliged to be out all night, then his allowance would have been two shillings for himself, one shilling for his pony and sixpence for each pauper he returned.

It was no surprise, therefore, that the parsimonious ratepayers baulked at having to take on such payments which they considered unnecessary and entirely avoidable by the simple expedient of refusing to issue any further certificates of leave. Not that the villagers minded overmuch: most preferred to stay where they were anyway because they knew that, if the occasion arose, they could at least claim on the poor rates of their own parish without any additional difficulty, however reduced that might be. The consequence was that a poor family obliged to remain stationary of necessity had to be satisfied with whatever wages or other income they could obtain.

THREE

THE BUILDING of the new road and the fencing and hedging, as stipulated by the enclosure commissioners, were all completed by the time harvesting began in the late August, which released those who had worked upon it for field work. The summer, as it turned out, was a wet one and, consequently, the harvest was delayed and there was a rush to get it in during whatever short spell of good weatrher came in between the rains, especially when a gale flattened much of the corn crop on the night of the ninth and tenth of August. However, when Jem sought work on his own account and joined the line at Glebe Farm hoping to be taken on as a day-labourer in his own right to help cut and gather-in the corn, he was told by a somewhat sheepish new tenant Henry Cadger that he had 'enough men already booked to do the work,' even though the corn harvest was the crowning work of the year and extra casual labour was always required. In fact, so great was the need to gather-in the corn harvest while even a short spell of good weather held that the long August break at the village's Dame School was always referred to as the 'harvest holidays' during which children worked in the fields alongside their parents and older brothers and sisters sometimes until late in the evening: everyone worked, often until darkness closed in and the normal red harvest moon rose in the eastern sky. Jem could only suppose that someone had forewarned the new farmer that one Jem Stebbings was marked down as a malcontent, who had spoken out strongly against the lord of the manor and the six largest farmers in the district as well as the Church and certain titled personages so it was best not to employ him if he, as a newcomer, wished to have the friendship and good will of the other farmers to help him make his way.

Thus, unable to find work in Hamwick Dean, Jem could only return to the drudgery and manifest unfairness of Joshua Jaikes's roundsman system and resume his traipsing to Merchant Staplers and Lower Rackstead each morning, which he did all during the harvest period, helping the farmers there gather-in their corn and barley. They were delighted to have so hard-working a worker for whom they paid so little and yet who did so much, especially as, in the rush to get-in the corn and barley, work in the harvest fields often continued until the moon rose and it was sometimes near to midnight before Jem returned to the cottage in Hamwick Dean, knowing that he would have to rise and leave it again at sun-up the next morning, which of course, was what Joshua Jaikes had intended all along. Come the October, however, even he was no longer needed and was told he would not be wanted again till the spring weeding: what work there was on the farms there, was solely for the hamlet labourers themselves: so Jem was sent by Jaikes to join the gangs undertaking verge-cutting and digging drains and lopping tree branches in the woods around the parish, though he was paid only four shillings weekly for it, even as a married man, which was precious little for rent, food and fuel to keep him and his family.

Fortunately, Mary-Ann and Thirza had been taken on by Henry Cadger as harvest labour, simply because no one expressly told the farmer who they were and, being a newcomer, he did not think to ask. So they were able to join the other women 'gavelling' behind the cutting team: and, though in past good years the wage would normally have been a high of fifteen shillings a week for a man and nine shillings and sixpence for a woman, this time it was a wretchedly low seven shillings a week for the men and five shillings only for the women, with half of the latter for the children.

Such was the plight of some that, when the cutting and carting were finally finished on Glebe Farm and, as custom decreed, a small patch of corn was left uncut in the last field because superstition had it that the man who cut the last sheaf would have ill luck throughout the following year, even the threat of ill luck did not stop someone from stealing into that same field during the night and cutting it anway. The same thing happened in the other fields on other farms where the custom was followed: corn could be ground to make flour for bread as readily at home as in a mill, even if that bread were unleavened the same as the Israelites had eaten before their exodus from Egypt.

Mary-Ann's and Thirza's work was short-term, of course, like that of all the other casual harvest labour: when it ended, she began to take in what washing she could, as she had been doing when Jem had first met her, helped by young Thirza, while young Jed spent the winter picking stones for Marcus Howie on his new land and bird-scaring for Joshua Godwin when, in his mother's view, had they still been working their leased land on the open-fields, he would have been sitting in the Dame School learning to read, to write and to count and to know the capitals and countries of the world and the names of the kings and queens of England. Instead, he was digging out flints from the ridges of turned earth with other children and placing them in piles behind him or walking up and down the winter-seeded fields in all weathers working a rattle to scare off the crows and rooks.

By the Christmas, half the population of Hamwick Dean and the two hamlets were back on parish relief, though they were to find the payment they received was only half what they had been given a year previously: for following enclosure, as the first weekly huddle of dispossessed husbandmen gathered outside the church door waiting their turn to go inside, the joint select vestry of the three parishes had felt obliged to raise the poor rate substantially, which not unexpectedly had alarmed the six rate-paying large farmers in particular, since they paid more than all others save the lord of the manor, who was not bothered either way. At the next Easter meeting of the select vestry, three of those farmers who had benefited most from supporting the enclosure Bill, namely Amos Peakman, Marcus Howie and Silas Kempen from lower Rackstead, had themselves nominated and approved as members of the vestry with the simple premise of their backers of reducing the poor rate, which, accordingly, they did, not once, but three times between that Easter and Michaelmas. In several cases, the dole was even refused to some: when one member of the select vestry saw a pauper tossing a piece of mouldy bread to his dog, a special meeting was convened at which it was voted to withhold relief from him and anyone else who kept a dog, since dogs ate food which the family might otherwise eat and they did not pay relief to feed dogs!

Their attitude hardened yet again in the January when they announced they would no longer be dispensing 'bread slips' to the needy as they once had done to the aged and the infirm as they left the church of a Sunday morning, paid for by a legacy from a former clergyman of the parish as a reward for their church attendance, a custom which not even Parson Petchey had dared to end. From then on, all some of the very old could afford was the poor quality bread from Samuel Thorn's or Andrew Norris's ovens, the reject loaves of which there were always a few which had been insufficiently yeasted to them to make them rise or had been left baking too long in the oven so that one day a loaf might be as dry as a seaman's biscuit to chew and the next runny in the centre like porridge.

For many such as Jem, the work the women and children had done during that harvest period was all that kept the family fed over the long, cold and bitter months of that second winter. It became a common sight to see people heading to the overseer's store on Forge Lane to plead with Joshua Jaikes for a small bundle of firewood, say, to put some heat into a cottage, or a blanket to cover shivering children at night and a few lumps of coal occasionally. Not that it did them any good: there was none: so little was actually being stored to give out to the poor by then that the building contained nothing but a half-sack of meal and a small pile of turnips: the days when the overseer of the poor, such as William Hurrell, stacked bundles of chopped firewood outside the door for those who required them or when the shelves of Caleb Chapman's outbuilding or the butcher William Hoskins's shed – when they were the assistant overseers – were filled with bundles of tallow candle, jugs of lamp oil and lengths of cloth and when sacks of turnips and potatoes were replenished every week were long gone.

Of course, if a man did not like the living he endured in England and wanted to break away from his poverty and his suppression by others, there was always the appeal of the new lands across the Atlantic or on the other side of the world: North America, Upper Canada, the Cape and even Australia were already luring disaffected young labourer overseas. A 'certificate of leave' would always be granted by the magistrates to emigrants, particularly large families, since it meant there would be fewer mouths to be fed from the poor rate. Nine members of the Belstead's family from Lower Rackstead, mother, father, grandmother and six children all under the age of ten, had climbed up on to Daniel Gate's wagon one morning amid tears and sadness from their neighbours, bound first for London and then a ship to America: and within a fortnight of their leaving, their neighbours, the seven-strong Barnes family, were also on their way by carrier for Liverpool to take ship to Upper Canada.

Three other families took note of the handbills which had been fixed to trees all over the Hundred, promising employment to weavers in the new cotton mills springing up around Manchester and in other towns with the queerest of names, like Ramsbottom, Rawtenstall and Oswaldtwistle and a score of other places of which they had never heard, though the work they would find there was little more than the same paid slavery of the farm labourer, life-shortening, always hard, always long and always brutal, dirty and dangerous. Those who went North left without a certificate, stealing away under the cover of night with only what they wore and what they could carry: one owed his landlord five weeks' rent and, with no chance of being able to pay and refused help by the parsimonious vestry, he simply locked the door of his cottage, muzzled the dog so it would not bark, walked with his family to Hamwyte and disappeared.

One feckless husband, Thomas Bell, a one-time husbandman, faced with rent to pay and food to put on the table, abandoned his wife and seven children and left them as a charge on the parish: a warrant was issued for him, but all that anyone knew was that, a week before he went, he had talked of travelling up the Great North Road on the eastern side of the Pennines into Yorkshire, where more and more mills for the new woollen industry were rising up in Bradford, Leeds, Barnsely, Halifax, Dewsbury and a host of other places.

Since he had no wish to return, he, too, did not bother to apply to a magistrate for a certificate: neither did five young bachelors, the Werrell brothers, Meshach and Abendigo, young Henry Hockley, George Appleton and James Mann, none of them above eighteen, who all disappeared from the village on the same night without telling anybody of their plans. Enclosure and its effect was adding Hamwick Dean's destitute to the great movement northwards to the industrial towns and outwards to the colonies.

Those who felt themselves obliged to remain in Hamwick Dean, as did most of the now landless husbandmen, did so knowing full well that, with so many men in the village and the two hamlets seeking work on the farms, of necessity, they would have to be satisfied with whatever wages they could obtain in the year ahead. For his part, Jem, having served for twelve years away from England, had no wish to leave it again: Hamwick Dean was his home for all its faults, and they were many, and it was home, too, to the wife and children he loved: so he stayed and that was to be his and their undoing.

FOUR

JEM'S AND MARY-ANN'S undoing began one Sunday morning in the early February when they and young Jed arrived late at church: they had set off late for no other reason than both parents had been awake for most of the night nursing Thirza. She had developed a fever from the damp which infiltrated the wall of their cottage on Arbour Lane and been put to bed the previous evening shivering violently and with her forehead wet with perspiration. All through the dark, dragging hours, Mary-Ann had remained seated at her bedside, intermittently bathing her forehead and her arms with cold water as her temperature rose and fell and murmuring softly to her to comfort her. Jem, too, had sat up with his wife, perching himself on a small stool by the long-dead fire with his back against the wall, occasionally dozing, but every now and again jerking himself awake to ask how the child was, particularly whenever she moaned or cried out.

At first light, however, Thirza's fever had abated: her breathing was more even, her forehead had cooled and she had ceased to toss and turn and was sleeping peacefully: the first rays of the sun were lighting the top of the great bank of cloud walling the horizon to the east when Mary-Ann and her lanky husband finally sank into their own bed: but they had slept only three hours before Jed, now eleven years of age, shook his mother awake, complaining of the lateness of the hour and wanting something to eat for his breakfast.

Jem's church-going had been intermittent ever since the shock of the enclosure had ended his days as a husbandman and reduced him and his family to poverty, so angered had he been at the Church's part in it: once every now and again was enough for him. Mary-Ann, however, had continued to go each Sunday and to take Jed and Thirza with her, simply to maintain an appearance of normality with the other villagers: she went also because she could pray to God and in hope that He would heed her prayers: for she did not blame Him for their troubles, but felt they were brought upon them more by others and were 'none of God's doing,' as she had said a hundred times. In that, she was no different from the other village women who crowded into the church and prayed each Sunday for peace and contentment and then went home to frugal meals and idleness and hunger and illness: but they prayed anyway and comforted themselves that 'one day the meek would inherit the earth,' thinking it applied to them.

It was only when Joshua Jaikes, in his capacity as the senior churchwarden, stopped her as she left one Sunday and warned her quite bluntly of the consequences which might befall her recalcitrant husband if his church attendances did not improve that she had determined, even before Thirza had been taken ill, that she, Jem and the children would all go together again that Sunday.

'You need to show your face again, Jem, for our sakes if not for your own, because we can't afford to pay any fine and Jaikes is just looking for the chance to do you a mischief, if I'm any judge of him,' Mary-Ann had scolded.

With Thirza seemingly recovered and sitting up to take her onion soup, she saw no reason to change her plans: having a sick child in the house was not an excuse to neglect the Lord, she reasoned to herself: more than ever, it was a time to pray in His House for the child's well-being. So young Thirza was left in the care of an elderly, widowed neighbour, who being frail had been granted dispensation of a kind not to make the long walk up Forge Lane and along Parsonage Lane to St. Bartholomew's each Sunday, being visted by one of the two curates as part of their duties: however enfeebled, she could still be trusted to sit beside a dozing child's bedside for a couple of hours.

Their late wakening and no other reason than that was why, when Mary-Ann, Jem and young Jed turned on to Parsonage Lane in a blustery wind, there was not a single person in sight ahead of them.

'Hurry up, Jem, we shall be late,' Mary-Ann called out impatiently to her limping husband, dawdling some twenty yards back, at the same time pulling her brown woollen shawl more tightly about her head and shoulders as spatters of sleet blew into her face. More than anything, she feared that at any moment the tolling of the single church bell summoning the indifferent, as well as the faithful, to prayer and communion would cease and they would have to enter after the service had begun, with all the disruption that would cause and attention it would bring.

Her husband, dressed in his one clean smock, which his wife had washed in the tub the previous evening and had dried above the hearth while the fire was lit especially for that morning's church-going, was as disinclined to walk any faster as might be any man who knew he faced near an hour of psalm-singing and knee-bending and a further hour of fire-and-brimstone sermonising from Parson Petchey. Such homilies as the hook-nosed parson delivered each Sunday were, to Jem's thinking, all of a hypocrisy: one needed only to look about one to see it all: to him, such things were said more for the women than the men: they seemed more willing to accept it all. They, like his wife, sat listening attentively with their little prayer book on their laps, eyeing each other's new shawls, if they had them, which few did, and whispering asides to those near them, mostly about others whom they did not like or about whom they knew some gossip: but they listened, nevertheless, while the men yawned and fidgeted and the youths played 'paper, scissors or stone' behind the backs of those in front till spotted and reprimanded by a hissing Joshua Jaikes in his role as senior churchwarden or his cohort, Lemuel Ring and once even by the parson himself, who, remembering the salutary effect it had during his brief excursion into the schoolmastering profession, boxed both transgressors around the ears and walked on.

As it was, Mary-Ann and Jem had still not reached the timbered porch with its red-tiled roof when the bell finally stopped tolling: the procession of the parson and the choirboys and the churchwardens had just emerged from the vestry where they robed when she pushed open the heavy porch door to the nave, with a final hissed plea for Jem to be quicker. Unfortunately, the chill draught which blew in turned the pages of those prayer-books which had already been opened and alerted everyone to the latecomers: it forced Joshua Jaikes, as the cross-holder at the head of the procession, to stop in the very act of beginning, thus disconcerting the two candle carriers and the choirboys behind, which did not please Parson Petchey at the rear, and, worse for Mary-Ann, caused three hundred or more pairs of eyes to turn towards her and Jed.

If Mary-Ann had been asked and if she had answered truthfully, there was one duty above all others which she detested having to perform whenever she attended the services on a Sunday and that was, like all the village women, to walk the length of the aisle and perform a curtsey, not to the holy table, not to the Calvary of the crucified Christ hanging from one of the pillars, but to the starchy, thin-faced harridan of a parson's wife, who sat in isolated splendour, prayer-book and hymnal in her lilac-gloved hands and never offered so much as a smile in return, but simply nodded her head in a cold, aloof manner as recognition of her status and due deference to it were paid before allowing the curtsier to take their seats, always ensuring the row immediately behind her remained empty so that she was separated from the 'lower country classes,' as she called them.

It was a practice she had instituted upon the death of the Old Squire and in which she had revelled alone for more than a decade till the arrival of the new lord of the manor and his wife. When they were in church, they occupied the Old Squire's pew directly in front of the chancel as befitted their status and, of course, also merited a curtsey: and, though not receiving anything nearing graciousness from the lord of the manor, the women did at least receive a shy, timid smile from the lady of the manor. However, as it turned out, both she and her husband were seldom in attendance since she was frail and at that time pregnant yet again and the lord of the manor himself seemed no longer to care about attending church, or religion at all for that matter, so the villagers curtsied Sunday after Sunday solely to Mrs. Petchey under the watchful eye of the churchwardens. All of them, Mary-Ann included, considered it an imposition and a humiliation and smarted under it: but none dared to voice any form of dissent: they were too afraid. The wife of a 'common day-labourer' did not inveigh against those 'put in authority over them,' but accepted it and showed her 'respect' by curtseying as was expected of her so as not to jeopardise in lean times what was doled out to them at the back door of the parsonage – pease porridge, onion soup or morning gruel or winter coals: if they were lucky, if they were considered to be deserving enough.

That Sunday morning once again only the parson's wife was seated at the very front: and, in view of the fact that the cross-bearer, the candle carriers, the parson himself and indeed the whole congregation were waiting, a hurried bob in the aisle might have been acceptable, so long as it was within the view of the parson's wife: but, late and embarrassed and in a hurry to allow the halted procession to proceed, a red-faced Mary-Ann darted straight into the usual pew just inside the door, pulling in young Jed after her. Unfortunately, as she did so the pew door banged against the side as she pulled it open and the noise echoed down the vaulted nave like a thunderclap, to be compounded a few seconds later as a sullen Jem followed her into the church and banged shut first the main door and then the pew door.

At the front, in her splendid isolation, the parson's wife waited for a few seconds and, hearing no footsteps in the aisle going towards her, turned slowly in her seat and, leaning out into the aisle, peered back down its length.

'Has the wife not forgotten something?' she demanded in a loud and imperious tone, not even knowing who it was and acting purely on the sounds alone.

Immediately, there was an intake of breath amongst all those who had already performed their own curtsies, as they had been taught: then a general murmuring arose: it was to the accompaniment of that sound that a blushing Mary-Ann rose from her knees, where she had begun her devotions, squeezed past Jed and Jem to open the door of the pew and, crimson-faced with embarrassment, made her way forward down the right-hand aisle to perform the gesture of respect which the haughty parson's wife expected of her. Again the eyes of the whole congregation, not to mention those of the impatient parson and the others in the delayed procession, were upon her as she returned to her place, past fifteen rows of staring faces either side of the aisle, with ten more rows looking at her from the sections by the organ, a dozen more behind the font and thirty more in the rows of pews against the south wall. The more churlish amongst them savoured the reprimand because it was against someone else and not against them and, therefore, it would be something about which they could gossip later: throughout the service those same women tittered and smirked behind their opened hymn-books or with their heads down in prayer at so flagrant a breach of village etiquette.

Even then, the matter might have rested there had not Mary-Ann, Jem, Jed and Thirza, well again after her illness, arrived late at the church a second time the very next Sunday: again entering the gate and hurrying up the short path to the porch just as the bell finished tolling, having struggled that morning to light their fire with the damp firewood which young Jed had collected the previous day. Mary-Ann, with Thirza in tow, was in the same scurry as before as she pushed open the church door, hurried across the cross-aisle and led her daughter quickly down the right-hand aisle to the front where both mother and daughter performed their bobs as was expected of them, again as usual receiving only the merest nod of the head in recognition from the Reverend Doctor's wife, before returning quickly to their usual places – without noticing that a change had occurred that morning.

Quite arbitrarily, the parson's wife, as the senior worshipper in the village's hierarchy present, had issued a decree that all the males, including boys above the age of ten, should sit on one side of the church and their wives and daughters and all other small children should sit on the other side. There was no rhyme or reason to it that anyone could see: it seemed to be just the whim of a woman who considered the mixing of the 'lower order' sexes in God's House was a breach of some arcane religious dogma which none in the village had ever considered might exist and would not have understood why if it had. True, the separation of the sexes at worship was practised by certain religions, but, to the knowledge of the villagers of Hamwick Dean, it had never occurred there, not under the Old Religion or the New, for that matter, not even during the brief reign of the Levellers and the Puritans. Nor did they understand why it was decreed only that they should do it: and, puzzled though they were, the villagers had all meekly obeyed, everybody, including the three large farmers, if with red faces and no little muttering of discontent, all assuming the parson's wife had taken her directions from the Reverend Doctor himself, at that moment robing in the vestry. Clearly, it would not have been mooted had the lord of the manor and his wife been present: she would not have dared: but they were not present and unlikely to be for sometime, according to word sent from the Hall, so it was.

It seemed to affect the women more than the men and youths: the women seemed to think it a matter of comfort or importance that they sat in church with their husbands and sons, those who had them, while the men and the boys grinned and smirked at the whole idea and rather enjoyed being able to lounge with their workmates and drinking companions and be able to whisper to each other about farming or other matters while they were supposed to be intoning their responses or praising the Lord in tuneless accompaniment to the small organ. To them, it was some 'daft woman's folly,' and, peculiarly, it suited them, not that the parson's wife would have wanted that: if she thought for one moment the men considered it a good idea, she would have abandoned it there and then and returned to the status quo.

However, so preoccupied was Mary-Ann with returning to her pew as quickly as she could after her curtsey, both she and Thirza walking back with eyes lowered and hands clasped before them as do the pious when returning from the communion rail, that she rejoined Jem and Jed without noticing that all the other women of her station now sat upon the same side as the parson's wife, that is, across the church along the south wall, all two hundred or more of them, and she had returned to what had become the men's side.

Immediately, there was that same audible intake of breath as had occurred the week before and once more a hush fell over the congregation as the churlish smiled yet again: then a furious whispering broke out: it was that which attracted the attention of the parson's wife and made her turn in her seat yet again to look towards the back: what she saw was Mary-Ann turn 'the wrong way' at the cross-aisle and return to her usual pew by the door. Beckoning to Lemuel Ring, who was the nearest churchwarden, the parson's wife declared in a strident voice loud enough for the whole congregation to hear: 'That woman is in the wrong seat. Kindly tell her to move. She should be on this side. She cannot sit where she is!'

Remembering his last brush with Jem when he had tried to block his path and had received a bruised ego for it, the grim-faced churchwarden came somewhat reluctantly to where Mary-Ann sat with her husband and children: 'The men and the women are to sit apart from now on,' he said in his normal nasal whine of a voice. 'Mrs. Petchey has said so. You are to sit among the women and girls on that side and the men are all to sit on this side – separated.'

It was the sniggering of the others for a second time, particularly the women across the way, that drove Mary-Ann to do it: she had been humiliated once and she was not going to be humiliated a second time in a week, not in a church before all the other villagers, not by *that* woman of all people! The anger rose up in her: clenching her fists, she stood up and, with open scorn on her face, declared in a voice which was meant to be heard the length and breadth of the nave and was: 'I am not going to move for you or anyone, Lemuel Ring. I was married in this church, joined to my man before God in it by the parson himself and I have sat in this pew with my husband more or less every Sunday since and I've carried two of my children from this pew here to that font there to be baptised and carried two more to be buried in the churchyard outside. I will not move for you or anyone – '

'You must move,' pleaded Lemuel Ring, casting an embarrassed eye back towards the front of the church where the parson's wife sat waiting. 'It is not for me, it's Mrs. Petchey who says the men are to sit this side and the women and girls are to sit that side.'

There was an abject tone to his pleading, which asked would she please comply so that he could go back to his seat farther down on that same side – the men's side – and then they could begin the service and he would not be embarrassed in the eyes of the parson and his wife and the congregation yet again.

'I am damned if I will, Lemuel Ring!' declared Mary-Ann, with an anger in her voice which surprised her husband, that a wife who normally sat so docile and meek in the House of the Lord should be so adamant about moving: but the insult and humiliation of the previous week was surging back into Mary-Ann's memory, reddening her cheeks: and worse, she was being asked by someone whom her husband detested and who was a known friend of his greatest adversary, Joshua Jaikes.

She could clearly see that the parson's wife had turned her face again to the front, as if expecting and anticipating that Mary-Ann would submit to her higher authority and comply without protest: and that infuriated Marry-Ann even more. Stepping out of the pew and storming forwards into the cross-aisle where all could see her, and with all the defiance she could muster, she directed her remarks down the length of the nave to where the parson's wife sat.

'The day I married,' she shouted, 'your own husband said, "Those whom God hath joined together, let no man put asunder!" Well, I tell you now, madam, certainly no woman ever shall and least of all you, for you are neither ordained nor capable!' And with that, she turned and swept out of the church, calling for her stunned husband and children to follow: it was the talk of the village for weeks afterwards.

Leaving the church did not mean that Mary-Ann was going to give up her faith simply because of the meanness and petty-mindedness of the parson's wife. At that time, a small group of Dissenters had in the past few months started to come over from Hamwyte, which had a long history of Dissenting, to hold meetings under an ancient spreading oak tree by the hump-back bridge at the foot of Chantrey hill, hoping sooner or later that some of the villagers would join them. Unknown to the parson, and in the hope of attracting more to their cause, they had even purchased a small area of spare ground on the edge of the village on one of the back lanes along the ridge-top towards Lower Rackstead, upon which in time they hoped to build a small chapel to hold their meetings. Its seller was a curmudgeonly old man, Aaron Phipps, a former husbandman who, since he was bed-ridden and soon to meet his Maker anyway, did not give a fig for parson and treated himself to one last nose-thumbing. Till then, they met under the ancient oak and only cancelled their gatherings when thunder and lightning threatened. What mattered to Mary-Ann was that they held firmly to the Bible, believed in salvation by grace, the hope of redemption, Heaven, Hell and the second coming of Christ: on that basis, she was prepared to be their very first convert and went with Thirza the very next Sunday and were welcomed as equals: Jem and Jed stayed at home,.

Sadly, in village life as it was then, one did not fall foul of one who considered himself the worthiest man in all three parishes, or his wife, or those who served or conspired with these, not without some form of retribution befalling them: and Jem and Mary-Ann had done all of those things.

FIVE

WHILE JEM, for the sake of his wife and children, was prepared to submit himself again if needs be to the indignity of Joshua Jaikes's working of the roundsman system in return for relief from the poor rate, the one thing which irked him more than any other was to see the wives and daughters of formerly independent husbandmen like himself hurrying along the lanes in the early morning, clutching a tin basin or a jug under their shawls and averting their eyes from anyone they passed. They were on their way to the parsonage, to wait humiliatingly at the back door for a dole of soup and bread or cold porridge from the cook or one of the maids. So long as there was a shilling left in the flour jar, Jem was determined that no wife or daughter of his would ever join the huddle of women and children standing on the steps leading up to back of the great house: indeed, he had always vowed that, if ever Mary-Ann defied him and went, he would not to touch a drop of any soup or oatmeal porridge she brought back.

That was a man's pride: the winter of 1828-29 had been a bitter one, with continuous severe frosts from mid-January to the end of that month: for Mary-Ann matters came to a head more practically one morning in the March when the flour jar had been empty of coins for a week and she awoke knowing that there was not so much as an onion or half a turnip even, let alone a crust of bread, in the cottage to give the children and no fuel at all for the fire.

'I have to go, Jem,' she cried, almost in tears, for she knew how much her words would hurt his pride. 'We have nothing left. There is nothing in the larder and the children are hungry. They have barely eaten anything for three days now. We can't live like this!'

What she said was true, but Jem was still too proud to acknowledge it. 'Go if you must,' he shouted, angrily, 'but I'll not take charity from them and their kind. I'd sooner starve before I'll go to that man for his Christian charity!' He spoke the word 'Christian' with an open cynicism which before would never have been there.

Mary-Ann, however, saw the hunger on the face of their son and daughter and went anyway: unfortunately, she had delayed so long that it was past nine o'clock when she and Thirza, carrying a pewter basin each, lifted the latch on the gate that led from the churchyard to the parsonage – the 'back way' – and went up the moss-covered path. Consequently, there was no one else waiting at the back of the great house when she climbed the steps and knocked: and, worse, the knock was answered not by the cook or by one of the maids but by the parson's wife herself.

'Yes?' she demanded, somewhat imperiously, glowering down at Mary-Ann and the trembling Thirza over her wire-framed spectacles.

'Please, ma'am, we've come for some porridge, if you please, ma'am,' Mary-Ann began, keeping her head lowered in the hope that she would not be recognised: but she was recognised.

'Are you not the woman who left the church?' the parson's wife challenged. 'You are the woman who has joined those other heathens at the bottom of Chantrey hill, are you not, praying to the Good Lord in the wide open under a tree like a bunch of barbarians when you should be kneeling in His own House?'

'Yes, ma'am, I am, ma'am,' Mary-Ann mumbled her reply: and lifting her face added: 'We still worship God, though, ma'am, and believe in Heaven and Hell and the Second Coming of Christ:.'

What Mary-Ann did not know was that, when Parson Petchey learned of the meetings being held under the oak tree, he railed against them from the pulpit.

'They are unorthodox Christians, these Dissenters,' he declared vehemently to his congregation. 'You must not associate yourself with them. This is the true House of God. You shall come here and only here or there will be no lasting Salvation for you, but eternal damnation instead. And any who do take up with these – these blasphemers shall not receive any charity from the church. They will receive no succour from us in their days of need – no soup or morning gruel or winter coals. Nothing, if they forsake this House.'

'Worship God indeed!' the parson's wife retorted as Mary-Ann stood humbly before her. 'It is sacrilege to worship the way they do! You shall get nothing here, woman. We do not give to those who desert us. There are enough in the village in want without us having to feed Dissenters as well. Be off with you. Be gone and do not come again.'

Sick at heart, Mary-Ann ushered a bewildered Thirza away: that day, not only did she return empty-handed but she suffered the added humiliation that, by the evening, through the gossip of the cook and one of the maids, practically the whole village knew that Jem Stebbings's family had been refused succour by the rector's wife. If it had one good outcome, it was that when Dick Dollery's wife, Eliza, and Enos Diddams's wife, Emma, who had been early enough to get a dole of porridge for their own families, heard the news, they brought a quarter loaf of bread and a half-jug of cold pease porridge round to them so at least they had something to eat for dinner and supper.

Come the Friday and Mary-Ann and Thirza were in the queue at the vestry to request humbly that they be added also to the list of those who needed help with their rent: notwithstanding the fact that they were near the front of the long queue waiting outside the church gate, she knew that the whispering in front and behind was about herself. Fortunately for her, Joshua Jaikes was abed with a severe cold that day – not severe enough for some, as Dick Dollery's Eliza put it laughing, though it was a hollow laugh: thus, he was not present or he almost certainly would have refused her or at least would have spoken up against the wife of his sworn enemy receiving anything. The other lay members of the vestry present, therefore, were able to grant Mary-Ann's request for rent assistance without his knowledge or that of the parson's or his wife, but only for a month: they were also able to give relief of two shillings so that she at least returned to the cottage with enough to feed the children and herself and Jem again for a few days, albeit on a diet of bread, onions, oatmeal and turnips again.

Her trials did not end there: two weeks later, when Mary-Ann crept out of the cottage and went directly to the cottage on Forge Lane in which the overseer, Joshua Jaikes, now lived, in the hope of obtaining a half-scuttle of coal and some kindling wood with which to light the fire and cook what food she still possessed, she was refused. As Mary-Ann approached, Jaikes was standing at the door of the empty cottage which was now used for storage of the items which the overseer was supposed to dispense to the deserving poor, talking to his cohort, Lemuel Ring: whether it was her imagination or not, Mary-Ann was not sure, but she thought she saw the two men smirk to each other when they saw her and she thought, too, some derogatory comment was made between them.

'We have no coal,' declared Joshua Jaikes, brusquely, as Mary-Ann made her request. 'We have been told no more is to be given out by order of the vestry because the warmer weather will be here in a month or so.'

'But how am I to cook?' pleaded Mary-Ann. 'I have nothing in the cottage I can use.'

'You could always burn a chair or a table – if you have one,' laughed Lemuel Ring: the two were still laughing when Mary-Ann left.

Such were the times then that a man could not just go out of his cottage and pick up wood whereby he might to heat his cold home: an Act of Parliament passed eight years before provided that any person convicted before a single Justice of the Peace of doing any malicious injury to any building, hedge, fence, tree, wood or underwood or copse, was to pay damages not exceeding five pounds. One clause even provided for every male offender under sixteen who did not pay damages and all costs and charges and expenses forthwith to be sent by the magistrates to hard labour in the House of Correction for six weeks. Thus, a child who broke a bough from a tree by the roadside, perhaps while swinging upon it for fun, might be sent to the magistrate, who might well be – and in many cases was – the owner of the tree, that is, the squire, the lord of the manor, a landowning clergyman or other rich landowner.

The Act was passed without any debate, enacted solely for the protection of enclosures and game reserves: it exempted entirely 'persons engaged in hunting and qualified persons in pursuit of game' – in short, the privileged, pheasant-shooting, fox-hunting, horse-riding gentry who could do as much damage as they pleased.

Early in the May, it so happened, young Jed went birds' nesting and foolishly chose to trespass on the lord of the manor's land to do it, climbing over the high clay-brick wall which bordered the estate and crossing a corn-growing stretch to where he knew the birds would be nesting. Having acquired his blackbird's egg, he was seeking to regain the safety of the road by climbing one of the oak trees which there line the long straight run of Hall Lane and then edging along a dead branch overhanging the lane as a matter of expediency since he had seen one of the lord of the manor's day-labourers approaching some two-hundred yards off. The agile Jed made the traverse along the branch easily enough, but, just as he was about to swing himself down, there was a loud crack and a good fifteen-feet of the dead bough snapped off, almost braining him and destroying some of blackthorn saplings newly planted along the wall as a screening hedgerow. For a few moments, Jed lay shaken and bruised, but when he recovered his breath, there being no one on the road, he decided the dead branch would provide at least a few days' fuel for his mother's fire and, despite the fact it was almost as heavy as him, he dragged it across the lane and pushed it into the ditch opposite. That night, when it was dark, he slipped out of the cottage, went back to the spot where he had hidden the branch and dragged it all the way home, taking a headland and field route so that no one would see him.

A few days later, however, Elijah Candler came trotting up to Jem's cottage in the parish constable's pony and trap: the fact that he had brought his pony and trap and was accompanied by Titus Broake's bailiff, Heginbotham, forewarned Jem that there was serious business afoot. By then, the bough had been chopped into small lengths and most of it had been burned on the fire, but, unfortunately, there was still sufficient evidence in the cottage that the family had warmed themselves with it and had cooked with it, namely five logs stacked by the grate.

'I'm sorry to have to bother you,' Elijah Candler began in his usual apologetic manner, 'but I have had a complaint against your boy, young Jed – a matter of stealing a branch and damaging a hedge on the manor estate.'

As mother's will, Mary-Ann flared up immediately on hearing the nature of the charge and who had instigated it. 'Shame on you, Elijah Candler! Shame on you,' she cried, 'chasing a boy for a man like that! Doing others' dirty work!'

She might well have flown at the constable had Jem not politely ushered the two men outside and pushed his wife back into the cottage with a sharp 'Quiet! I'll deal with this.' The two visitors understood Jem's action and did not take it amiss: they accepted the need for men to talk things out quietly amongst themselves without a woman's ranting interruptions: as it was, even then, Jem had to hold the door firmly shut from the outside so that Mary-Ann could not pull it open and burst out, though she still shouted from inside.

'It was me who brought the branch back, not the boy,' declared Jem. 'It was too heavy to be dragged by a boy. You only have to look at him, he's as thin as a fencepost. He could never have pulled it all that way, nigh on a mile or more. It was me that did it. I broke it off for fuel and dragged it here by myself. There was no one else with me.'

'But old Jeremiah Coulson says he saw a boy dragging the branch away towards your cottage,' protested Heginbotham. 'He is a witness. I can put him up before the Justices if you wish and he will say the same.'

Jeremiah Coulson was an old husbandman due to reach his sixty-fifth year in a few months: dispossessed of his own acreage by enclosure, he was then employed as a roundsman to do the necessary but more menial tasks, like cleaning out the cowsheds, spreading muck, clearing and deepening the ditches and other water channels in wet weather or trimming the thorn hedgerows after the first burst of spring growth.

'We all know old Jeremiah is half-blind,' declared Jem. 'It was me he saw, most likely he thought it was a boy because I was bending over as I pulled the branch.'

When Heginbotham began to protest again, Elijah Candler silenced him with a wave of the hand. 'What Jem says is true enough,' he said. 'Old Jeremiah is as blind as a bat and I have to act on the evidence I have. I have a man here who says it was him that took the branch and you can't get no surer evidence to obtain a conviction than that, can you – a man's own confession? When a man confesses to a felony, I have to accept that he is telling the truth or for what other reason would he do it?'

Heginbotham let out a sigh of mild exasperation: he was a man of the world and knew as well as Elijah Candler the true reason why Jem was making his confession: simply to prevent his ten-year-old son from being sent to the Steadleigh House of Correction, twenty-three miles from the village, to spend two months amongst the ruffians, thieves and deviants who languished there, even amongst those in the children's wing: for he knew that most probably the boy would return knowing more ways to break the law than he ever did before he went in..

The cooper-cum-parish constable wished that he did not have to arrest one with whom he had once passed many a long evening of drinking and talking in the Wayfarers': but he had been re-elected as the unpaid parish constable for a third time at the Easter vestry and, by arresting Jem for the theft of one oak bough, property of Titus Broake, lord of the manor, and taking him to the bridewell at Hamwyte, he was only doing the duty others expected of him. What troubled him most was that he knew also Jem was without work, on parish relief of four shillings a week and so was unlikely to be able to pay any fine imposed, which meant a certain six-week sentence in the House of Correction.

Out of Heginbotham's hearing, as he led Jem to where his pony and trap stood ready to take him to the bridewell at Hamwyte, the cooper murmured his apology. 'Sorry, Jem, but I has to do it – it's part of the job.'

SIX

THE FOLLOWING DAY Jem was put up before the magistrate at Hamwyte, a well-to-do parson from the village of Dark Leyton, seven miles north of the town, who, being a fairly large landowner himself, viewed a felony committed against one of his own kind more seriously than if committed against a simple cottager.

That morning there were eleven others standing with Jem at the bar of the court: the first to suffer the reverend magistrate's opprobrium was a labourer from Langridge, who, unable to find work and having no money, had left his wife and five children chargeable to the parish. He had been brought back by the parish constable, with the churchwarden and the overseer of the poor of the same parish as witnesses, and was committed to Melchborough Gaol to await trial at the next Quarter Sessions.

The remaining seven were all charged with the same offences as Jem: the first two, brothers, John and Thomas Dibden, pleaded guilty to cutting and stealing a quantity of wood from a duke's estate at Lower Heding, a village eight miles northwest of Hamwyte: they, too, found the reverend magistrate in an unforgiving mood. Both were fined twelve shillings and sixpence, to be paid to that village's overseer, as well as the five shillings value of the wood and seven shillings and sixpence in costs to be paid to the complainant, the duke's bailiff, or both would receive one calendar month in Steadleigh House of Correction: neither could pay.

The next offender was a gangling day-labourer of no more than sixteen years of age by the name of William Newbury, from Trepplestone, to the northeast of the market town, who had been seen scaling wooden rails, part of a fence around a field belonging to a large farmer, and then sitting on them, though for what purpose other than idleness was not stated. He admitted his offence as charged and was fined eight shillings and sixpence, to be paid to that village's overseer, and three shillings costs and a shilling and sixpence to be paid to the plaintiff: but, since he could not pay any of it either, he, too, received a month's hard labour in Steadleigh.

An Inworth man, Richard Jones, admitted unlawful possession of part of a tree and was fined a pound and ten shillings to be paid to the overseer of the poor at Inworth, and ten shillings costs and two shillings, the value of the wood, to go to the farmer, or two months' hard labour in Steadleigh: he also could not pay.

Another youth by the name of Joseph Richings, from Salter, had cut off a beech tree bough, the property of some knighted landowner, by the name of Sir Tolles Beckwith Hunt: he was fined twenty shillings, to be paid immediately to the village's overseer, two shillings damages for the knighted landowner, who owned a five-hundred-acre estate, and seven shillings and sixpence costs to the complainant, his bailiff, or receive two months' hard labour in the House of Correction, which he accepted with a shrug.

An abandoned wife, named Mary Sandalls, from Cumvirley, next admitted breaking down and taking away part of a fence to use for firewood for cooking an evening meal for her six children: she was fined four shillings, with three shillings and sixpence costs, also to be paid immediately to Cumvirley's overseer of the poor and the complainant

'I cannot pay, your worships. I have no money,' she said, sorrowfully, her head bowed and tears of shame and humiliation running down her cheeks.

'Fourteen days in Steadleigh should help you to mend your ways,' sighed the reverend magistrate wearily, before turning his eyes to Jem, who was then pushed forward to the front of the bar by the town's constable, a local haberdasher, as the woman was pulled back.

Like the others, Jem admitted the theft of one oak bough, length estimated at fifteen feet, value two shillings, and, being unable to pay immediately the fine of twenty shillings imposed and the two shillings value of the wood, with three shillings and sixpence costs to the complainant, James Heginbotham, he like the others was sent to the Steadleigh House of Correction to serve six weeks, with three weeks to be spent at hard labour.

A father and his two young sons, neither of whom were above the age of twelve, charged with stealing a quantity of potatoes growing in an enclosed field at Greater Tottle, followed Jem. Each was fined ten shillings, plus fifteen shillings, the value of the potatoes, and a further five shillings costs, fifteen shillings and the costs to go to the complainant and the residue to go to the overseer, or each was to spend one month's hard labour in Steadleigh.

In former times, Steadleigh had been the place where thieves, beggars and other petty criminals were put to work in an attempt to reform their criminal ways as well as to punish them for their wrong-doing: some would do productive work, such as making small tools and ornaments or other items to sell to passing visitors, while others would do actual work commissioned by a local tradesmen, such as making mats and weaving baskets. Its capacity was fifty inmates, but such were the times then that there were never fewer than seventy inmates at any one time: and in a single year eight hundred or more might pass through its doors. For the most recalcitrant, the repeat offenders and those condemned to hard labour, there was no such work as making tools or weaving mats: for them, there was two or three weeks on the crank handle, which was what Jem was set to.

Alone in his cell and under the eye of one of the guards, he turned a crank handle attached to a set of cogs, which pushed a paddle through a box of sand without any product from it: a cog on the machine counted the number of revolutions by turning another cog so that, whatever happened, the paddle had to be turned: a prisoner could not be idle while not being watched. Unfortunately, Jem was required on occasions to use his crooked arm and, when he did, invariably he turned the paddle more slowly: in consequence, he fell foul of the turnkey for even deigning to reply to one of his taunts and, as an extra punishment, the paddle was screwed tighter still to make it even harder to turn. Only on the seventh day, the Sunday, was he relieved from this pointless drudgery.

After three weeks of that, he was finally put to work weaving mats from rushes, but on his fifth week again fell foul of the same turnkey when one of his rush mats was torn up by the guard as being poorly made: for his second punishment, Jem was put on a two-hour shot drill, which was also intended to be hard labour without reward, whereby he was set to lifting an iron cannonball to chest height, carrying it a measured distance of twenty-five yards, then setting it down, before returning for a second and then a third and a fourth, till he had carried the required number of cannonballs the requisite distance: this same pointless exercise was then repeated to another place and, after that, to another place till the turnkey considered he had extracted his necessary revenge and ordered an exhausted Jem to return to his cell.

Unhappily, Mary-Ann was not able to visit her husband in the weeks he was in Steadleigh: in the previous century, relatives of necessity used to take food and clean clothing in to the prisoners, but that was no longer necessary as the authorities now provided them with meagre meals of gruel and bread, with occasional servings of gristly meat and vegetables, potatoes, turnips or peas, mostly, boiled in a stew. Thus families no longer visited so often and were restricted to two visits a year only since the authorities felt it better if the convicted were kept away from the influence of their loved ones. Indeed, the only visitor Jem had to his cell in the six weeks he was there was the chaplain, who pleaded in prayer for him to show and to feel contrition for his sins and to whom Jem listened politely and agreed with every word he said, since he could not tell him exactly why he was there and so thought it the easiest of options.

Meanwhile, back in Hamwick Dean, misfortune followed upon misfortune for Mary-Ann, Jed and Thirza. At the previous Easter vestry, Amos Peakman, Marcus Howie and Silas Kempen had been joined by Joshua Godwin and also by the other large farmers from Lower Rackstead and Merchant Staplers, James Allen and Thomas Godbear, and, surprisingly, too, by three of the 'turncoat farmers from the Merchant Staplers, Richard Shadwell, John Dicker and Henry Sweetapple, thus creating a prepondrance of fifteen farmers amongst the twenty-five who made up the select vestry. The tenant farmers were complaining of the new higher rents being charged by the wealthy absent landowners from whom they leased their land and declared themselves unable either to pay more into the poor rate since they were struggling to meet the new tithes as well. In the very first week that Jem was in Steadleigh, the 'farmers' vestry,' as the villagers now called it, cut the relief yet again, which amounted to just ninepence weekly for Jed and Thirza and a shilling and sixpence only for Mary-Ann. Nor were rents to be paid for anyone who fell into arrears: too many were similarly suffering hardship to pay the rent for everyone. Only the older pensioners and truly impotent poor were to be given help: the more able bodied others would have to fend for themselves, especially one whose husband was a convicted felon at that very moment languishing in Steadleigh House of Correction.

'We can't go on paying everyone's rent,' snorted Amos Peakman. 'We have enough to pay with the old pensioners. Any others that can't pay their own way can always go to the poorhouse.' He found no dissenters, though at least three of the new members did have the good grace to lower their heads, but none voiced any objection: the vestry was hardening its attitude towards paupers in every direction.

At the same time, the tenants of the row of six cottages on Arbour Lane where Mary-Ann and Jem lived discovered that they had a new landlord: a month earlier, the Bishop of Melchborough, still looking for funds to complete the repair of his cathedral church in Melchborough, which was proceeding very nicely, had deemed the six cottages, which had long been neglected, as being too costly to repair: so within a fortnight of Jem's arrest and incarceration, on the misguided recommendation of Parson Petchey, who thought a new owner might be a blessing in disguise for those who lived in them, they were sold to a wealthy merchant from Wivencaster, whom no one knew or had ever met.

He, as it turned out, was not to be so munificent as the Church: for that was how he had become well-to-do, by adhering to the letter of the law and refusing to allow anyone credit: with him, everything was to be paid in cash promptly on the due date. Unhappily for Mary-Ann, he absorbed the rent arrears as part of the sale, much to the bishop's delight: his first action was to raise the rent by sixpence a week and his second was to demand that all arrears be paid immediately.

With only the reduced relief coming in and the vestry unwilling to help, there was no prospect that Mary-Ann could pay the rent herself, particularly as she was so far in arrears.

The eviction came suddenly in the fourth week of Jem's absence: one morning, there was a loud hammering on the door: men's voices were shouting outside and when Mary-Ann opened it four men pushed their way in, toughs from Hamwyte. Two carried cudgels but, on seeing that were dealing solely with a woman and two children, they brusquely informed her they were there to repossess the cottage as the rent was nine weeks overdue and they would be obliged if she did not cause any trouble. A sad-faced parish constable, Elijah Candler, was with them to enforce the possession order from the magistrate and behind him was standing Joshua Jaikes, who allowed her to pass without so much as a comment or the offer of a helping hand: all Mary-Ann could do was to wait outside as her furniture and goods were dragged out and piled by the roadside. Even as they watched another shame-faced villager, the wife of a day-labourer who had some employment at the time, in want of a better cottage than the hovel which she was renting, was waiting to move in her five children and her own furniture and goods.

They passed the night separated, with Mary-Ann and Jed sleeping with Enos Diddams's children and Thirza sleeping with Dick Dollery's six daughters, who made a great fuss of her: in the morning, helped by the two wives, Mary-Ann loaded their few poor possessions on a barrow borrowed from John Romble and went out along the

Lower Rackstead road, where she had once seen while blackberryinga crude, low, two-roomed, timber-framed hovels which some squatter had built for himself and his family and which, post-enclosure, he had abandoned and gone back to his own settlement village rather than risk a forced march there with a rope tied around his neck as one would tie a lead on a dog.

No other word but 'hovel' could describe it, but it was the best of a half-dozen such dwellings which at one time or other had been thrown up around the parish, all now abandoned: part wattle and daub, part home-made brick, part splintered fencing poles found by the roadside or taken from some farmer's land, none of it was consistent, but bore all the hallmarks of work done in a desperate hurry. The roof was formed from old pieces of timber covered over with turves cut from the verge itself and laid end to end and sagged all along its length: and where the poles did not quite fit at the 'gable' ends and the front, the holes were patched with odd pieces of wood, while at one end a lopsided chimney built of mortared brick was so precarious in its construction it seemed that the first violent winter gale would bring it crashing down on the occupants inside. The two windows fronting on to the road were small, taken from some long-demolished cottage and inserted and filled round with dried mud and straw, hardly letting in light enough to dispel the gloom of the interior: to keep out the draughts, rags had been stuffed into the gaps where the small panes were missing and where the frames did not fit properly. Inside, the floor of its supposed 'parlour' was of bare earth, with a grain sack hung over each window for a curtain and pulled back on to a nail to let in light: the door fashioned from two planks was hinged by leather strips nailed to the frame and dragged upon the ground every time it was opened and closed.

In the centre of the floor, Mary-Ann placed her table, which was itself showing signs of much repair, with the four wooden chairs grouped around it: against one wall, away from the door, she set her darkwood, worm-eaten dresser, with a lower cupboard for food, a drawer for their few spoons, forks and knives and above three shelves on which to stack the cracked crockery. Opposite, under one window, she placed her small sideboard, which had only three of its legs and was supported on the fourth by a small column of bricks: on it stood a blue vase, given by a villager wanting to get rid of their own clutter: in it that day, however, when Mary-Ann had finished, was a bunch of wild flowers and a sprig of cow parsley picked from the verge by Thirza.

There was only a single bedroom, divided from the 'parlour' by a shoulder-high wattle screen: this Mary-Ann further divided by tying a length of string across it and draping a blanket over: on one side slept Jed and Thirza, on the other herself and, in due time soon she hoped, their father, though the beds themselves were no more than furze-filled matress on the dirt floor, each covered by a blanket made from strips of calico, sacking and other material sewn together. However, it was home of a kind and was mostly dry, except when it rained too heavily and water ran down the face of the chimney and collected in a puddle in the empty grate.

SEVEN

WHEN AFTER six weeks Jem returned from the Steadleigh House of Correction, he bore the marks of his ordeal: he was much thinner, more subdued and his limp was more pronounced, but he still hurried up the long hill from Hamwyte, feeling that only a return to his family would buoy him and act to restore his spirits. It was as he walked down The Street again that he first noticed the curious glances of those he passed, though he supposed it to be simply because they would all know that he was returning from Steadleigh and all that fact implied: but instead of Mary-Ann standing outside the door of the cottage in Arbour Lane, there was another woman sweeping the path: and the children playing outside on the road were unknown to him and eyed him with some apprehension.

'Where is my wife?' Jem asked in some consternation.

Fortunately, the woman was an acquaintance of Dick Dollery's wife, Lizzie, and knew of Jem and where he had been.

'I'm sorry to say, your Mary-Ann and kiddies were evicted, Jem,' she said sympathetically. 'They went two weeks agoo. The Church don't own the cottages n'more. Sold'em all to a new landlord, a man from Wivencaster. Mean type. I'm told she owed rent and hadn't been able to catch up. The vestry's not paying for anyone now. Put out all her furniture on to the road, they did. She's up the Lower Rackstead road somewhere. Down one of the lanes. In one of the places there – ' Her failure to use the word 'cottage'was deliberate. ' – Don't know exactly where, but Lizzie Dollery will be able to tell you. She'll know. I'm sorry, Jem, but the place was going begging and it's got more room than the one we had – '

Jem, however, was not listening: he was hurrying back up The Street in the direction of the ridge-top road.

Eventually, after asking several people, he found his new home down a small muddy lane, well off the main way, threequarters of a mile along the ridge-top road, built up against the high bank where the way curved and left a flat patch of verge. The sight of it was a shock, but the state in which he found Mary-Ann, Jed and Thirza was an even greater shock: for the past three weeks they had eaten nothing but bread and raw onions: the skin on the roofs of the children's mouths was blistered so that they both sat miserably on small makeshift stools by a barely smoking hearth and cried when they finally saw him: Mary-Ann, too, was subdued and her speech constrained by the rawness of her mouth, while the so-called 'tea' she poured for him as he finally sat in his new 'parlour' was nothing more than most of the other villagers drank – hot water stained with crushed acorns to give it taste and colour. Such was their plight on his return: somehow he would have to find a means to feed his family, even if it meant having to submit himself to the roundsman system again: but first he would try on his own account.

One result of the enclosure of the open fields, the common pasture and the waste in Hamwick Dean had been the creation of three new farms of seventy to a hundred acres on the land which had once been farmed by the husbandmen, each tenanted by an incomer who rented their consolidated parcels from one or other of the absentee landowners who had benefited from the awards: in the same way, three new middling farmers had also set up in Lower Rackstead and two more again in Merchant Staplers, none leasing more than seventy acres.

The first of the new farmers to arrive in Hamwick Dean was a Highland Scot by the name of Angus McCreef, all the way from the mountainous County of Ross, who took over the tenancy of eighty-five acres on the former waste at the foot of Chantrey hill in the February, beholden to Titus Broake, of course: by the time of Jem's return, a small cottage had been built on the land. He had been followed by William Worden, from Cambridgeshire, whose arable open-fields in his home village had been turned entirely over to grass for cattle following enclosure by some lord, with the result that a hundred men and youths were idle: indeed, there was no work for anyone save a few shepherds and cowherders. He had arrived in the March to set up on eighty acres along the Merchant Staplers road and had his cottage built there by bricklayers from Hamwyte almost at the same time as the third newcomer, a similarly dispossessed farmer from Norfolk named Robert Lenny, erected a cottage for his wife and six children on a leased parcel of seventy-three acres along the Lower Rackstead road.

Jem was hopeful that one or other of them, not knowing him or his history, might give him employment of some kind, helping with the hay-making or weeding or even fence-building: but, like Henry

Cadger, as soon as he mentioned his name, they, too, shook their heads, saying they had enough hands already to do what little work there was. Whether someone had forewarned them as well, Jem never knew, though he could not blame them: in so small and so hierachal a community, it would have been an unwise act for anyone to offer him employment if the lord of the manor, perhaps, or one of the larger farmers, or even the overseer of the poor, or any other for that matter, had 'advised' against it, especially if they were a newcomer setting up and dependent like Henry Cadger upon the goodwill of their brother farmers.

The following morning, he walked over to Merchant Staplers in the hope that one of the three middling farmers there might take him up again: but he was told by each that they had enough roundsmen from their own hamlets to do their haymaking and weeding of the crop-bearing fields. To make matters worse, it rained heavily as Jem walked back and he reached the 'cottage' drenched to the skin.

Thus, having no money and a need for food, all Jem could do was reluctantly to go back to the vestry early on the Friday morning and to offer himself again for work, willing to do anything, coppicing or ditch-digging, say, in the hope of being granted immediate relief of a shilling or two, enough at least to feed his family, though he did not hold out much hope of a sympathetic hearing.

After waiting for a half-hour on the road outside the church with the other claimants and conscious of their whisperings about the eviction of his family and his time in Steadleigh, Jem was finally ushered last of all into the gloomy room, where he found Amos Peakman, as the chairman, seated in the central chair, with Joshua Jaikes as the clerk at his right-hand and five of the other farmers alongside him and, from the looks upon their faces when he entered, in no mood to give out any relief other than was absolutely necessary to a convicted felon. They were there to safeguard their own interests and to make sure the poor rate was not raised for any reason or mis-spent on the idle poor. Only Elijah Candler, Samuel Thorn and Caleb Chapman, seated together at the other end of the table, exhibited any sign of sympathy and half-smiled a welcome to Jem.

'What have you come for?' demanded Amos Peakman, bluntly, squinting at Jem through the small glasses he wore when reading.

'I have come to offer myself for work,' Jem replied, deliberately affecting a humble position with his head lowered, for he knew better than to stare them in the face. 'I have no work and no money and there is no food or fuel in the cottage and I have two children going hungry.

My wife does what she can, but we are destitute. I am hoping the parish will give me work.'

His use of the word 'cottage' drew smiles from the farmers, for they all knew of his eviction, while Joshua Jaikes just stared at him with a contemptuous look on his face, as if he considered Jem should not be there at all. 'Have you not just returned from gaol?' the overseer-cum-clerk demanded abruptly.

It was no more than Jem expected, so instead of replying to him, he addressed his reply courteously to the chairman. 'Yes, Mr. Peakman, I have. Six weeks with hard labour in the House of Correction at Steadleigh, serving part of my time on the crank-handle and the rest of it making rush mats.'

All that elicited from the farmer was a hurrumph, as if embarrassed by his truthfulness. 'You were in gaol for stealing were you not?' he queried.

'I was, and I am humbly sorry for it,' Jem replied, knowing that this was what they would want to hear, still keeping his tone humble. 'I broke a branch off a tree which was hanging over the wall. I dragged it home for the fire. I know I did wrong, but we had no heat in the cottage that day. It was May, but still like wintertime. The branch was rotten and would have fallen and at the time I did not see any harm in it. It would have been of no use to anyone if it had been left to rot on the ground.'

'It is not for you to say whether it should be left to rot on the ground or not,' Amos Peakman retorted. 'That is what the laws of this land required you to do, but you chose to steal it. You took for your own purposes something which you knew to be the property of a gentleman, the lord of the manor, Mr. Broake no less, did you not?'

'I did and I have been punished for it,' Jem acknowledged, keeping his head bowed, for he did not want to give them any cause to refuse him. 'I do not deny what I did, except to say that I did it for my little ones and my wife, to give them heat when they had none.'

All this time, Elijah Candler had been sitting quietly listening: his sympathies lay with Jem, but there was nothing he could say in Jem's defence: if he did, it might, he knew, make matters worse, not only for him, but for young Jed, too, and perhaps even for Jem himself, who had deliberately owned up to a crime, as decreed by the law, to spare his young son: all he could do was to point out that Jem had served out his punishment.

He was quickly cut short by the chairman in a manner which suggested he would brook no disagreement on it: 'His reasons, admirable as they may seem to you, have no bearing on this matter. The man committed a felony and so is a felon.'

'I would not have done it had I not been in such desperate straits,' Jem told him. 'I was a husbandman for nine years, as you know. I kept myself and my family and, in all that time, I never asked the parish for anything, not for so much as a bundle of firewood, or a shilling from the poor rate – I cared for my wife and my children by myself and tried to see to it that they never went hungry even when the rain washed out my crop in those bad summers. In spite of all those things, I managed till I lost the land. It is only since I lost my land that I have fallen – ' He paused, looking for the right words. ' – on hard times.'

Another hurrumph from the farmer: 'Have you been offered work at all?' he wanted to know, for the Poor Law system then would refuse a labourer relief if he were unemployed simply through having refused to accept low wages as the vestry considered that they had no right to interfere between the labourer and his master on matters of pay, which was why wages were so low.

'None.' The answer was given truthfully.

'Have you tried?'

'I have, three times since I came out of the House of Correction, but I have not been able to get any. I have been told there is nothing to be had,' replied Jem, truthfully, averting his eyes from those of Richard Shadwell, John Dicker and Henry Sweetapple; for he did not want to give them cause to speak against him. 'If I could be given a certificate of leave, I would willingly walk as far as Salter or Gledlang even to see if there is any work there, or maybe Maydun or Wivencaster, but without a certificate I have no hope of finding anything.'

'You would not be able to find anything if you did,' Amos Peakman told him bluntly. 'Others have already been over to Salter, Gledlang and Cobwycke and a half-dozen other places and they have all been told to get back here because there is nothing for them over there. And we don't want our parish constable or our overseer here having to ride all the way to Wivencaster to bring you back, not with all the costs that would entail. We don't want any more of that.'

For some reason, Amos Peakman was eyeing Jem suspiciously. 'What this vestry has to decide is whether you are a genuine pauper,' he declared in the priggish self-rightousness of a wealthy and well-fed man addressing a more humble and ill-fed fellow. 'In my view, the welfare regime we have had in this parish in the past has been too liberal. It encouraged fecklessness and idleness and drunkenness, not to mention immorality, and discouraged honest labour.' The fact that the low wages he and others paid might also have affected a man's keenness to work did not occur to him.

As he spoke, he was staring straight at Jem as if he would be able to read the answer there on his face. 'If you are one of the idle poor, you will be sent to the new poorhouse at Inworth and be set to work there,' he said bluntly.

'I am here to work,' Jem declared, straightening up and lifting his head to show his determination.

'Any kind of work?' queried the parish clerk, overseer of the poor and surveyor of the roads, Joshua Jaikes, raising one eyebrow.

'Yes, any kind,' Jem answered. 'If there is work to be done, I will do it.'

At that point, Jem was asked to step outside so that they could discuss his request: after a few minutes waiting in the road, he was called back in by Elijah Candler.

'We cannot send you and your family to the poorhouse at Inworth as you have a place,' Amos Peakman told him, 'and, besides, I am told the poorhouse is full already with more needy inmates, the sick and the elderly and the orphans. The best we can do for you is to set you to work in return for a wage. You appear to be able-bodied, but whether you are deserving or not is another matter. We cannot offer outdoor relief, but we can offer you paid work – '

As Amos Peakman delivered the verdict, Jem could not help noticing that Joshua Jaikes was smirking, or at least trying to hide his smirk: Marcus Howie and Joshua Godwin were staring coldly at him in the manner of men who had no sympathy for him and considered he had brought the plight in which he now found himself upon himself, while the three 'turncoat' farmers, Richard Shadwell, John Dicker and Henry Sweetapple, did not meet his eyes, as if ashamed of their earlier decisions: again, only Elijah Candler, Caleb Chapman and Samuel Thorn revealed any sympathy.

Finally, the chairman turned to Joshua Jaikes. 'Mr Jaikes?' was all he said.

Jaikes realised what the tone of the call meant and replied instantly. 'Yes, Mr. Chairman, we have quite a number working on the old roads already, bringing them up to the same state as our new road. He can join them. We have much work to do. The old roads are in a poor state after the recent rains, as we all know. They have been neglected for too lomng. There are large puddles on the Hamwyte road where the drainage is poor and at the bottom of the hill towards Merchant

Staplers on the way to Langridge and the ridge-top road is heavily rutted.'

'And wages?' queried the chairman.

'I would respectfully suggest we pay him four shillings for the week, that is eightpence a day,' replied Joshua Jaikes, still with the smirk upon his face.

'Good, then that is settled,' said Amos Peakman: and, once the detail of Jem's hours had been fixed and the place where he was to begin decided, he was sent him out with a dismissive wave of the hand. The meeting wass over: the farmers had to get back to their work: they had wasted enough time on the paupers...

EIGHT

THE ROAD-MENDING schemes upon which the vestry committee set the unemployed and the paupers of the three parishes, poorly paid as they were, with a married man earning a mere four shillings a week, were funded from a special highways rate, the contributors to that fund being the same proprietors who paid into the general poor rate, such as Titus Broake, the large and middling farmers, the tradesmen and the other property owners, so they had a vested interest in ensuring that the work was done not only expeditiously but properly. They had deduced that the simplest way to reduce the amount paid out in relief was to stop people asking for it: and the way to do that was to give them hard and unrewarding work, like stonebreaking and road-mending, and pay them a pittance for doing it.

For that reason, Joshua Jaikes maintained his harshness, since any laxity or failure on his part would have reflected on himself and, at the next vestry election, he might well have found himself losing the paid posts of vestry clerk, overseer of the poor and parish surveyor. In short, it paid him to be harsh with the poor unfortunates whom he supervised in the vestry's name: and since Parson Petchey seldom concerned himself with the mundane matters of the real world when the spiritual world was in such greater need of his contemplation, he was able to rule with a free and very firm hand, an opportunity which a man of his character was not likely to scorn.

The next morning, when Jem reported to him at the cross-roads at eight o'clock, he had expected others to be there, but found himself alone in meeting the overseer, who rode up on his horse, for he seldom liked to walk.

'I have a special job for you,' declared Jaikes, still with the same malevolent smirk as he had showed the previous day. 'You are to be on the cart, delivering stones.'

Jem knew full well what he meant: one of Jaikes's latest innovations had been to introduce a two-wheeled parish cart, smaller than a farm cart, only up to the height of a man's chest, for performing the more menial practices of dung removal and collection of cow pats and horse droppings on the road – except there was no donkey to pull the cart, no ass and no horse either. It was meant as a deterrent to any idler seeking parish relief when he should, in his and the vestry's opinion, be able to find work elsewhere and Jaikes's practice was to harness into the shafts whatever poor unfortunate of whichever parish came to him for relief and whom he considered was able-bodied enough to pull it, especially if it were one of the several simpletons of the three parishes who might not think it so much of a humiliation to stand between the shafts, like 'Prickle' Witney when he had returned from his last roundsman's tramp. Jaikes would laugh and smile and walk beside him with a whip, which he delighted in cracking above his head, though never actually hitting him, which amongst the idiot kind was enough to instil wide-eyed fear and to send him scampering forward along the road with the loaded cart while Jaikes followed grinning to himself, bent solely on inflicting humiliation and nothing else.

One time he had even put an able-bodied woman between the shafts to pull a lighter load: on another occasion, he had made two youths of no more than fourteen years, whom he considered too recalcitrant towards him, pull the cart, loaded with cow dung and horse manure the whole three miles to Hamwyte. It took them a half-hour just to manoeuvre the heavily-weighted load down the steep hill past Chantrey wood without letting it go, while Jaikes rode alongside, warning them not to let it go 'or else!' On the way back, he made them stop on the hill on Mope Lane to load a pile of flints taken from Glebe Farm's new arable fields: the two sweating and exhausted youths then had to pull their heavy load up the rest of the steep hill to the parsonage, which lay at the junction there, and spread the shattered flints in a puddle in front of the parsonage gateway, a service for which Jaikes was paid two shillings, while the youths received nothing other than their weekly dole. Another time, the same two youths were made to trundle a load of sand and gravel all the way to Lower Rackstead just to fill a pothole in the single road that ran though the hamlet.

Jem, it turned out, was to take the cart threequarters of a mile or so out of the village to where the new road ran and an uneven track led off to the village's gravel pit, which had given the Gravel Pit field its name and from which over the past hundred years ton after ton of sand and gravel and flints had been extracted to be carted away and strewn upon the roads which passed through the parish. Normally, a horse or a donkey harnessed in a fair-sized cart would have been backed up to the pit and it would have been part of the work of four or five paupers on poor relief to dig out the sand and gravel and load it on to the cart, which then would be trundled to where yet more paupers were filling in the potholes and puddles.

As the sun rose on what was to prove one of the few hot June mornings of that year, Jem was led along the new road to the old gravel pit, which was about thirty yards square and some five feet deep and part-filled with water, which meant he would have to stand up to his knees in weed and slime while digging out the sand and gravel which there lies just under the sub-soil.

'Get this cart loaded,' ordered Joshua Jaikes with a barely disguised smirk. 'We just want the sand and small gravel today. They need to be taken to where the other men are working along the ridge-top. It is two-and-a-half miles there so I expect you to take a good load as I don't want too much going backwards and forwards and time-wasting.'

Then he stood back and watched as Jem slithered down into the pit and began to dig the gravel and sand out of the bank, thus constantly undermining it and enlarging the pit itself: it was heavy work and Jem was soon sweating profusely as he shovelled the heavy sand and gravel up on to the bank, which was itself at shoulder height to a man standing in the pit. The only way to ease the work was to adopt the rhythm of movement similar to the one men used when pitchforking up sheaves in the harvest field.

In the meantime, having set Jem to work, Jaikes trotted off on his horse, with a promise that he would be back in an hour 'after breakfast' to ensure his latest pauper was not slacking and that he expected the work to be done by his return: so Jem worked steadily, trying to pace his effort, every now and again, when he considered he had a large enough pile on the bank, clambering out and, taking a sieve hanging on the side of the cart, shovelling the sand and gravel on to it to separate the larger flints, everything larger than his thumbnail, before tipping them on to a pile nearby.

Eventually with Jaikes back and the cart more than half-full of the sand and smaller gravel and level almost with the backboard, a sweating Jem leaned upon his shovel, wiped his brow and declared, as if he expected the overseer to agree with him: 'Surely it is enough now, Mr Jaikes? If we put in any more, I shall not be able to pull it.' He used 'Mister' so as not to give his long-time adversary cause to find fault with him on his first day, but gritted his teeth as he did so.

Though it made sense for Jem to load only as much as he could reasonably pull by himself, when he stood between the shafts and gripped the two handles and lifted and pulled the cart a short way to test his strength, the perceived ease with which he managed it did not suit Joshua Jaikes. 'There's not half enough in there yet,' the overseer sneered. 'You can get another two-hundredweight or more in there.'

One did not argue with an overseer of the likes of Joshua Jaikes, for he would as soon dismiss a man from the parish's employ as hire him and Jem did not want to risk losing his only source of relief for himself and his family and, for ever after: so he descended into the pit again, without protest, and heaved another three dozen or so shovelsful of sand and stones up on to the bank.

The harness which Jaikes had had fitted comprised a broad leather belt, which buckled around the waist of the unfortunate who stood between the shafts, while two other leather straps passed over his shoulders and a third band went across his forehead so that by leaning forward all parts of his body were then exerted to pull the loaded cart: legs, back, shoulders and head. Fortunately, when Jaikes pronounced himself finally 'satisfied' with the weight of the load – or more to the point, the height of it – Jem managed to jerk the cart into motion by rocking it backwards and forwards for a short time as he stood between the shafts and then, with a great effort, to haul it along the uneven track to the road.

'We'll take this lot along the ridge,' declared Jaikes almost nonchalantly, as if no effort at all were required to move a load which probably weighed almost a ton. 'We'll dump that and be back for a second load before you know it!'

He laughed out loud as he said it, as if at his own wit, but made no attempt to help Jem, simply riding alongside on his horse, delighting in the other's struggle. Even to get the cart moving at all on the road, Jem needed evey ounce of his strength and his breath, for from there to the village the Merchant Staplers road rises gradually, no more than a foot or two in every fifty yards, but uphill nevertheless. It flattens briefly at the beginning of The Street, but then resumes its rise at the top end on to the ridge-top itself so that to maintian his momentum Jem had almost to run as he pulled, for there could be no stopping or slacking.

The trouble was, by the time he reached the ridge-top, it was past ten o'clock and the sun was above the treetops so there was little shade: fortunately, the years on the land had hardened Jem's muscles and thus, by virtue of the strength of his arms, even his bent arm, he was able to maintain his momentum as he trundled the cart through the village, conscious of the many eyes upon him, with Jaikes all the time riding alongside and urging him to keep going, as if to prove himself in command. Had he been a youth or a woman, Jem knew that the overseer would not have kept himself from shouting abuse as well: but there was something in Jem's determination as they progressed, almost a scorn for the overseer, a defiance of him, that deterred him from overstepping that boundary that day. Instead, he contented himself with the sight of one who had once defied and belittled him reduced to the status of a beast of burden: that, for the moment, was enough.

The men working on the ridge had expected that when the cart came up with its load of sand and shingle, there would be at least two with it, as there normally was, albeit one in the harness pulling and the other pushing against the backboard, for it was a task which required at least two who were physically fit alternating their roles, especially uphill. What they saw instead was a solitary figure in the harness struggling up the final part of the ridge-top road where it reaches the crest, his mouth agape as he gasped for air, almost on his knees, his face cortorted with the effort of it all, his shirt soaked with sweat and sweat shining, too, on his arms and streaming down his face and chest as if he had been doused with water: and beside him, riding high on his horse, the hated overseer. An angry shout went up as a half-dozen of the men threw down their tools and hurried back to help the struggling man, amongst them Dick Dollery, Enos Diddams, Thomas Judd and William Stubbs.

'Good God, it's Jem!' cried Dick Dollery and, whirling on Joshua Jaikes, he shouted angrily: 'This is no way to treat a man, especially a man with a limp and a crooked arm! This load is far too heavy for one man to pull. There ought to be two or three pushing a load like that!'

'He loaded it himself,' declared Joshua Jaikes, flinching at the unexpectedness of the men's anger and suddenly worried that he had perhaps overstepped the mark after all. Yet he was still ready to add a further lie to excuse himself: 'I told him where you were working. I told him it was a couple of miles or more. It was up to him how much he loaded on to the cart. If he thinks he can pull that much, then who am I to stop him?'

'The bloody overseer, that's who!' shouted Enos Diddams, seizing one of the shafts to take the weight off the straining Jem, while more hands did the same on the other shaft. 'No man ought to be expected to pull so much. You should have had someone to help him. Where are Peter Doe and Daniel Hockley! Why didn't they help him?'

Joshua Jaikes could not tell them that that very morning he had sent the two named youths, both sons of former husbandmen, whom he constantly assigned to dig out the sand and gravels, to another part of the parish to dig a ditch to run off the previous week's rains: he wanted no witnesses to Jem's ordeal.

Aware perhaps that an answer on that question would be got from the other two eventually, Joshua Jaikes adopted an officious tone as his only means of defence. 'They are working elsewhere today,' he retorted, 'doing what I told them to do. Peter Doe will be back at the gravel pit tomorrow. Today he has other work to do. It is my job as the overseer and surveyor to give the orders. I tell the people what to do. I am in charge.

When one of the other men declared angrily, 'You could have helped the man yourself, you could have given him a push,' the overseer simply shrugged his shoulders: his indifference had returned. 'It's not my job to pull the cart. It's his and yours,' he snapped. 'If he wants parish relief, he has to work for it. And so do you. So get back to work, all of you, or I'll lay the lot of you off. There's others who'd be glad to take your place, so mind what you say. Back to work, the lot of you.'

It was enough of a threat to stifle the anger of the rest for the moment: they released Jem from the harness as he barely had the strength to do it himself, gave him a long drink of ale from the jug they had collected from Caleb Chapman's inn that morning on their way to their work and allowed him to rest by the roadside. It was noticeable, however, that when Jem went back for the next load, Joshua Jaikes ordered a youth named Shadrach Coe to accompany him and help to haul the cart up the long hill on the return: and the load thereafter was only half what Jem had hauled the two miles by himself.

Whatever the feelings of the men, Joshua Jaikes was clearly determined to heap humiliation upon his old adversary whenever and however he could: his only concession was to direct one of the normal diggers, Peter Doe, to return to the gravel pit the next day to help him dig out the flints, sieve the smaller ones from the sandy soil and then to help haul the cart for the rest of that day. Jem, however, was under no illusions as far as Joshua Jaikes was concerned: even though the overseer-cum-surveyor of roads no longer attempted to influence his load, he persisted in keeping Jem in the harness: after the men had argued with him along the Lower Rackstead road and had forced him to back down, that grudge had deepened.

For his part, Dick Dollery was still seething about the overseer's treatment of Jem when the two sat again in the Wayfarers' that Saturday evening for the first time since Jem's return, drinking their tuppence worth of Caleb Chapman's ale: 'Don't worry, Jem,' he growled, 'his day will come. His day will come.'

NINE

JEM CONTINUED to haul the cart all through the rest of that July when torrential downpours soaked him to the skin, caused ditches to overflow and created small lakes on the fields where the corn was growing, giving rise to all manner of blights and drowning the shoots in places. Indeed, such was the force of the swollen Langwater's flow on its upper reaches that it washed away an old packbridge at Blanc Leyton and at Tidwolton, amid the saltmarsh below Maydun hill, even altered its course. Unhappily, the rains extended into August, flattening much of the corn, which meant the harvest was worse than any previous year and very late: consequently, many of the men were back in the fields, being employed at a shilling and sixpence a day to get-in the wheat and barley, work which to them was more important and more satisfying than road-mending at eightpence a day.

For Jem, however, being a marked man and unemployable, there was little else he could do but soldier on pulling the cart, delivering stones and sand to those who remained mending the roads, for there were still a dozen or so whom no one would employ, mostly the recalcitrant youths: and, so as to give Joshua Jaikes no cause to find fault, he made sure that he was up with the sun, that he was in his place at the gravel pit even before the usual digger, Peter Doe, arrived and that there was always a pile of stones or a pile of shale and sand at the various road-mending sites for the men to break or to spread, for he knew that, if there were not, Jaikes would declare the both of them slackers and threaten to dock a day's money or more from their relief.

In a single day, he and Peter Doe might make two trips to the six men who were still working down the bottom of Chantrey wood, two more trips to the men along the ridge-top road and two more again to whoever was working elsewhere: but, since the cart was no longer overloaded, they were able together to manage the long haul up the Merchant Staplers road to the top of The Street, hard work though it was. Once over the ridge-top, if they were going downhill past Chantrey wood, the descent was a matter of Jem in the harness keeping one hand on the long-handled wheel brake while Peter Doe hung on to the tailgate all the way down, his feet scraping the earth, so that the cart did not run away from them: on the return uphill, of course, it was empty and easier to pull.

As part of his task, Jem was ordered sometimes to trundle the cart on his own to one or other of the farmers' fields and pick up a load of flints which had been lifted by the younger boys and girls of the village, the nine-year-olds and ten-year-olds, at fourpence a day, Jed and Thirza amongst them, for all worked now. Late one afternoon he picked up a load from the roadside by Amos Peakman's newly enclosed fields around Goat Lodge and, since it was downhill all the way, trundled it by himself to a spot along the Maydun-to-Wivencaster road where a youth named Silas Tuttle had been working alone for the past fortnight.

Tuttle, eighteen years of age, red-haired, heavy boned, with a lantern jaw and a disfiguring mole on his chin, was known for his surliness and his willingness to raise his fists and take umbrage at the merest hint of a disagreement with his opinions. He was being punished for having shown that same irritability towards the overseer when reprimanded by him and bitterly resented it: the grinding boredom of sitting alone by the side of the road all day in all weathers with no one to whom he could talk to pass the time, monontously wielding a long-handled hammer to break the various flints into small pebble-sized chippings, only added to his unfriendliness.

When Jem reached him, Tuttle was seated on the ground, with his hammer raised, about to strike a flint between his splayed legs. 'I don't need any more. I have enough already,' he growled in a resentful tone when the load of stones was tipped on to the ground nearby.

The sun that day was hot – hotter than it had been for some time – and the sky cloudless: Jem had paused to rest before making the long climb back up the hill to the gravel pit hauling the cart when, unexpectedly, a gig came bowling along from the direction of Maydun and its driver reined in alongside them.

'Am I on the right road for Hamwyte?' a red-faced man, with a high black hat, black topcoat and a set of red mutton-chop whiskers, asked, tugging at the collar and buttons of his black surcoat because of the extreme heat of the day to reveal a clergyman's white cravat. He spoke with an accent which had a distinct West Country or Cornish burr to it.

At the man's question, Tuttle, simply let out a sigh of exasperation. 'No, thee are miles out of thy way, man,' he said, wearily, for he showed no more respect for a parson than he would for anyone else: it was almost as if he were blaming the clergyman for his stupidity in getting himself lost.

'You need to go a mile farther on and take a left turn up the hill by the guidepost,' declared Tuttle, pointing with his hammer. 'Thee'll come to a village street. Go straight on there, over the ridge-top and down the hill on t'other side and no doubt thee'll find thyself in Hamwyte eventually, if thee doesn't get lost again.'

Having received his instructions, however, the clergyman made no attempt to move off, but instead eyed Tuttle curiously as if interested in what he was doing, like one who had not seen a man doing such work before. Then, looking about him, he unexpectedly began to enthuse about the weather, the countryside and the perfection of the day. 'Such fine countryside around here,' he declared, smiling to himself. 'Such a lovely day after all the rain...' And such wonderful profusion in the hedgerows, such an abundance of bird life and such wonderful animal life, too. Did they not think so being country dwellers? And what were those flowers there, those pink ones. And those purple ones there? And the flowers in the hedgerow, what did they call them? Such wonderful pretty things, did they not think? 'All God's Creation! All God's Creation! Sent by God to bless us all.'

For one who had walked three miles to his stonebreaking task even as the sun came up and had sat alone for hour upon hour with no one to whom he might talk through a day of heat and thirst, in the open without the comfort of a tree's shade, Tuttle was in no mood for such facetious homilies: the man's prattle was interrupting his work and the need to meet that day's quota of broken stone which Joshua Jaikes had set him.

'I can't say that I takes much notice of flowers and birds when I am working at this,' he replied, sarcastically, striking at another flint between his legs. 'What I will say, though, is, if it is a part of God's Creation to make it rain on us hard enough to sting our faces when we are seated out here doing our work and give us all manner of ills, if it is part of God's Creation to send us howling winds in winter cold enough to cut through our bones and, if it is part of God's Creation, to give us blizzards fierce enough to freeze a body to death out here if he has not enough clothing to keep himself warm, then it is a queer kind of Creation you speak of!'

The clergyman chose not to hear the sarcasm or the irritation in Tuttle's voice: he simply smiled and enquired, almost as if he felt that he had a right to such information: 'Is this your normal work?'

'No, it's what we do to get our money from the parish,' retorted the surly Tuttle, squinting up at the man through the bright sunlight like one who had only one eye.

'And is this your only work?' the parson asked next, undeterred.

'Aye, it is for me,' Tuttle answered. 'Spring, summer, autumn and winter. It's work, that's all, work to earn money. If I did nothing, I would get nothing. No doubt we shall be here all winter as well.'

'Can you not get work for the coming winter on the farms?' the man in the gig asked, puzzled by the reply.

'Farmers'll only employ older married men for winter work round here because they'll take what they're offered without making a fuss over it,' Tuttle brusquely informed him in the manner of one who expected the clergyman to know such things. 'They 'on't take on the younger men because they knows they would want more than the farmers are willing to give. Even then, they're not taken on all the time, just when they are needed, like now for harvesting. Round here, most of the men are driven on to relief in the winter months – married or bachelor, it makes no difference to the farmers. For most on'em, once the harvesting is done, there 'on't be no work on the farms till the spring, if they're lucky, and they'll be back road-mending like me.' He banged the hammer down hard upon the flint between his legs and sent a fractured splinter flying against the horse's foreleg which unsettled the animal and forced the clergyman to tug at the reins to bring it under control.

'Are you married?' the clergyman asked after a short pause, having pacified his horse. 'You are a young man yet.'

Tuttle scoffed at the man's question. 'Married! Me? Huh, I am in no hurry to wed and have the likes of some half-arsed parson lecture me on a Sunday morning about marrying too quick and bringing little'uns into the world when they are better left out of it, like I have heard with my own ears in our own church. We poor all has too many children, we are told. That is why we are poor, they tell us. My answer to that is, what is the point of a man lying abed with a young wife if he don't put her infamily way? En't that what marriage is for? To have little'uns by? Least, I always thought so. En't that why we men have been given what we have been given and women have been given what they have been given? – ' He said it with a certain malicious relish, knowing that the implied crudity of his comments would irritate the clergyman. ' – En't that the reason for us being on this earth? "To go forth and multiply!" like it says in the Bible. And when a man does do it, he is wrong to do it, they tells us. Religion! Huh! T'is all chaff, all chaff.'

The clergyman coughed loudly. 'Yes, quite, quite,' he stuttered, realising the impudence of the youth's remarks: and, keen to change the subject, looking down at the small pile of shattered stones which was no more than a few inches high and foot round, he added somewhat condescendingly: 'You seem to have done a great deal. How long have you been at your work?''

'What time is it?' enquired Silas Tuttle, gruffly, as if to say, 'How would I know how long I have been here? I have no fancy pocket watch. I have to judge the day by the sun, when it shines, that is.'

The man in the gig fumbled inside his coat and pulled out a silver-cased fob watch and announced grandly: 'Five minutes after four.'

'Then I have been at this nine hours, since seven this morning, Tuttle informed him sourly, 'and I doubt I will have done half enough to suit our esteemed overseer and surveyor when he comes, since he is never satisfied with anything.'

Tuttle's exasperation was genuine, for a good two hours of work still remained before he could end it: like all stone-breakers, he had a daily quota to fulfil and knew that Jaikes would insist upon it being fulfilled when he rode down to check upon him. If the overseer-cum-surveyor were not satisified with the work done, Tuttle faced the prospect of having to work another two hours or so to complete it, and then to walk the three miles back home: hence his replies spoken as one who wished to get rid of a pest.

'My, my,' said the clergyman, tut-tutting through his teeth. 'Do they pay you much for your work?'

'I gets four shillings a week, sir, because I have a family,' Jem answered truthfully, speaking up for the first time..

'And I gets two shillings and sixpence a week because I don't have no family yet,' answered the youth, deliberately omitting his 'sir.'

'And how do you live upon two-shillings-and-sixpence a week?' the man in the gig asked, incredulous at the fact that Tuttle received so little.

'I don't live on it,' said the youth, sharply, 'I poach. I take anything which ought to be free to all of us – rabbits, hares, fish if I can catch'em, pigeons, too, doves, pheasants, any animal I sees and which no man has a right to say they own and no one else does.'

'But the punishment for that is fearful,' said the driver of the gig, aghast at the casualness of the youth's confession. 'You would have to trespass on another man's land to do that.'

'Aye, and I do?' shrugged the youth, as if he did not care one way or the other, which he did not. 'I goo where there is free food to be had for the taking, all provided, as you say, by the Good Lord. All God's Creation!' He dropped another flint between his legs and struck it forcefully with his hammer. 'And if I hadn't found other means to eke out my wages over the past six months, my mother and my brothers and sisters and me, we would all have been business for you and your kind long agoo because we should not have been able to keep body and soul together.'

'But the risk!' protested the clergyman, 'the risk of imprisonment, of transportation – '

'When you are hungry, when you have no food in the house, you do not care how the rabbit or the guinea fowl is got so long as it is in the pot and bubbling away,' said the youth with a shrug. 'It is better to be boated to Van Diemen's Land for fourteen years than to starve to death here. At least you would be alive and breathing air and not pushing up daisies from a pauper's grave!'

The clergyman reddened: the youth's casual confession to a felony had shocked him to the core: whether it was true or done for just that purpose, he was unsure: but he suspected that most probably it was true. Enough was enough: he did not wish to hear anymore: he tugged at the reins to warn the horse and, with a click of his tongue, set the animal trotting on its way.

'Damned fool of a parson!' snorted Tuttle, returning to his stone-breaking and giving the new flint an extra hard blow to dissipate his anger. 'What does he know about work and a working man when he has never done a day's work in his life? What does he know about hunger, him and his kind, when they have never been hungry? Damn them to hell, I say, the lot on'em!'

'It wasn't smart to say what you did,' Jem told him, though he said it with a smile, for he, too, had been startled by Tuttle's casual admission and his total indifference to it.

'T'is true. If I did not goo poaching every now and agin, I should starve,' declared Tuttle, 'and so would my Old Lady and my brothers and sisters – ' He paused and looked across at Jem with a wicked grin upon his face. ' – If thee wants to come with me, I'm going to have a goo at the pheasants they breed in Chantrey wood tomorrow night. One of the lads knows where they are. T'is meat on the table when all is said and done. If you fancy coming along, we'll all be meeting in the Carpenters' Arms tomorrow night. There's four on us – '

'Chantrey is Titus Broake's land now,' said Jem, who was in the act of turning the cart, somewhat alarmed at the youth's nonchalance. 'He owns the wood. You don't want to get caught in there by his gamekeeper.'

'Who, Jonathan Trott?' The youth scoffed at the name of the gamekeeper, whom Titus Broake had hired from Lower Rackstead. 'It'd take a better man than him to catch us, four of us to him – we won't get caught. Besides, no one knows we're going. We only decided ourselves last night. You're welcome to come, if you want and the others agree. We have two guns. You was a soldier, I heard, so you ought to be able to shoot straight enough. We'd be in an out a lot quicker if we had someone like you with us.'

'No thanks,' replied Jem. 'I'm not a man to go poaching. I've already had one visit from Elijah Candler and Broake's new gamekeeper, looking for evidence they didn't find, upsetting my wife. I don't want another.'

TEN

TWELVE YEARS before, in 1817, pauperism, desperation and discontent had fuelled the riot in Hamwyte for which five men had forfeited their existence on this earth: of the nineteen others who had been transported to the other side of the world, to New South Wales and Van Diemen's Land, none had yet returned, if they were still alive to return, and none knew whether they were or not. That same hunger still existed and, in Hamwick Dean, sent the same kinds of desperate men and youths crawling at night into the dank undergrowth of the woods there – and indeed sent others crawling the same into woods and copses in ten thousand other places throughout the country – all seeking to put on their tables the food which they could not obtain by waged employment.

Unhappily, the belief amongst the ruling elite was that only a brutal system of punishment would ever deter the poor from their criminal ways: to them, land ownership was precious and poaching was an intolerable infringement upon their domain: they considered all wild life that moved across their preserve belonged to them. None seemed to realise that a man whose family was starving would throw caution to the winds if he knew that a covey of fat pheasants was being bred in a nearby wood and that the only table they were ever likely to grace would be that of the very man whom they blamed for their misery – in the case of Hamwick Dean, Titus Broake: that same ruling elite seemed not to understand that poaching was rife because many of the people of rural England were near to starving.

When thirteen years before, in 1816, the advent of the Peace and the sudden discharge of thousands of soldiers and sailors on to the labour market and the sudden fall in grain prices had brought mass unemployment, hunger and inevitably crime in their wake, the Parliament of landowners and gentry had passed a Bill, which for its harshness had no parallel in the laws of any other country: under it, any person found at night in any forest, chase or park, unarmed but with a net for poaching, was to be punished by transportation for seven years to Van Diemen's Land or New South Wales. The severity of such laws raised considerable disquiet amongst the more liberal minded and, in the following year, the Act was repealed, to be replaced by another Act which, though it softened the law to the extent of withdrawing that punishment from persons found with just nets, but without guns or bludgeons, it still decreed that anyone found with a gun, a crossbow, firearms of any kind, a bludgeon or any other offensive weapon while poaching, was to be tried at Quarter Sessions and, if convicted, still to be transported for seven years: and further, if the offender were to attempt to return to England before their time, they would be transported back to New South Wales or Van Diemen's Land for the rest of their lives. Even that Act had been replaced by yet another Act, which allowed a person convicted before two magistrates to be sentenced to three months in gaol for the first offence, to six months on the second conviction, with the harshest form of punishment, transportation for seven or fourteen years, being retained only for the third offence.

When Silas Tuttle invited Jem to join his nocturnal foray, it was the third of these Acts which appertained, not that Tuttle cared one way or the other: such were the times that, despite the draconian laws, the gaols and Houses of Correction throughout the country were filled by those convicted under the Game Code, many of them, like Tuttle, youths of eighteen or under: their youth, however, did not prevent them from being transported.

Of course, not all poachers were paupers of the parish or starving labourers: some men were poachers from the love of it, regarding their regular sallies into the woods and fields around their respective villages as much of a sport as those who had taken up the new sport of shooting game: but the majority of those who crept through hedgerows to lay their traps or slipped from tree to tree through the darkness or padded stealthily along woodland paths did so from distress. Others, however, were organised gangs, operating often at the behest of some poulterer or butcher in a nearby town, stealing turkeys or chickens or lambs or even whole sheep or whole cattle to order: for the stolen carcass of a sheep or a bullock, say, could earn them more in a single night than they were paid in a week of work: and some coach drivers to London would willingly carry stolen game or a sheep's or butchered cow's carcass, unbeknown to their passengers.

What was a known fact was that, in Chantrey wood, there was game aplenty to be had: for, having acquired the wood's hundred-and-nine acres in its entirety as part of the enclosure allotment, Titus Broake had, as a man now of even greater wealth and status, taken up the new sport of shooting for pleasure, which had become prevalent amongst the richer classes as a source of leisure: indeed, he had hired his gamekeeper, Trott, from Lower Rackstead, for that very reason, since he had kept game on two estates there, one owned by Her Ladyship no less. With Trott's skill in rearing the birds, Titus Broake had been able to hold several shoots already, inviting several of his well-to-do friends from Hamwyte and Melchborough, to shoot there, like him, all men of some wealth and influence, including the Lord Lieutenant of the county and the County Sheriff no less, all done with a purpose in mind, of course, a hoped-for knighthood and a seat in Parliament as one of Hamwyte's two Members since old Sir Benton Brierley's health was on the wane.

Like other gentlemen of England, Titus Broake took to guarding this special amusement by methods which even the aristocrats of France had never used on their peasants before the Revolution: a man or youth who sought to poach on his preserve risked being maimed for life in any one of a number of vicious traps and other devices which his gamekeeper Trott had laid. For what galled Titus Broake was the seeming belief amongst some around Hamwick Dean and Hamwyte that they could poach the pheasants on his land with impunity: Trott had found the evidence on a path through the wood, had seen the torn leaves and twigs ripped from the outer branches of the trees bordering it by the volleys of pellets, yet he had not been able to catch a single one of them.

The pheasants continued to vanish and evidence of rabbit snares had been found in a half-dozen places: it was almost as if some of the villagers regarded a brace of pheasants or a couple of rabbits as their right, like an unregulated form of poor relief. It was none of his doing that there were so many poor in the village: that so many of them lived in poverty: that they bred so fast and idled their time away, drinking in the two ale houses. The need for enclosure to feed the population and expand the country had been obvious to everyone except the husbandmen and small farmers of Hamwick Dean and the other places: it had already helped to reduce the village's population: and that very month, two further families had departed under the cover of darkness.

Poaching, however, was a different matter: it was becoming rife: indeed, the majority of cases he and his fellow magistrates heard at the court in Hamwyte were of people charged under the Game Laws, almost one in seven of all convictions, and all of them seemed to have a grudge against the landowner or to complain that they did. So when it came to poaching, he needed only to look to the poorest in the village for his culprits: it was a simple matter to him – find one who bore him a grudge, like that Stebbings fellow, the one with the limp, the one who had been a soldier and so knew how to handle a gun, and probably his boy, too. After all, the father had been in the House of Correction, sentenced to six weeks, with hard labour on the crank-handle for stealing a branch from his land, so Heginbotham had reported to him – and had deserved it, too! It was the same Stebbings fellow who had spoken out against him over enclosure and had sold the land he had been given and then done nothing with the money save sit in his cottage and brood and probably spend it all at the Wayfarers' Inn with his cronies.

After Trott had found a pheasant dropped on a path in Chantrey, he had told that fool of a parish constable, the cooper, Elijah Candler, to go round to Stebbings's cottage with his gamekeeper to look for tell-tale plucked feathers: they had not found any 'evidence,' as the parish constable called it, but, put all the facts together – the grudge, the need, the soldier's skill with a gun – and it was obvious who was the most likely perpetrator. It stood to reason that it was likely to be him and his son, since they were most in need and he had heard from Trott that, since he had returned from Steadleigh, he was even living in some self-built hovel along the Lower Rackstead road, not a half-mile from Chantrey itself.

ELEVEN

THE CARPENTERS' ARMS, though no more than two rooms of a cottage with a dirt floor, rough tables and benches for its customers and a plank for a bar upon which stood a single barrel, did have two attractions which had always drawn the day-labourers there over the years. The first was that Jack Tickle always charged a mite less for his home-brewed ale than did Caleb Chapman, even though it was just as good and regularly tested by the ale tester, the former Little Court clerk, Josiah Bright: second, of late, it had become the place where plots could be, and were, hatched, which saw men and youths stealing across open land towards woods and warrens in the dead of night and returning some hours later with bulging sacks slung over their shoulders: and, since beer cost more than many an unemployed man or youth could regularly afford, a bundle of wood taken from a copse, a few turnips lifted from a field, a partridge or a pheasant shot before it could rise or a rabbit caught in a snare helped to pay a regular drinking man's debt to the landlord.

Others drank there, too, of course, for various reasons: because their fathers had always drunk there, because they could not abide the unrelenting dourness of Caleb Chapman at the Wayfarers', because the one-time independent husbandmen and traders drank at the other place, because Jack Tickle was more generous in allowing a man to put a drink on the slate – for which he exacted extra on payment, anyway – and, for some, because they were barred from other places because of arguments or fights.

One who did like to slake his thirst there occasionally, simply because it was the nearest hostelry to his cottage and mill along the Merchant Staplers road, was Abel Tedder, the corn miller: as the moon came up over the top of the trees late that evening, he decided to visit the ale house and join some male company and also to forget his troubles, which then were great.

Normally at that time of the year, he looked forward to continuous work milling the grain, particularly over the winter and into the spring as the farmers brought their grain to him: but two poor harvests in succession had altered that: though there had been a good grain harvest in Twenty-Seven, by coincidence and poor luck, it had been followed by a bad harvest in Twenty-Eight: which had been exceedingly wet. Twenty-Nine had proved even worse and the larger farmers all over the Hundred, as well as the new middling farmers, desperate to get in their grain and not knowing what lay ahead, were rushing it to market at Hamwyte, Wivencaster and Melchborough and selling it rather than storing it as they used to do, which did not augur well for the miller's work that winter: hence his troubles.

Abel Tedder was making his way up the long hill from his mill when he saw Jem Stebbings hauling the empty parish cart a hundred or so yards ahead: he was surprised to see him on the road so late and supposed that he must have made a late delivery of stones to one of the road-mending sites so that, come the morning, there would be enough stones to enable whoever was there to begin. He could not but help feel a pang of sympathy for the former husbandman: for he knew that it was all a part of Joshua Jaikes's humiliation of him, just as he had humiliated others in the past, and he marvelled at Jem's fortitude and forbearance. Over the weeks, the miller had seen the former husbandman a dozen or more times about the village, hauling the cart with a load of sand and shingle or a load of stones: in fact, he had seen him only the previous day, pulling the loaded cart past his windmill down the hill towards Merchant Staplers and the Maydun road, where the mouthy, headstrong, surly Tuttle youth was working.

To the miller's eyes, from the way the former husbandman walked, heavy footed, with a rocking motion to keep the cart moving, he looked to be completely exhausted: by his reckoning, most days Jem Stebbings would probably cover a dozen miles to-ing and fro-ing between the gravel pit and the different road-mending sites.

The distance between the two was too great for Abel Tedder to catch Jem: he guessed that he was heading home: for he knew that, after unharnessing himself, he would leave the cart overnight on the verge outside his cottage – or the tumbledown hovel built half into the bank on the Lower Rackstead road which he called a 'cottage' and which the miller had once passed on one of his trips out of the village.

Normally, at such an early hour, the Carpenters' Arms would have been empty as most of the men did not begin their drinking till well after eight, which was why he was surprised to see the sullen-faced Tuttle seated with five others in the tiny backroom of the Carpenters' Arms and even more surprised to see the much older Dick Dollery sat with them, since, in all the years that Abel Tedder had been drinking in the Carpenters' Arms, he had seldom been a customer there and, indeed – if he were not mistaken, which he was not – was one of the most regular of all the regulars at the Wayfarers' Inn. So why had Dick Dollery deserted his normal place? That was the first question which came into Abel Tedder's mind: the second was, 'Why was he with the mouthy Tuttle youth?'

He had no reason to believe they were there for any other purpose than to drink and to smoke away their troubles, for the air was already thick with pipe smoke: however, had he pushed open the door a minute earlier, he would have heard the answer alluded to at least and some interesting conversation between Dick Dollery and the four others seated with him – Tuttle, an even younger village youth named William Skinner, at sixteen the 'half-lad' of the group, a Merchant Staplers youth of nineteen named George Goffin, whom Abel Tedder had seen but did not actually know, and John Threadneedle, an older married man in his mid-twenties with two young children whom Abel Tedder and everyone else considered to be a sensible type and so was surprised to see drinking in the company of three at least whom he knew to be hare-brained, namely Dick Dollery, Silas Tuttle and young Skinner.

'I'd bet five shillings I won't miss a shot tonight,' Dick Dollery had declared a minute earlier.

'You had better not,' was the reply from William Skinner with a laugh. 'I risked life and limb on Salter church roof to get the lead for this caper.'

He had indeed: and a small part of that lead which had kept the raindrops from falling upon the heads of the pious folk of Salter – drops which were now caught in a wooden bucket next to the pulpit – lay in a bulky double sack at Dick Dollery's feet, pushed from view under the table, for much of the lead had been melted down and turned into small round pellets of the kind poachers like: and wrapped in the same bulky sack were two hunting guns and a pistol, Fortuitously, as the guns were being slipped under the table, the landlord, Jack Tickle, turned away to busy himself elsewhere: seeing no evil and hearing no evil, he could always profess to knowing no evil.

'Well, boys, damn the flincher!' declared the Merchant Staplers youth, George Goffin, raising his pot to make the toast, though, in effect, it was not an actual toast, but a threat to all of them at the table that, whatever their venture that night, none must cut and run from it.

'Damn and blast the first that flinches,' repeated the red-headed Silas Tuttle, who had assumed the leadership of the affair, raising his own glass and swallowing the last of his ale in one gulp.

Abel Tedder, had he heard it, might have wondered, too, what the last sentence spoken aloud was about: for as he pushed the door shut, Silas Tuttle said to a nervous William Skinner: 'And this time, don't drop the bloody thing!' The miller was not to know, of course, that it was an allusion to a previously shot pheasant, dropped on a path and lost, one that had led to Elijah Candler and the gamekeeper Trott visiting Jem's 'cottage.'

At that, realising someone else had come into the tavern, their talk was more whispered and eventually passed on to other subjects, though they remained drinking till well into the late evening and left the inn just before half-past ten. Outside, they walked in casual pairs up The Street, turned at the cross-roads on to the ridge-top road and, hidden by the darkness, padded stealthily on towards Lower Rackstead. Part way along that road, they halted under the shadow of one of the trees by Goat Lodge Lane and Silas Tuttle, who had been carrying the sack, now pulled out two long-barrelled game guns, one of which he gave to George Goffin and the other he handed to Dick Dollery with the comment: 'I hope you do know how to shoot because the targets won't be as stationary as the ones you shot at in your the Volunteer days.' The pistol he stuck in his own waist belt: from the sack also were produced two lengths of wood, each about three-feet long, which were taken by William Skinner and the older John Threadneedle: the sack with the pellets was also handed to young Skinner to carry.

The sky was a mixture of dark clouds and bright moonlight: after a last look round to ensure that no one was spying upon them, they climbed the hurdle gate there and set off across the ploughed field towards the dark mass of Chantrey wood rearing up like an impenetrable black wall on the skyline: all was done silently, as if each man knew his part. Once in amongst the shadows of Chantrey, the five poachers crept forward some forty of fifty yards and the three guns formed a line while the two with the bludgeons went wide to act as beaters to make the pheasants rise: and the pheasants were quick to fly once the men started.

They were not to know that word had reached Titus Broake that a poaching foray was to be made sometime that week into Chantrey: none knew by whom it was passed first, though it was not unknown for a 'blower' to be planted amongst the poaching kind to learn of just such ventures. This time, it was more likely to have been a man standing at the plank bar of the Carpenters' Arms on a previous night, overhearing the plan being mooted and mentioning it to someone else, who passed it on again till it reached the ears of the new gamekeeper, Trott, and eventually Titus Broake himself.

The lord of the manor's response had been immediate: Trott was detailed to act as a watch, which he had done over three nights, armed with two pistols, and accompanied by two other men not known in the villagers, both poor labourers from Higher Rackstead in need of money, one named Henry Brewster, the other William Southgate, who were also armed each with a long-barrelled pistol and a flintlock gaming piece.

Tuttle was the first to fire his pistol and brought down a pheasant and Trott, hearing the gunshot, began running towards the sound: at that time, he and the other two watchers, Brewster and Southgate, were separated not only by the denseness of the trees and the brush but also by some fifty or sixty yards: thus, he was alone when he came out of the trees on to one of the dozen or so rides which criss-crossed the wood and unexpectedly found himself not thirty yards from the five poachers, all with neckerchiefs tied over their mouths.

At that very moment, Dick Dollery was taking aim at a pheasant which had risen overhead from the undergrowth: their backs were turned to Trott so they were oblivious to his approach: as Dick Dollery fired and the bird fluttered down, his four companions shouted with delight.

'Stand where you are or I will fire!' commanded Trott loudly when the cheering had subsided. 'I am armed. I mean to take you rogues tonight if it is the last thing I do.'

TWELVE

FOR A MOMENT there was stunned silence as the five poachers sought to discern from where the command had come: then, turning, they saw Trott standing in the middle of the ride, a pistol in each hand.

By then, Tuttle had reloaded his own pistol and when he saw that Trott was alone and that no one emerged from the shadows to join him, with all the arrogance of youth, he went forward a few paces to place himself in front of his comrades as if daring the gamekeeper to carry out his threat. Even with a brace of pistols in his hands, a solitary man, standing alone against five others, three of whom were themselves armed, would not have the gall to fire, he reasoned, neither to harm any of them and certainly not to kill any of them just to protect his master's game.

'We are armed, too,' Tuttle shouted and waved his own pistol to show the gamekeeper.

Hardly had Tuttle uttered the words than there was a flash in the shadows under the trees and a ball whistled over their heads, tearing at the lower twigs and embedding itself in the trunk of an ash tree: seconds later, even as the twigs and leaves showered down, Brewster, the first of the two watchers to reach the scene, stepped out into the moonlight. He, too, had come running and, on seeing five figures, three of whom were armed with guns, facing the gamekeeper and one of them waving a pistol at him and shouting defiantly, he had fired into the trees above their heads in the vain hope of panicking them into making a run for it: instead, all five stood their ground.

The lanky gamekeeper was experienced enough not to be fazed by the sound of an unexpected gunshot: better, he could turn it to his advantage. 'I told you to stand where you are,' he shouted, as if the whole thing were planned. 'The next one will not be so high. You are on private land. These are private woods and what is in it belongs to its owner and he don't hold with no poachers!'

Behind Tuttle there was a muttered curse, then a flash and the report of a gun: George Goffin, panicked by the first shot, had raised his own long-barrelled firearm and it had accidentally discharged:

thirty yards away, the figure of Trott, silhouetted against the lighter sky of the ride, doubled over, dropping one of his pistols as if it had become red hot and clutching at his hand. 'The damned rogues have shot me!' he cried as if incredulous that it should have happened to him 'They have shot me! I am hit, dammit, I am hit!'

As the lanky gamekeeper stumbled away to get out of range, half-cursing and half-weeping with the pain of his wound, Brewster, anxious to follow him and not to be left to face five armed poachers alone, thrust the long-barrelled gaming pistol into his belt and unslung the flintlock gaming piece from his shoulder, which he then swung up to point at the five who had just wounded his governor and began to retreat backwards towards the shadows in a state of some panic, obviously fearing that the next shot would injure him. 'I'll fire if I have to,' he called out as a warning, 'I will, I'll fire!'

The moonlight was bright enough even at a distance of thirty or so yards to read the expression of panic upon his face: almost as if by instinct, Dick Dollery sensed what was about to happen. As the former farmworker crossed the divide between moonlight and the dark, he flung himself sideways: an instant later, there was another flash and he heard the passage of lead shot whistle past above his prone form.

From behind, there was a high and loud shriek of pain: at the end of the line, William Skinner, the sixteen-year-old carrying the sack, in half-turning away, had taken a cluster of the pellets from Brewster's gaming gun full in the left side of his face: some had gone into his eye, some had embedded themselves in his cheek and slashed across his forehead and the rest had torn off half of his ear.

'They've shot my eye out! I'm blinded! I'm blinded!' he shrieked and lurched away into the darkness, howling like a dog as the blood streamed down his face, desperately trying to stem it with his neckerchief and his shirtfront

The second watcher, Southgate, meanwhile, who had been farther away when he had heard the first gunshot, had come up more stealthily, not wanting to blunder into any crossfire: he emerged on to the ride some fifty yards back, just where the injured Trott was leaning against a tree for support, moaning with the pain of his wound and attempting to bandage his shattered hand with a neckerchief of his own. At that point, the retreating Brewster joined them at a run: from somewhere in the darkness, they could all hear the moans and wails and weeping of the wounded Skinner.

Tuttle, at that time, was creeping forward at a crouch through the shadows, his pistol cocked, determined to avenge his injured friend by chasing the wounded gamekeeper and his two watchers from the wood: having gone some thirty yards and seeing nothing in the shadows, he fired a speculative blast into the darkness in the general direction of the moaning sound, hoping that act alone would be enough to persuade the three to retreat and leave them to their business. By chance rather than aim, the pellets cut through the leaves and branches near enough to the three watchers to make them believe they had been spotted: they turned and fled, their curses and cries in the quiet of the wood seeming to be amplified amongst the vaulted lower branches of the ancient trees.

'We've got the blighters now,' a triumphant Tuttle shouted and, pausing only to ram some more shot down the barrel and put some powder in the pan, he set off at a run after them and fired again in the general direction of the noise of the fleeing men as they crashed through the bushes and undergrowth, but without much hope of hitting anyone. Indeed, all that happened was that the blast of the gun made the three run even faster so that, in their desperate attempt to find a way through the old hedgerow surrounding the wood, they tried to barge their way through it, ignoring the pain of the thorn scratching at their arms and faces.

Unfortunately, poor William Southgate was the slowest: his coat became caught on the spiky thorn branches and he was only halfway through, with his head in the open field and his feet in the wood still, when he was seized and held by the agile Tuttle and Goffin, who had caught up. Southgate's two companions, if they heard his cry for help at all as he tried to disentangle himself, ignored it and continued to flee across the ploughed field towards a barn and other buildings which, along with a small two-storey house, had been erected on one of three new farms created since enclosure, this one tenanted by the Scots incomer, Angus McCreef. If anything, the howls Southgate was letting out as Tuttle and Goffin pinned him to the ground and began kicking at his legs and punching his back with their fists only made them run all the faster. By then, Tuttle had taken possession of Southgate's flintlock and was about to use the butt to batter at the trapped man's arms and legs, his head, too, if he could reach it: fortunately, Dick Dollery came up and was in time to pull off both.

'Stop for God's sake or you'll kill him!' he cried: and, as the surprised Tuttle and Goffin paused, as much to complain at the other's interference in their sport as anything, a bruised and scratched Southgate tore himself free from the thorns, completed his wriggle through the hedge and went at a yelping, limping run across the field after his friends, giving out a curious panic-stricken whimper of fear as he did so.

However, Tuttle and Goffin, along with Threadneedle, who had also come up, were not finished yet: like three men chasing a fox or a rabbit, excited by the hunt and their perceived superiority over their quarry, the three set off after Southgate, as much to put the fear of God into him as anything else. Crashing through the hedgerow, ignoring the thorn spikes, yelling and shouting and laughing with the fun of the chase, they gave no thought to the poor wounded Skinner some two-hundred yards behind them with metal pellets embedded in his eye and his cheek and one ear lacerated, trying vainly to stem the flow of blood down his cheek and neck.

It was left to Dick Dollery to retrace his steps to where he found Skinner sagging against a tree trunk, one hand clutched to his bloodied face, moaning quietly to himself.

The three other poachers, meanwhile, continued across the field and were prowling in amongst the farm buildings of Angus McCreef's place: there, for the next twenty minutes they crept up and down, uncaring of the farmer and his wife peeping out of their bedroom window, scouring first the barn and then unsettling the horses in the stable before pointing their guns at the wagon shed, Tuttle all the time demanding: 'Where are you, you blighters? I'll teach you to shoot at me! I'll teach you, so help me! Where are you?'

The first two, Trott and Brewster, had hidden themselves not in the obvious barn but in a small pigsty thirty yards away, while the bruised and battered Southgate had managed to clamber unseen on to the top of a hayrick where he lay moaning lowly. In the end, unable to find their quarry in the darkness, Tuttle and company returned to the wood to see how Skinner was: they found him with Dick Dollery, who had bandaged the youth's wounds as best he could, enough to stem the flow of blood from the holes in his cheek and what remained of his ear, though he could do nothing for the poor youth's eye or the pain it was giving him: there was blood everywhere, on his face, all over his neck and shoulder and down the front of his clothing.

'We must get him back. We need some light to see how bad he is,' Dick Dollery told them.

'I'm not going back yet,' declared Tuttle, somewhat selfishly, 'not till I've got what I've come for and that's a half-dozen pheasants or partridges. I want something for my trouble.'

'Put it to the vote,' suggested Goffin, also unperturbed by Skinner's moans: so they voted, with just Dick Dollery raising his hand to go back and Tuttle, Goffin and Threadneedle voting to remain, at least a further hour, especially as there was game to be had and they were unlikely now to be hindered by Trott and the other two watchers.

So while Dick Dollery took the first two pheasants they had shot 'for my missus' and led the wounded, groaning and complaining Skinner back through the woods, the others remained and shot another six times and bagged four more pheasants for the sack before again disputing whether to continue or whether it was wiser to go home: Tuttle and Goffin were for staying, Threadneedle was for leaving and, after a fierce argument, he, too, left with two birds.

In the meantime, Trott and Brewster had emerged from their hiding place and had knocked on Angus McCreef's door, seeking aid: on hearing their tale, the farmer sent his eldest lad of ten running all the way to the Hall: it took him a good half-hour to cover the two miles and then there was the time it took to bang on the big oak door and wake the household, to pass on the message to the servant who answered it and for her to wake her master. Immediately, he heard what had gone on, Titus Broake sent the maid to rouse the scrawny footman, Hepplethwaite, and have him saddle his horse: meanwhile, he armed himself with two pistols and, cursing the fact that his bailiff, Heginbotham, was absent back in Yorkshire on a family matter, he quickly mounted and was soon galloping up the long hill towards the village and Chantrey, where the arrogant Tuttle and the foolish Goffin still remained, each armed with a gaming gun, beating the undergrowth and merrily continuing to fire at anything that rose up, and totally oblivious of the time and the fact that the dawn was lightening the sky.

On reaching McCreef's farm, Titus Broake had the farmer arm himself with his own gun, since he was his tenant, and join him along with his son, the bandaged Trott, plus Brewster and Southgate, the latter having finally come down from his hayrick hiding place now that reinforcements had arrived.

'I mean to have these beggars tonight,' declared an angry Broake as they set off towards the wood. 'I know who they are! At least, I know who one of them is. I'll shoot the lot of them before I'll let them take any of my birds!'

He meant it, too, such was the nature of the man and his anger at people who seemed to believe they had a right to take what was lawfully his.

Goffin spotted them first as they came across the ploughed field. 'There's six of them!' was all he shouted, which was warning enough for Tuttle and the two of them were away towards the darkness, zigzagging through the brush and undergrowth, carrying their sack of birds with them, till they reached a high bank near the edge of the wood overhung by brambles and gorse which threw deep shadows across the ground.

'We ought to make a run for it,' suggested the nervous Goffin, who was crouching down. 'We could be up this bank and away. They'd never catch us.'

No,' declared Tuttle, crouching also and, at the same time, reloading his gun. 'They'll be expecting us to run. They'll be watching for us as we cross the open field. We'd be easy targets and I don't want a pistol ball up my backside. We're better off here in the shadows. Besides, they don't know exactly where we are. We've got guns, too. They won't be expecting us to put up a fight.'

'But it's getting daylight. I think we should go,' pleaded Goffin.

'And I say we stay here till we're sure,' growled Tuttle firmly, priming his powder. 'I am not running from any damned landowner who thinks he can lord it over me.'

The discussion went on for a full minute or so, with Tuttle determined to show that he was not a coward who ran at the first sign of trouble and Goffin wanting to climb the bank, cut through a corner of the wood and be away along the Lower Rackstead road.

'We're bloody staying!' was all Tuttle would snarl back at him each time the nineteen-year-old pleaded, gripping his gun more tightly as his anger mounted at his companion's nervousness.

They were still arguing noisily when suddenly, above them, a voice called down out of the darkness: 'Stand where you are, the both of you, or we will fire!' On top of the bank, six feet above them, stood Titus Broake and his party: they had circled round and crept up on the two while they had been engrossed in their argument on whether to stand or run: now it was too late: now the first glimmer of dawn glistened on the barrels of five guns, three pointed straight at Tuttle's head, the other two pointed straight at Goffin.

'That's the one who shot at us, I'm certain of it,' came the pained voice of the gamekeeper, Trott: he was looking at Goffin when he said it, but no one seemed to notice in the half-light of the dawn.

Again it was Tuttle who spoke up to defiantly. 'You shot at us first,' he shouted up, somewhat petulantly, as if that would exonerate him: then rather boldly, though with the neckerchief across his face, he stepped out into the moonlight and, looking straight up at Titus Broake, added: 'And if you don't stand back, you will get the same again. I've got a gun, too, and it is pointed at you just as yours are pointed at me.'

The taunt was too much for Southgate, who was standing alongside his master: still seething from his earlier treatment at the hedge and the delight the two had taken in what they had done there, he fired before anyone could prevent him. At that short distance, any wound was liable to be fatal: Tuttle took the blast full in the chest, gave a queer gasp as if all the air in his lungs were bursting out, spun round and pitched full-length on to the ground.

For a second or so there was a stunned silence: all eyes were on the still figure lying half in and half out of the shadow thrown by the high bank, as if they could not believe what had happened, for it was clear that Tuttle was stone dead. Goffin, in his own panic, was the first to react: dropping his gun, he bent quickly, scooped up a flint as big as his fist and hurled it upwards straight into Southgate's face, catching him in the mouth and nose and making blood spurt. His cry of pain was enough to distract the others atop the bank: before anyone could leap down and seize him, Goffin was away, minus his gun, darting along the track and crashing through the undergrowth into the depths of the wood.

Titus Broake, Trott, Brewster, Southgate, Farmer McCreef and his young son all gave chase, of course, but Goffin was far too fleet of foot for them. He headed eastwards as if making for the lane that led to Lower Rackstead, intending eventually to turn south towards Merchant Staplers, a diversion which at least took his pursuers away from the Hamwyte road and the edge of the wood and the sound of a cart being trundled quickly down the hill towards Hamwyte.

THIRTEEN

TWO HOURS EARLIER, Jem, in just his shirt, had answered a frantic rapping on the plank door of his 'cottage' to find Dick Dollery standing outside, clutching two dead pheasants and supporting a moaning and sobbing William Skinner, still holding his bunched shirt-front over his bloodied face: the excruciating pain of his eye wound more than his actual blindness had rendered him near hysterical.

'We ran into the gamekeeper in Chantrey wood,' gasped Dick Dollery, who was about all in. 'We was after a few birds, me and a couple of others, and Billy here got shot in the face by some cove they brought in to keep watch. Don't know who the hell it was. I reckon he's lost his eye and his ear.'

They both helped the wounded and groaning Skinner into the 'cottage' and, rousing young Jed and dragging his bracken-filled mattress from behind the wattle divide, they laid Skinner on that in the parlour part, forcing the twelve-year-old to stand shivering by the crude hearth, for there was no fire to give him any warmth: by then, Mary-Ann and Thirza had also risen, awakened by the victim's moans and the voices at the door.

A cursory inspection of Skinner's wounds showed that there was nothing either Jem or Mary-Ann could do that would help him other than to offer him some water from their pail to wash away the blood: Mary-Ann offered to bathe his eye, reckoning on a woman's touch being more gentle than that of a man, but, such was the pain he was in, Skinner became agitated at the very suggestion of anyone even touching his wounds.

Jem had seen bad wounds on the field of battle and had helped men to bandage their own injuries several times during the Peninsular War, but that was an arm or a leg or a shoulder where a bandage could be wrapped around to keep out the dirt and dust: he knew that wounded very often broke out in a fever and sometimes died quite quickly of their injuries unless a skilled surgeon tended them: and Skinner's eye wound, in particular, was serious.

'He needs to see a surgeon,' declared Jem, 'someone to treat his eye and his ear and take out the pellets. There's a surgeon at Hamwyte, a Mr. Topham – back of the Black Bear – an old chap – he was a surgeon in the Royal Navy, retired now, who still does things now and again. We can take the lad to him. He'd see to him, I'm sure, and he'd do it with no questions asked, so long as we pay him. Five shillings should be enough to pay him to pick the pellets out and bind up his eye and ear. We just say a gun went off in his face, though I have no money to give.'

'His father'll have to cough up, it's his son,' Dick Dollery answered matter-of-factly with a shrug: till then, he had not thought beyond getting the youth to his friend's 'cottage,' simply because he did not want to take him through the village streets to his own home. 'I might be able to rustle up a shilling or two, but I don't think I can stretch to five shillings. Not that kind of money. T'is more'n a week's relief. I can't afford that and neither can you.'

'I have a little, a sixpence or two,' Mary-Ann said, but the tone of her voice told Dick Dollery that she knew it was far from enough.

'No,' said Dick Dollery raising one hand to refuse her offer, 'I shall have to go round to his folks' place and ask them for it – and, if they can't afford it, there's still one or two who owes me a shilling here and there from way back.' He said it with such nonchalance, it was as if waiving money owed to him was an everyday occurrence.

'He'll lose the sight of the eye anyway, I reckon,' said Jem, looking sympathetically at the groaning youth, who, unable to find a position to ease his pain on the mattress, had risen from it and was now balanced precariously on one of the little handmade stools, rocking backwards and forwards in an attempt to gain the relief he sought, rather like a person does with toothache.

'How are we going to get him to Hamwyte?' Dick Dollery asked. 'It's three miles or more there. He can't walk, not all that way. I had the devil's own job getting him this far. Every step is an agony for him. That's why I come to you – you are nearer and he can at least get inside and rest. I daren't take him to my place till the coast is clear because they may well be watching.'

To Mary-Ann, it was obvious: the means was standing outside the door: Jem had trundled it home the previous evening. 'Take him in the parish cart,' she declared. 'At least, it will be put to a better use than it has been of late with you pulling it.'

'You ought to do that bastard Jaikes,' growled Dick Dollery: the sight of Jem trundling the cart about with his loads of stones and sand had become the talk of the Wayfarers' when Jem was not present and the talk of the Carpenters' Arms as well.

'Meet him on a dark night somewhere and do him proper, like,' added Dick Dollery and meant it, too.

'One day,' said Jem, equally as grimly, 'one day I will.'

As he spoke, he was stepping into his brown breeches: there was a greater urgency at that moment: it was only a matter of a minute or so before he had pulled on his holed boots, thrown on his ragged, black topcoat and rammed his wide-brimmed black hat on his head: then, with Dick Dollery taking one arm and Jem the other and Mary-Ann holding open the rough plank door, they lifted the bloodied and pained William Skinner off the stool and helped him outside to where the cart stood, watched by a wide-eyed Jed and Thirza

Skinner was placed in the back of the cart and, with Jem harnessing himself in the shafts and Dick Dollery pushing from behind, they quickly trundled him the threequarters-of-a-mile to the cross-roads, where they separated: Dick Dollery hurried to the youth's family cottage to inform them of what had happened, while Jem, one hand holding firm upon the wood brake, wheeled the cart down the long hill, past the thick-trunked trees and underbrush of Chantrey wood as quickly as he was able, having to ignore Skinner's moans as it bumped over the uneven surface.

Somewhere far off came the distinct report of a gunshot and men's voices shouting to each in the depths of the wood, but then growing fainter as if they were on a chase away from where Jem was standing. As the voices faded, Jem did not hesitate and covered the last hundred yards of the hill and the curve of the way round to the hump-back bridge almost at a run: for once over the bridge, it was a flat trundle into Hamwyte and, therefore, of no great difficulty for him.

Dick Dollery, meanwhile, had awakened Skinner's father and mother to apprise them of what had happened: there was, naturally, consternation and wailing and desperate, resentful cries of 'I told him not to go! I told him not to go!' from the mother: and, from his six younger siblings awakened by the rapping at the door a silent and awed curiosity as they learned that their big brother had been blinded in one eye by a gunshot and also lost a part of his ear.

From the father, however, there was just a stoical acceptance of his son's fate: 'How bad is he?' And when told, 'Bad enough, he'll lose his eye most probably,' he simply nodded his head, as if resigning himself to it, before uttering with a deep sigh: 'Well, I suppose we'd best get over there and see what can be done. I have a shilling or two put by for a rainy day. If that's what it'll take to pay the surgeon, then that's what I'll have to do – ' And to his wife, weeping and wailing and carrying on. ' – It en't no good you gooing on like that, woman, What's done is done. We have to thank Dick here and Jem Stebbings for what they are doing. Though t'is five shillings I can't afford, we can't deny the boy the attentions of a surgeon if he is in pain, can we?'

Henry Skinner had, as it happened, known of his son's mission that night, indeed had sanctioned it with a casual, 'Don't get caught, boy. If you've a mind to goo poaching, I won't be able to help ye if thee gets caught and has to goo up afore the beak, particularly if you're on Titus Broake's land. They're all friends together, those people. They look after theirselves and don't care a farthing or a groat for the little man. You'll be boated for sure if they catches thee.' The term 'boated' was common currency then, a euphemism for transportation.

With the coins jingling in his purse, Henry Skinner and Dick Dollery hurried back through the still-sleeping village and down the hill to catch up with Jem, which they managed to do just a few hundred yards from the surgeon's house, where he had halted a third time to regain his breath and also to allow them to catch up since it would have done no good to knock upon Topham's door with no money to pay him: he would want to see that first of all.

Fortunately, the surgeon's house was on the same road into Hamwyte, a hundred yards short of the junction with the High Street and, apart from a coach coming out of the back gate of the Black Bear as they approached it, no one else was about at that hour of the morning: so they were able to slip in through the wide gateway and, by rapping gently on the door, attract the attention of the kitchen maid, lighting the first of the house's fires.

When the surgeon was finally called and came down the stairs, he was at first put out at being disturbed so early and complained of it all the time he examined the wounds.

'He's got three pellets in his eye,' he said brusquely. 'They'll have to come out. The eye's gone. I can't do anything with that. Ear's the same. Can't do much with that either except stitch together what's left. I don't have to ask how he got these wounds, but when a man comes to me with a face full of buckshot I am allowed, I think, to draw my own conclusions.'

'I'm his father,' said Henry Skinner sternly, as if challenging the surgeon.

'Don't worry, sir, you secret is safe with me,' the surgeon reassured him, but with a certain indifference, having guessed what had been the nature of the business which had led to the wound: after all, it was not the first gunshot wound he had attended since he had retired from the Royal Navy and the scenes of many a battle with the French.

'I can patch him up, but it won't be the best I can do. I've patched many a man worse than this on board ship, but I have not the instruments with me that I used to have. Still, we can but try. Get him up on the table and hold him down. Use as much force as you need to, but hold him still. Knock him unconscious if you must, for this is going to be painful. I'll do the eye first. It looks the worst. I'm going to have to use the forceps to get the pellets out and I'll have to probe for the one that's deeper in his eye ball. That isn't going to be easy. He'll holler for that one so you may have to gag him. When his eye is done, I'll do his cheeks and then I'll have to put some leeches on his ear and get them to clean that up so we can see if there is anything left worth sewing together. If not, it'll all have to come off.'

Skinner was given three mugs of rum to drink and only when that had taken affect did the surgeon set about the task of extracting the three pellets from his eye with a pair of tiny forceps: the father, Jem and Dick Dollery were hard put to hold him down and had to lie upon every part of him lest they be kicked, punched or bitten. Horrific as it all was to the others, it was less so to Jem: he had seen many a man held down while a surgeon did his grisly business and had himself been held down when the ball had been removed from his thigh at Badajoz: for even slight musketball wounds carried the deadly potential of infection as a ball would take with it small pieces of uniform, as well as dirt, and if it hit bone then the resulting splinters added to the infection and there was always the risk of a man just bleeding to death. Fortunately, the musketball which Jem took in his arm at Salamanca had also been hooked out by a surgeon's finger: if it had been otherwise, the ball would have been left and allowed to work itself into a shallower position before being removed: this could take years and some veterans carried the lead balls inside them for the rest of their lives without them ever working themselves nearer the surface.

Having done Skinner's eye, the surgeon next picked out the pellets embedded in his cheek with the same forceps: then he cut away the hanging flesh from the youth's ear and applied leeches to all the wounds to cleanse them, during which the youth again had to be held down. After that, what was left of his ear was washed and sewn up with cotton twine and bandaged, the bandage covering the whole of his head from his jaw to his forehead, with only the one good eye peeping from underneath it.

Jem had left by then, glad to do so: it was not that he was squeamish, rather that he had to get the parish cart back to the village or someone might wonder why he had taken it so early down the hill towards Hamwyte where no one was working on that part of the road. Worse, they might even guess the reason why: so he had to be careful.

When he arrived back at the cottage, it was sometime after seven: he half-expected to see Joshua Jaikes waiting for him at the guidepost at the top of the hill, but, fortunately, there was no one so he went back along the ridge-top road to call at the 'cottage' and reassure Mary-Ann that he had returned unobserved.

FOURTEEN

AS HE ENTERED, Jem was surprised to see Mary-Ann seated in one corner with Jed and Thirza clutched about her: in the dim light, he caught a brief warning look from her, but, before he could do anything, he was seized from either side and his arms pinioned behind him: his gaolers were Trott and Brewster. At the same moment, Titus Broake stepped out from behind them: and behind him was Elijah Candler, the parish constable. It was pointless for Jem to struggle: to have done so in so confined a space might well have led to injury, not only to himself but to his wife and children also: besides, apart from conveying the wounded Skinner to Hamwyte, he had nothing to hide. They would not know about that even if they inspected the cart, for by the time Skinner had been helped off at the surgeon's house, the blood on his face and clothes had all congealed to black, anyway, and Jem had wiped up what he could of it before setting out on his return. So he simply resigned himself to being held: to them, struggle would suggest guilt: he would have to convince them that he was not one of the poachers, for it was obvious why they were there.

'I said I would have you and now I do,' Titus Broake crowed, taking up a position directly in front of Jem, a broad smirk on his face. 'I'll teach you damned thieves to come poaching on my preserve. You'll wish you hadn't for a long time after I have finished with you! The law knows how to deal with thieves like you who go poaching at night-time. You're in for a long stretch, a long, long stretch, after all the trouble you and your kind have caused this night.'

Jem was not going to be intimidated by a man's face thrust close to his own: enough sergeants had done that during his army service. 'I have never poached on anyone's preserve,' he replied, calmly. 'If you are looking for a poacher, you have the wrong man.'

'Really?' demanded Titus Broake, raising one eyebrow in a cynical manner. 'And what the devil are these then, rooks?' As he said it, he produced two pheasants from behind his back and brandished them in Jem's face.

Jem knew instantly what had happened: the birds were the ones which Dick Dollery had brought in while helping Skinner and then had neglected to take with him in his haste to get the injured youth out on to the cart and off to the surgeon at Hamwyte: they were still lying on the table when the four men had entered. On any other day, had a brace of pheasants appeared in the cottage, Mary-Ann would have said a prayer of thanks and had them plucked, gutted and hung in no time at all: but at that early hour, she had been concentrating on boiling up the turnip and onion mash for the children's breakfast and had not thought to put them out of sight.

Titus Broake kept his eyes fixed on Jem. 'You were one of them and this is all the proof I need. I know these birds. They are mine, are they not, Mr. Trott?'

'They are, sir,' came the answer from the gamekeeper. 'They are ringed. They belong to the manor – on my life, sir, on my life. They're manor birds.'

Titus Broake stepped back with a dismissive flourish of his hand as if to say no further discussion was needed. 'There you are, constable,' he snorted, 'there is your proof if ever proof were needed. No doubt he has been out getting rid of the rest, for I have no doubt more birds than these were taken. And if I am not mistaken, they are probably hanging on some butcher's hook in Hamwyte this very minute and that is where he has been while we have been waiting here – disposing of them. Do your duty, constable, arrest him. Take him to Hamwyte bridewell and have him locked up. The courts will deal with him.'

'Elijah, I swear, I was not there,' Jem tried to protest again, hoping to appeal to the parish constable as the only likely source of reason amongst them. 'You know I tell the truth. You have the wrong man. I am no poacher.'

Elijah Candler looked at Jem as if he were mildly disappointed in him. 'Jem,' he said in a solemn, disapproving tone, 'the evidence is too strong agin thee. Worse, and sad I am to say it, I am told by Mr. Trott here that one of them that was with'ee was the Tuttle boy and I am told that he is dead.'

'Tuttle dead?' Jem could scarcely believe it: in the corner, Mary-Ann opened her mouth as if she were about to speak, perhaps to tell them of Dick Dollery and Skinner, but a sharp, unseen, reproachful sideways glance from Jem stopped her: Jed and Thirza, meanwhile, shrank back further into the cottage's gloom.

'Aye, took a blast full in the chest. It killed him outright,' said Trott bluntly: and, since Elijah Candler had not yet been able to view the body, he calmly filled in the details. 'He's still lying back there where we left him under the bramble bank, with a great big hole in his chest, dead as a doornail. Nothing could be done for him. Bill Southgate's standing guard. We shall have to remove the body later today, I expect. We have to either ask the parson as the other magistrate here or send over to Hamwyte for someone else to come over to view the body. He has to be independent, like – ' He glanced somewhat sheepishly at his master, who was a magistrate himself, and the look was met with a disdainful sniff. ' – Till then, he'll have to lie where he is – not that he'll know any different, mind.' He smiled at his little witticism and Brewster smiled with him.

'That's what comes of going into the woods to steal other people's property and shooting at my gamekeeper,' Titus Broake declared with a snort. 'I have no sympathy for the boy. He knew what he did was against the law and he has paid with his life for it. It is too late for him now, he has escaped his punishment, but your punishment, Stebbings, is yet to come.'

'I still say I was not there,' Jem retorted.

Elijah Candler let out an exasperated sigh: 'T'is useless to deny it, Jem. All the facts point to you as being one of them, The proof is here, Jem, these two pheasants – '

Damning as the evidence was, there was still in the parish constable's voice a certain sympathy, as if he wished that he did not have to say what he was saying, but he was the parish constable, carrying the parish's truncheon and had his job to do.

'Any other time, I might have been minded to believe ye, Jem,' he said with a slow shake of his head, 'but we have come here and we have found two pheasants lying on the table in your cottage. We know they were taken from Chantrey wood because both Mr. Broake and Mr. Trott have identified them as from there and they know their own birds because, like they say, they are ringed. They was lying on your table, Jem, when we entered. I saw them with my own eyes. T'is known you and Tuttle have worked together. You was together two days agoo. You was seen by myself taking a load of stones to him. And the next night he is shot dead poaching and two ringed pheasants are found in thy cottage – ' He paused and shrugged as if unwilling to go on and state the obvious: both Broake and Trott were smiling thinly: the parish constable's unexpected powers of reasoning surprised them.

' – I have to ask you, Jem,' Elijah Candler continued, quietly, 'who else was with you and Tuttle because, according to Mr. Trott, there was five of you in the wood and, with one dead, God rest his soul, that leaves four others to account for. One is you and that leaves three and one of they three, I am told, ran away from the wood towards Lower Rackstead after Tuttle was shot. He got away for now, but that still leaves two others to account for. Of they, I am also told, one was hit and wounded when the shooting started – '

'He was yelling his head orf so we know he was hit bad,' interrupted Brewster, bluntly, tightening his grip on Jem's arm. 'Hit in the eye, we think, by the noise he made, just after Mr. Trott was shot in the hand – ' Trott held up his bandaged hand as if to confirm everything. 'Yelling and screaming, he was, last we heard of him.'

Conscious of Mary-Ann's disquiet in the corner, Elijah Candler tried one more time. 'Tell us who you were with, Jem,' he urged quietly and somewhat sympathetically. 'It will go all the better for you with the Justices. We can tell the magistrates you were repentant when we took you and that you only did it to feed your family.'

Jem heaved a sigh. 'I can tell you nothing, Elijah,' he said. 'It is true that I know Tuttle and I have spoken with him a few times and that I delivered stones to him two days ago, but I can't tell you what I do not know. I was not there. I swear it, Elijah, I swear it on my dead mother's grave. I was not there!'

'Jem,' sighed Elijah Candler, 'if you was not there with them, where was you when we come here almost two hours agoo? Two hours we have been waiting here. Your wife says only that you were gorn off somewhere. Your children say the same. Then you comes back with the cart. I ask you, Jem, where was it you went? It will goo better for you if you tell us. And then there is the matter of the guns, Jem. If you has a gun hidden here, you had best give it up now. T'will be all the worse for you if you don't.'

Jem knew that he could not say anything without implicating his friend, Dick Dollery, and the wounded Skinner: he could not tell them how the two pheasants had come to be left in his cottage or where he had been. All he could do was to allow Elijah Candler to take out a length of rope and loop it around his wrists behind his back, though he did not do it overly tight and seemed to show Jem some sympathy as he led him outside. One outside, however, Trott produced a second rope and, while Brewster held him, the gamekeeper looped it around Jem's neck and would have drawn it as tight as might a hangman had Elijah Candler not ordered him curtly to loosen it.

'I know this man. If he says he 'on't run, then he 'on't,' the parish constable said sternly.

They walked him back into the village and round to the parish constable's house, where his gig was harnessed and Jem was helped up as several of the stupefied villagers looked on, not knowing yet why. That way he was conveyed back the three miles to the Hamwyte bridewell, forced to kneel all the way as the cart bumped and bounced its way over the potholes and ruts and down the long curving hill: and while Elijah sat at the front holding the reins, Trott, sat alongside the kneeling Jem, holding on to the rope halter around his neck, keeping it tight so that he would not attempt to jump out and occasionally allowing it to jerk accidentally.

They were almost at the bottom of the long hill, where it curved to the left, when Jem saw two figures standing under the overhang of the trees up the narrow Mope lane as if to avoid them: neither Elijah Candler nor Trott saw them: it was Dick Dollery and Henry Skinner, returning from Hamwyte. The wounded William Skinner remained under the watch of the surgeon for the rest of that day until the wagoner, Daniel Gate, halted his team outside the house late that same evening and the youth climbed on to it and was taken off to Wivencaster by his father.

It was noticeable amongst the villagers that, as soon as the news of Tuttle's death and Jem's arrest and everything else that had happened had spread around the village, young William Skinner no longer seemed to be about the place. 'Gone up North,' his father said, 'gone to see if there is any work, some place called Stockport. They say there's mills there and work if a man has a mind to goo.'

When he returned years later, he would be wearing a black eyepatch and combed his hair over one ear, which was half cut away and told everyone he had had an accident tending some machinery in a cotton mill.

FIFTEEN

DICK DOLLERY'S first thought on hearing that his friend had been arrested was to go to Elijah Candler and give himself up in Jem's place: but he was quickly dissuaded from that by his irate wife, Lizzie. 'Have sense do, man!' she scolded. 'I have never heard anything so daft! You'll do no good giving yourself up. If they have found the birds at his cottage, he is done for. If you go to Elijah Candler, they'll just put the two of you in gaol together and then where will we be? You keep your mouth shut. If they knew it was you there, Elijah Candler would have come for you by now. The best we can do is to see that Mary-Ann and the children do not suffer. It's them we must think of now, them and our own.'

There was sense in what she said: for even when Trott passed him as he walked up The Street to the Wayfarers' the day after Jem's arrest, the gamekeeper gave him no more than a cursory glance and showed no sign of recognition: therefore, so long as his name was not mentioned, he was likely to be in the clear. The name which was on everyone's lips, quite naturally, was that of young Skinner and the question being asked was: 'Where has he gone?' Only Abel Tedder and Jack Tickle ever gave Dick Dollery queer looks when they met him.

Dissuaded from giving himself up, Dick Dollery went to Mr. Able to ask him how much he would charge to appear on Jem's behalf at Hamwyte magistrates' court: friend though Mr. Able was of the drinkers in the Wayfarers', he was first and foremost a lawyer and for him to represent anyone in a magistrates' court in order to cross-examine witnesses still required a fee of one guinea paid in advance. However, out of the goodness of his heart, he did let it be known that he would accept half the fee paid up front in coin, for the purpose of his book-keeping, and for the rest to be paid in ale or porter over the bar of the Wayfarers' in the months ahead, if that were acceptable to the innkeeper, which it was. It suited Caleb Chapman because he was assured of the money, it suited Mr. Able because he would not have to pay a penny piece over two or three next months and it suited those who could not raise the whole fee for Jem's defence at one go, like Dick Dollery, Henry Skinner, Enos Diddams, John Romble and others, because at least he would have a defence of some kind.

Mr. Able would at least be able to question the likes of Titus Broake and the other witnesses on such matters as the definite identification of those with whom they had fought in the woods, dark as it was, which when mentioned in the inn made Dick Dollery go white-faced, even though he was the one who was doing all the collecting. And just as Dick Dollery looked very glum as he sat drinking in the Wayfarers', so, down at the Carpenters' Arms, Jack Tickle spent the whole evening before the case was heard nervously fidgeting and repeatedly polishing his pots, which he had never been known to do so industriously before, and hoping that no one had seen five figures, one with a heavy sack thrown over his shoulder, leaving his premises that night. Further, one of his regular drinkers, Jack Threadneedle, peculiarly, had ceased to drink there and, equally peculiarly, had suddenly taken to walking all the way to the Bull at Merchant Staplers: and, when asked, he also refused to contribute so much as a single farthing to Mr. Able's fee for Jem's defence, reasoning to himself and telling nobody that, once they had a man convicted over the matter and in Melchborough Gaol, honour would have been satisfied and they might drop their pursuit of the rest.

The law then specified that some types of offence could be dealt with summarily by magistrates without a jury: and often a lawyer had hopes that the prosecutor might drop an action between the committal and the trial, as had been done on occasion in other cases for reason of cost alone. This was not to be the outcome for Jem and when he was taken from the bridewell three days after his arrest and put up before the magistrates, unsurprisingly, Titus Broake, as the wronged landowner, a magistrate himself, a pillar of the community and a friend of the Justices seated on the bench before him, was the first to push forward and stand at the bar to give evidence, stating unequivocally that Jem Stebbings, of Hamwick Dean, was already a convicted felon, whom their honours might well remember they had sentenced to be incarcerated for six weeks with hard labour in the Steadleigh House of Correction only a few months previously for stealing wood from himself.

'When he was apprehended by myself, my gamekeeper and a steward, in the company of the parish constable, we found him to be in possession of two birds from my preserve. They were lying on the table in his cottage when we entered,' he declared solemnly while the clerk scratched away.

The magistrate, Aloysius Grimwade, a portly merchant, with mutton-chop whiskers, raised his eyebrows and tut-tutted in sympathy, which caused Titus Broake to press his case even harder, declaring that it was not just a matter of poaching alone, heinous a crime though that was. 'The case is far more serious than that,' he somewhat pompously informed his colleague, as though only cases involving himself were important. 'My gamekeeper was shot at three times at least and severely wounded in the hand and another of my stewards was beaten savagely with the butt end of a gun when he was caught entangled in a hedge. There is the matter of their injuries to consider. Your worship must bear in mind that whoever shot three times at my gamekeeper did so with the intent to kill him. It is my belief that one of them was the man who stands before you in the dock, the rogue Stebbings, a convicted felon. As a magistrate myself, were I seated up there with you, I would not hesitate to commit the defendant to the Quarter Sessions at Melchborough where he can receive the greater punishment. The evidence demands it.'

'After all, two plump pheasants do not fly in through the door or windows of a hovel and lie down and die on their miserable table, do they, your worship?' said Trott somewhat smugly later in completing his evidence after Titus Broake: it drew the expected laughs from those about him, including from the magistrates and, for once, from Titus Broake himself.

After that, it was perhaps a foregone conclusion, even to Mr. Able – who had seen enough of it in his thirty-five years at the bar – and when he sank back on to his seat with a sigh, Jem found himself being returned to the bridewell to await trial at the next Quarter Sessions before a bench of county magistrates. He remained in the bridewell for three weeks, which at least allowed Mary-Ann to visit him almost daily with Jed and Thirza, standing outside the small, brick building midway along the High Street and calling to him through the small barred window just as she had done all those years before to her brother, Will, on the night before he was hanged.

Before proceeding to trial, cases were heard first by a Grand Jury of twenty-three men, who decided whether there was a case to answer: the Grand Jury at Quarter Sessions generally came from a panel of summoned jurors, customarily from its more well-to-do ranks, while at Assizes they were 'gentlemen of the county,' usually, in effect, magistrates themselves. The Grand Jury met in private, so was able to exercise its own brand of discretion: for instance, though prosecutions heard by the Grand Jury might be dismissed as 'not found,' if the jurors found a case fit to proceed, they awarded it a 'true bill' and it proceeded to open court to be heard in public.

Mr. Able's hopes that it would declare the case 'not found' were dashed the same as they had been of the case not proceeding further than the magistrates' court, which was not surprising since Titus Broake was, and was entitled to be, one of the number on the Grand Jury who pronounced upon it: and, influenced to a considerable degree by him, the other jurors adjudged the depositions a 'true bill' and the case proceeded to open court to be heard in public before the bench. The triple discharge of the gun or guns was cited as their prime reason for proceeding, that and the defendant's previous incarceration, which drew suspicions of having poached as a revenge, as well as his 'refusal' to name any 'accomplices,' of whom there were noted to be 'at least three still abroad.' On the plus side, however, it was also remarked upon by several fairer minded members amongst the twenty-three that no weapon of any kind had been found in the accused's cottage and that none had specifically identified him as one of the poachers either, by voice or garb, neither Trott nor Southgate or Brewster, but he did have the two birds in his cottage: so, on a vote of fifteen for and eight against, greatly to the chagrin of Titus Broake, he was duly charged solely as a 'receiver.'

Happily, Mr. Able was prepared to accept a similar arrangement regarding his fee to be Jem's counsel for a second time at the Quarter Sessions.

As it happened, the bad weather had continued even into the next month for on the day in October when Jem was chained with four others, put on a cart under the guard of Hamwyte's two parish constables and taken to Melchborough, several inches of snow fell over that county and elsewhere in the South.

Peculiarly, too, instead of being taken into the new gaol on the Hamwyte road itself, they were taken directly to the 'new' Shire Hall in the centre of the town and, together with ten others, all were put in the cramped cells underneath, the easier to be brought up and put to the bar the next morning.

Suffice it to say that, when Jem was put up to the bar the following morning, it was with forty others, all charged with similar offences under the Game Code: indeed, an impartial observer, had there been one in the court, might well had deduced a certain growing frustration amongst the ranks of the county magistrates and petty jurors at the seemingly never-ending procession passing before them – men and youths of every age who, in their eyes, seemed to consider they had a right to trespass on another man's property and to poach his game with impunity and always gave 'hunger' as the same excuse.

While a man might grumble in an evangelical tone, as had Enos Diddams only the evening before to a peculiarly quiet Dick Dollery in the Wayfarers', that, 'God sent these animals for the peasants as well as for the princes. He will not let His people be oppressed. He will assist us in our undertaking,' the squires and the justices, who were often one and the same type if not one and the same person, were more minded to close in round a man whom they wanted to rid from their parish, woods and warrens. Thus, it was when Jem, convicted thief, now apprehended as a poacher and, though denying himself to be that, then certainly a 'friend' of them and a 'receiver' of what they poached – when he was finally called forward in the mid-afternoon, the thirty-eighth that day, and Titus Broake repeated his evidence before the Quarter Sessions county magistrates and jury, the latter the very same men who had formed the Grand Jury, it seemed as though the sentences were being increased as time wore on solely according to the number of those who had gone before: in short, justice was dispensed more and more harshly according to the number of cases being heard.

In giving their evidence, Trott, Brewster and Southgate, being a mite more fearful than their master of a lightning bolt from Heaven after they had taken the oath on the Holy Book to 'tell the truth, the whole truth and nothing but the truth, so help me God,' mercifully stated under questioning by the chief county magistrates and Mr. Able that, truthfully, they could not say beyond a reasonable doubt that the defendant in the dock was one of the five poachers. The five had all been masked with neckerchiefs across their faces and their hats pulled down: they had worn dark clothing and it had been such a dark night, only half moonlit, and much of the time they were under the shadows cast by the trees in a dense wood.

Further, in reply to Mr. Able, all three said they could not recognise any of the men in the woods, either by voice, clothing or form, as being from Hamwick Dean: and Brewster and Southgate, being from Higher Rackstead, had to state that they did not know anyone from the village anyway and so would have been hard put to be sure of any of them. Even after sitting in the Wayfarers' and the Carpenters' Arms on two different nights drinking with the men there and watching them closely, they were still unable to identify anyone. It was not surprising they did not recognise anyone since none of the three escapees, so to speak, was at either place on the nights they visited. In fact, on the night that they were in the Wayfarers', Dick Dollery had walked in, unbeknown to them, had seen them and had walked straight out again and for the next two weeks had the good sense to do his drinking down at the isolated Shoulder of Mutton, a mile-and-half away on the Maydun-to-Wivencaster road. Likewise, the night they were in the Carpenters' Arms, John Threadneedle was at the Bull at Merchant Staplers and George Goffin, who normally drank there, was a mile away at the Compasses in Greater Tottle.

When Trott, midway through his evidence, saw Titus Broake frowning hard and the magistrate and one or two of the jurors raising their eyebrows in surprise, the gamekeeper, wanting to continue in the lord of the manor's employ, truthfully stated that he had identified the two pheasants found lying on a table in the defendant's cottage as being from the wood because they were of the type raised there and ringed personally by himself: and Brewster was able to add that the defendant had been out when they entered his cottage and, when he returned, pulling the empty parish cart, he would not give them an explanation of where he had been. They supposed he had been over in Hamwyte disposing of the other birds at some butcher's or at some inn there: for they knew for a fact that any one of the five landlords of the inns in Hamwyte would slyly tip the wink to a customer whom they knew to be a poacher that they would welcome two or three brace of birds if they could be 'found' somewhere and no questions asked.

When Mr. Able queried why a man would need a cart to transport the half-dozen birds which the gamekeeper had counted as missing the day following the shooting, Trott simply shrugged his shoulders. 'I suppose because it was easier for him to hide them in,' was his answer.

Elijah Candler was called next, as the parish constable who had carried out the arrest of the defendant: somewhat sheepishly, for he knew what opprobrium he could bring down upon himself: he gave an honest account, occasionally glancing across at Jem as he did so. 'I am Elijah Candler. I am the parish constable of Hamwick Dean and in trade as a cooper. On the morning in question, even before the sun was truly up, I was called from my bed by a man whom I now know to be Mr. Brewster, of Higher Rackstead, who was acting as a watcher in Chantrey wood for Mr. Titus Broake, the lord of the manor of Hamwick Hall. Mr. Brewster had been sent by Mr. Broake to summon me to the home of the defendant before you, Jem Stebbings, which I duly did. The defendant's cottage lies on a backroad along the top of the ridge at Hamwick Dean, about a half-mile from Chantrey wood. Inside the cottage, I found Mr. Broake waiting with his gamekeeper, Mr. Trott, along with the defendant's wife and two young children. It is true, your worship, that when Mr. Brewster and I entered the defendant's premises, we found two birds lying on the defendant's table which Mr. Trott identified as belonging to the lord of the manor's preserve. The defendant was out of the cottage at that time and only returned an hour or more after I got there. Though we searched the cottage, we found no guns or powder and pellets. It is also true that when questioned, the defendant denied all knowledge of ever having been in the Chantrey wood that night, but, despite asking him, he would not say where he had been so early. I had asked his wife where he had gone so early and she had told me she did not know, only that he had gone out and she thought he had gone to work. Similarly, neither of his children would say anything about their father. I could not get a word out of either of them, your worships. When the defendant finally returned, it was about eight o'clock by my watch and he was quite breathless and perspiring. He was in dark clothing and was wheeling the parish cart for some reason, though he would not say for what purpose he had taken it so early. I can only assume he was disposing of something, but I do not know what. There were stains at the bottom of the cart, but they were covered by dirt and I could not say what they were.'

Elijah paused as if he were thinking over the evidence he had given, assessing it, ensuring that it was truthful and would not injure Jem's cause beyond the facts of the case as they were known to him. 'I would like to say,' he resumed after a while, 'as regards the character of the defendant, your worships, that I have known Jem Stebbings for a number of years, ever since he come back from the wars, as a friend and a fellow drinker at the Wayfarers' Inn in Hamwick Dean, and I can say honestly, as the parish constable, too, that I have always found him to be an upright and honest man, hard working, and that his previous transgression in taking wood for his fire from the plaintiff's tree – ' He paused again, for he still believed that Jem had covered for young Jed, such as any man would do, for a child could be charged as well as a man then and the House of Correction, even in the children's wing, would be far worse for a boy of ten.

'– I can honestly say,' he went on, 'it was out of character and the act of a desperate man. In this case, I have been told by a man in the village that he saw the accused returning to his home late on the evening that the offence was committed and felt that the defendant looked so exhausted after his day's work and had been at it so long that he does not believe, your worships, that he would have been likely to have gone out again that evening to go poaching, having returned so late to his dwelling, so to speak.'

It was a good effort by Elijah and would redeem him in the eyes of the other villagers when word of his plea spread: he was, after all, only the parish constable, acting unpaid, though it did puzzle him, being as Jem and Dick Dollery were such great friends and always sat together and drank together in the Wayfarers', why Dick Dollery had not appeared at the magistrates' court to give his support as one would have expected of a friend? And curiously neither was he in court that day. Both Jem's wife, Mary-Ann, and Dick Dollery's wife, Lizzie, were present: so why not Dick Dollery himself? Elijah Candler did not know it, but Jem had already sent word by Mary-Ann when she had visited him during his time in the Hamwyte bridewell that Dick Dollery was not to go anywhere near the magistrates' court or the Quarter Sessions: he was to do nothing which would draw attention to himself and the appearance of one of the poachers in court to watch the proceedings might be just the thing to stir the memories of Brewster or Southgate or even Trott himself: it was as simple as that.

When Jem was asked by the chief county magistrate what he had to say for himself, he declared boldly: 'I acknowledge, your honour, that the two birds found on the table in my cottage most probably came from the wood, but I cannot say anything more about how they got there, except that I was not in the wood that night myself and do not know what might or might not have occurred there.'

'Cannot say or will not say?' the chief county magistrate muttered, more to himself than to the jury alongside him: it was clear the defendant was covering for others and, if that were so, then the law would have to deal with him more harshly than it would have done had he been a mere receiver: after all, there had been an attempt to shoot and kill both the gamekeeper and the two stewards in this matter.

'I urge you to put aside your friendships and tell us truthfully what you know,' he declared in the manner of one reprimanding an errant schoolboy. 'Now is not the time to play the gallant friend. The jury does not look well upon a man who deceives and attempts to pull the blindfold down upon them. If you are, as I suspect you are, hiding the actions of some other person or persons, then I urge you to tell it to this court, for the sake of your wife and children as much as for your own sake. Your family have as much right to have you home with them as the law, which, as things stand at this moment, has to put you in gaol for a considerable length of time.'

Though the petty jury at the Quarter Sessions was responsible for giving a verdict on the guilt of a suspect, it was regarded as normal for this jury to act on guidance from the presiding judge or county magistrates: and in this case, the county magistrate declared to the jury that, other than the charge of receiving the two shot birds, to which the defendant had admitted in his own testimony, they could find no other evidence that the prosecution had made a valid case. For instance, no weapon, recently discharged, had been found in his cottage despite a search and none of the actual participants had been able to identify him as one of the five masked poachers, all of which seemed to anger Titus Broake, for his cheeks reddened visibly and his gamekeeper and his two stewards, glancing across at him with good reason. remained fearful for their positions on the manor estate.

Jem's case was to be one of forty-two brought before the petty jury that single day of the Quarter Sessions so the jurors did not even bother to leave the courtroom to consider their verdict, but declared him guilty on the charge of being a receiver and proceeded to the next case.

As a result of the general feeling of the public against the Game Laws, petty juries in some cases of poaching were, peculiarly, often quite reluctant to give a verdict of 'guilty': indeed some twenty per cent of the charges that came before them were dropped. However, the county magistrates of Melchborough felt they could not do it this time because the defendant had admitted to having the birds in his possession, which were proved to have been stolen.

It was a widely held view that county magistrates at Quarter Sessions were more serious than judges at Assizes – calling up a wider range of differing sentences for similar offences and also with an ability to exercise personal discretion as they 'possessed local information and a knowledge of the individuals accused so they had better opportunities of discriminating as to the degree of punishment which is likely to effect the reform of the offender or secure the peace of the district.

The magistrates' sentence was, in view of their friendship with the plaintiff, to be expected: the accused was sentenced to twelve months' penal servitude in the new Melchborough Gaol with hard labour, eight weeks of which were to be spent in four fortnightly periods on the tread-wheel.

This time, Mary-Ann was at the trial, walking the whole way to the county town through the night, with just Dick Dollery's wife, Lizzie, as company, determined to be there, arriving in the early hours and waiting half the morning to gain entry: Jed and Thirza she left with Emma Diddams. Unhappily, the old courthouse being a small place and so overcrowded with the relatives of the others, she barely got inside the door and, in the crush of bodies, saw no more than the top of Jem's head as he stood at the bar before being taken away.

SIXTEEN

WITHOUT A DOUBT, Melchborough's new gaol, built at a cost of fifty-seven thousand pounds to a new and modern design on several acres of ground threequarters of a mile from the centre of the town, was the pride of the county authorities. It was enclosed by a brick boundary wall some twenty-feet high, supported by stone columns every thirty feet, with midway along its hundred-and-twenty-yard frontage an imposing Egyptian-style entrance lodge of Yorkshire stone over which was positioned 'the drop' or place of execution so that the populace of the town and surrounding villages might gather on a broad gravelled concourse between it and the Hamwyte road to watch such events. Where such matters affected them and their livelihoods, it was known that certain nearby landowners and large farmers would sometimes send their workers to stand and watch an execution if the poor unfortunate happened to be a rick firer or a cattle stealer – as a warning to any others who might be thinking of doing the same.

Within its walls, four blocks of cells, each of three storeys, radiated out like the spokes of a wheel from the central hub of the warders' tower, the two upper tiers being reached by galleries: separate from them were four small airing yards radiating from another central semicircular tower from which the warders peered into every yard through small bull's-eye windows without being observed by the prisoners trudging round and round in silence, while grasping a knot on a rope tied fifteen feet from the next knot.

The new gaol had taken seven years to complete and had been open only since the previous year, replacing the town's medieval and smaller gaol at the bottom of the High Street, close by the river and stone bridge at the entrance to the market square, which by then had been taken over solely for debtors, while the old House of Correction adjoining the latter held the town's female prisoners.

It was late in the afternoon when the forty-one prisoners convicted that day were marched across the gravelled concourse, all chained in a line by a stout curb-chain drawn through the eyelets of their handcuffs. No sooner had the great doors of the lodge clanged shut behind them and they had entered into the gloom of the cobbled yard than they were commanded to halt: a wait of a minute or so ensued while the accompanying courthouse warders handed their caption papers to the chief warder of the gaol. Then a signal was given and one of the six warders waiting for them went quickly along the line withdrawing the curb chain: having done that, the same guard went along the line a second time unlocking their cuffs and handing them to the courthouse warders, for the irons would be needed to bring across the next day's batch.

In the pause, Jem and the others were at least able to rub their sore wrists, for the irons had chaffed them all the way and Jem's skin was red and raw.

'Fall in! Form a line!' the chief warder commanded, curtly: and without waiting for the bewildered prisoners to comply, the other warders began roughly pushing and pulling them into line: that done, it was, 'Left turn, up the steps, march!' No delay was allowed. When the confused prisoner at the front of the line, looked about him in some bewilderment, he was seized and pushed roughly towards a doorway at the top of some steps, where, with another warder at his shoulder, he was hurried along a short, darkened corridor into a long bare room lit by oil lamps.

A second line was quickly organised, with the same pushing and pulling as before. 'If any of you have any letters or locks of hair, or other keepsakes, you are to give them up now,' ordered the chief warder, a burly, sidewhiskered man, with a barrel chest and round stomach. 'If you do not and they are found on you once you are in the prison, they will be destroyed. Do you all hear?'

'I have a Bible,' a pale-faced, round-shouldered youth piped up somewhat shame-facedly: and from inside his shirt, he produced a small bound copy of the New Testament, much thumbed and with a gold cross incised on its front, and held it out. The chief warder took it as if it were soiled itself and, holding it by the spine, shook it carefully to see if anything would fall out: nothing did. Then he did a surprising thing: he dropped it on to the table and said: 'Bibles are allowed. Reclaim it when you are through.' And eyeing the line, he puffed out his chest and commanded in a severe, no-nonsense voice: 'Everyone is to strip! All clothes off for the medical officer's inspection! Look lively, look lively! Let's make you presentable. You don't have anything that other men don't have unless it's the pox!'

The other warders laughed at the joke, even though they had heard it many times: indeed, it was shouted at every batch of prisoners who passed through.

There was immediate consternation amongst four of the youths, not one of whom was above the age of sixteen: clearly, they had not been subjected to such a direction before and at first made no move to obey and seemed about to protest, which, as Jem knew from his six weeks at Steadleigh, would only bring a harder punishment down upon them. So, he and two of the other men, former soldiers like himself who had faced such orders in the army, gave them a lead, slipping off their jackets and pulling their shirts over their heads: for Jem had no illusions that, had the youths persisted, they would have found themselves being forcibly stripped by the warders. Timorously, the younger men followed their example.

When they were all naked, their clothes were scooped up and thrown in a pile in one corner: then they were lined up facing the doorway which they had entered and one by one were sent across the passageway to another small room, lit by a flickering lantern, where the medical officer waited: Jem was the fifth to go across.

The medical officer was a surly, bearded man with rimless glasses: he was standing before a small square of carpet placed on the stone flags. 'Feet on the mat,' he commanded in a bored fashion as Jem entered; then, in the same bored fashion, he ordered: 'Open your mouth. Lift up your tongue!' With that, he peered closely into Jem's mouth and having satisfied himself that no money or anything else, such as a key or a lock-pick, were being secreted there, he next instructed, 'Turn round, head down!' and began examining the roots of Jem's hair and behind his ears to ensure nothing was hidden there either: that and other places.

That done, it was, 'Arms above your head!' and after that, 'On all fours, head forward, raise your feet one at a time. Higher!' Then, 'Hands out! Turn them over!' as he was examined for any private marks: for many of the county's regular thieves would have five dots tattooed between their thumb and forefinger as a sign that they belonged to the 'Forty Thieves', as their brotherhood was called.

'Any of your family insane?' the surgeon asked with another bored sigh after finishing the examination and ordering Jem to stand again.

'No, sir,' replied Jem and waited as the answer and his general description – height, colour of hair, hue of complexion, colour of eyes – was entered in the medical officer's book, again with a weary sigh.

'Right, that will do. Next door to the bath.' The merest nod of the head told Jem in which direction to go. 'We need to get you lot scrubbed off before you meet the governor.' He ended his examination of Jem with another loud shout: 'Next!'

Steam was drifting out through the door of the communal bath as Jem entered, which at least told him that the water would be warm, if not hot: just inside the door, another inmate holding a pair of large shearing scissors and a cut-throat razor was waiting. He motioned for Jem to sit on a stool placed on the wet floor: then he expertly snipped off all of Jem's hair as close to the scalp as he could manage with his scissors: that done, he roughly lathered Jem's cheeks, chin and neck and scraped them with the cut-throat, though again it was expertly done by a man who knew his trade.

Nearby, two warders in large canvas aprons were standing by a square sunken bath, each with a long-handled brush in his hand, scrubbing vigorously at the milk white skin of the youth who had preceded Jem. No sooner had the barber announced that he had finished shaving Jem's cheeks and neck than the pale-skinned youth was ordered out of the bath and Jem was told to step in and take his place. He was immediately ducked under the warm water by the two warders pushing at his head with their long brushes: they then set about scrubbing his skin with a roughness and a lack of care of those who were bored at having to do the same task endlessly. Fortunately, Jem was given no more than a minute of this treatment before he was ordered out and the next man ordered into the same water.

After that, he was half-directed and half-pushed along the passage to a large room where another warder standing behind a counter issued him with the prison's grey flannels, grey shirt, brown coat, stockings and ill-fitting leather boots. He was also issued with a cloth cap, called a 'peak,' which was the same as any other cap except for the fact that it had a cloth mask with slits for the eyes which had to be pulled down over the face and which the governor insisted all prisoners wore, especially when joining the company of others, such as exercising in the yards or going to the chapel. The conceived object was to prevent them from communicating with each other and to hide the face of one inmate from another so that supposedly each retained their anonymity, since for the whole of their term, each prisoner would be referred to only by his given number.

Having dressed and slipped on the crude, prison-made boots, Jem was again ordered back across the passageway to yet another small room in which the governor's clerk sat at a table, making out the register-number for each of the newcomers, then matching them to their caption papers prior to entering their names and details in the prison book: he was also responsible for assigning prisoners what work they would undertake.

'What have you been?' inquired the clerk, brusquely.

'I was a soldier, then a husbandman till I lost it all, sir,' Jem replied, remembering to address everyone as 'Sir' so that he would not incur the ire of anyone who felt he should be so addressed.

'Have you been in prison before?'

'Steadleigh House of Correction, sir, for six weeks,' Jem replied smartly.

'Hard labour?'

'Yes, sir.'

'How long have you been out?'

'Four months, sir.'

The clerk looked up from his writing, one eyebrow raised in surprise. 'What work did you do there?'

'Mat-making, sir, with rushes.'

'Can you make a mat?'

'Yes, sir.'

'You are to serve time on the tread-wheel,' he declared, almost casually, at the same time writing something alongside Jem's name. 'We'll put you on other work till then. You'll do your time on the tread-wheel later.' Then it was: 'Dismiss. Wait outside in line with the others.'

Jem did as he was ordered: when all had been bathed, shaved, dressed, had their details recorded and had been given their numbers, they were lined up again and marched into a long reception room with a bare wooden floor, which, save for an oak table and four chairs, was devoid of furniture..

By a hearth at the far end, where a fire blazed, three people waited to receive them: one was a tall, lean, stiff-backed man with spectacles, who was warming his hands at the fire with his back to them and made no attempt to turn and acknowledge them as they clomped over the wooden floor.

'In line, get in line! Hats off for the governor!' shouted the chief warder.

Once more Jem and the others were pushed and pulled into a straight line: Jem, used to sergeants and corporals doing the same, did not mind: but some of the younger men resented hands being laid upon them, showed it on their faces and so were treated all the more roughly. That done, the governor, with a final vigorous rubbing together of his hands, stepped away from the fire and for the first time condescended to inspect them, raising a disdainful eyebrow every now and again as he looked along the line.

With a smart salute, the chief officer handed the various caption papers brought from the clerk's desk to the governor: however, he made little attempt to read them, merely turning over a few of the sheets, wrinkling his nostrils and then, as if disinterested, dropping them on the table.

'Read them the rules, Mr. Hopkins,' the governor ordered in a bored tone as beside him the assistant-governor, a short, dark-haired, cold-faced man, looked along the line with the same disdain.

In the dull monotone of one who had done it a hundred times before, the chief warder recited a long litany of rules for discipline, for daily duties, for keeping their cells tidy, for daily attendances at chapel and exercise in the airing yard, as well as transgressions which were liable to bring punishment down upon them, such as disobedience, refusing to work, disturbing the prison by shouting, whistling, singing obscene and other songs, passing obscene notes or making obscene drawings in books and chapel-stalls, misconduct in chapel during services, talking at exercise with other prisoners or by knocking on cell-walls or communicating through water pipes, for trying to scud letters out of the prison over the walls; for wilfully destroying prison property, for assaulting officers, using bad language to officers, fighting and arguing with fellow prisoners, plotting to escape, attempting to escape, feigning suicide or threatening to commit suicide, for having a dirty or untidy cell, for purloining bread, meat and other victuals, for having tobacco in their possession, any and all of which were likely to render the transgressor to suffer some form of punishment, usually seven days' or more confinement to the dark cells in the basement of the prison on a diet of bread and water. He finished with the admonition: 'All these are posted up in your cells. So read them!'

Finally, it was time for the governor to address them: he fixed each in turn with a piercing gaze, as if trying to ascertain their character, whether they would cause trouble or no, whether they were villainous or no, and then declared solemnly, without yet having read any of their caption papers properly: 'You have all been committed here by the county magistrates and rightly so, in my opinion. You will be held in the felons' block on ward two. You have all heard the rules of this prison. They are to be obeyed without question. I trust I make myself clear on that matter. That way you will save me the pain of having to punish you for any breach of those rules. It is my duty to ensure they are strictly carried out and I make a point of never swerving from it. In this gaol, all intercommunication amongst prisoners is strictly forbidden. You will not speak or call out to any other inmate at any time. Is that clear? – ' He waited for the 'Yes, sir,' before continuing sternly. ' – And though you might think an infringement of this rule a trivial offence, rest assured I do not look upon it in such a light. I take it most seriously. It is a breach of the rules and any attempt on the part of any man to hold communion with his fellows will be punished immediately. Understand that. Obey the rules and you will pass your time here without suffering the indignity of the punishment cells and you will not want to spend time in there, I am certain.'

He then turned to the third man warming himself by the hearth, a podgy, sad faced, bespectacled chaplain of some thirty years of age, already balding, with large ears, squinting eyes and frown lines creasing his forehead as if he had a permanent worry to concern him. 'Mr. Hunt,' said the governor by way of invitation, 'if you would like to address the prisoners.'

The Reverend Cornelius Hunt edged his way forward a little and then, clasping both hands in front of him, as if about to begin a prayer, he addressed them in the manner of a schoolmaster chastising a line of wayward 'parlour' pupils at some private boarding establishment whom he had caught smoking a warden's clay pipe of tobacco in some secluded copse away from the school's premises.

'As chaplain of this prison,' he began in a solemn, hand-wringing manner, 'the most painful part of my office is to be visited by the loved ones of prisoners and to witness the great affliction which those who are incarcerated here as convicts bring upon their families by their disgrace and punishment. I beg of you all, therefore, while confined in this gaol, to conduct yourselves well and to turn your thoughts to the one Great Being, who is still ready to receive and to welcome you to a share of His love. I ask you to remember that, though all the world might shun you in your shame at being brought here, as you have, in chains for the felonies you have so foolishly and so wantonly committed, and that, though you have hardly a friend left to say a kindly word for you, there is still One who has suffered on this earth for your sakes and who is ever ready to plead for mercy – where mercy is most needed – on your behalf. I hope that you will all do this so that when your loved ones see you again or write to you to learn some tidings of you, they will he able to soothe the anguish in their hearts with the assurance that you intend to become better men and might still live to be a comfort and a joy to those upon whose heads you have brought down such shame and such sorrow.'

Several of the men bit their lips and hung their heads at the mention of their 'loved ones,' their wives and young children, as much to hide their moistened eyes as their reddening faces and one even muttered a 'Bless you, sir!' Even Jem himself could not prevent a tear from moistening the corners of his own eyes as a vision suddenly came into his mind of a sad-faced Mary-Ann, sitting in their cottage, lit by candlelight, and Jed and Thirza, innocently enquiring where their father was and when he would be returning home and she biting her own lip and letting a tear trickle down her cheek. The thought of how his family would fare from that day forward now struck Jem and it took all of his willpower for his own lip not to tremble.

SEVENTEEN

THE CELL in which Jem was placed was thirteen feet long by seven feet wide, with an arched ceiling some nine-feet above: the only daylight entered through a small barred window high on the end wall: in one corner stood a stone water-closet pan, with a cast-iron top hinged to the wall: beside it was a copper basin to which the supply of water was provided by a cistern from above. The bed was a square hammock of canvas stretched between rings on opposite walls and, since it was still early evening, was hooked to one side: two coarse blankets were folded in a square on a small shelf alongside.

On a small, hinged table-flap fixed to the centre of one wall lay a Bible, so that the next prisoner, whoever he might be, might seek solace amidst its pages by the light of a shaded gaslight above, seated upon a stout three-legged stool. Inside the door to the right were two triangular shelves to hold his eating utensils, a tin plate, spoon and tin knife: by the door, too, was a hand-spring linked to a bell, which when pulled caused a small metal rectangle bearing the cell's number to project from the wall so that a warder patrolling the gallery would know which man was signalling for his attention, though the act itself was usually discouraged with a measure of sharpness and often indifference. Also on the wall just inside the door were pasted three sheets of paper, two of them displaying the words of the morning and evening prayers which every prisoner was expected to recite to obviate his sins: the third, printed in larger type, was a further reminder of the rules and regulations of the gaol.

At that time, a growing number of reformers who concerned themselves with the redemption of convicts were beginning to advocate a 'separate system' for the inmates of gaols in which each prisoner not only had his own 'separate' cell but, in it, ate alone three times a day, worked alone, passed the greater part of the day alone and, except when going to chapel daily and taking exercise daily, remained alone for the whole of his incarceration. It had originally been introduced by a prison reformer at the Gloucester House of Correction and fifty years before had been made the subject of an Act of Parliament: however, its use had languished till the newly appointed governor of the newly built Melchborough Gaol had decided it had some merit.

The aldermen, magistrates and gentry of the town's Court Leet, who conducted their business once a month in the 'new' Shire Hall overlooking the market place, believed it would be more likely to produce the required reform of an inmate's ways and character than the old way of free association and so had been quick to adopt it. Not unnaturally, they now considered their new gaol to be 'perfect' and a model institution for other counties to emulate: and, since it had the necessary tread-wheel and other sources of labour for recalcitrant prisoners as well, it was their hope that detention there would prove to be 'a salutary school of sound and lasting reformation' for the criminal types of the county, the numbers of whom, for some reason unfathomable to the townsfolk, seemed to be growing monthly, almost as if the criminal classes from the rural areas were setting out deliberately to fill the two hundred and eighty spaces allotted for them.

They also boasted that their new gaol allowed the different categories of inmates to be separated as well, with a whole floor of one of the new tiered wings being set aside for those on remand and awaiting trial at the courthouse and, though not yet convicted, most probably soon to be: the rest of that wing housed the growing number of minor offenders, while the three other wings were for those convicted of more serious offences and, therefore, in for longer terms or, as many were at that time, awaiting transfer to the transportation hulks.

The problem was that cells for those on remand or merely convicted of misdemeanours were being taken up by an unexpected and continual flow of men and youths being brought to court from all over the county, charged with any one of a dozen counts under the Game Code, hence the reason Jem had been held in the Hamwyte bridewell for three weeks and then put overnight with the others in the cells under the old courthouse: the gaol was too full to receive him and the others on the wagon with him. The situation was only eased while he was standing at the bar by putting fifty of those already sentenced the previous week to varying terms of transportation on to wagons and trundling them down to London and either shipping them on barges upriver to the new Milbank Gaol, specially built for holding those to be boated to the other side of the world, or downriver to the hulks moored at Greenwich, which themselves were full to bursting with men and youths facing exile from the country of their birth: some were even being taken straight down to the hulks at Portsmouth for immediate transportation.

As Jem sat in his cell that first night, a supper of a pint of gruel, badly cooked, the kind of stirabout he had got used to eating in the army, plus a slice of bread, was brought to him at five by another inmate pushing a trolley. 'Make the most of it,' said the accompanying turnkey coldly, 'you'll get no more till morning.'

Jem, however, was too sick at heart to think about eating: instead he sat upon his stool and when the bell rang, he unfolded his hammock, as the warder had instructed him, and hooked it up: all round there was a brief outburst of noise like bedlam as warders shouted, men shouted and the keys rattled and doors clanged shut: then suddenly there was silence. It was the early hours of the morning before he fell asleep: the severity of the sentence, the time he would be away from Mary-Ann, how she would fare, how the children would fare – all of that troubled him greatly.

When he did fall asleep, he seemed hardly to have done so before he was awakened by the clanging of the six o'clock bell: there, Jem's old army training came to the fore, for he quickly slipped into his day clothes and, no sooner had he done that, than a warder opened a small trap in the door and pushed a hand brush and dustpan into his cell. 'Make the place tidy and stow your hammock,' he ordered, addressing him solely by his identification number.

A short while later, the same warder pushed through a piece of cloth and ordered Jem to polish the floor, which being of smooth flags took a sort of shine when rubbed long enough: again it was a matter of meeting the warder's standards: if it were not done to his satisfaction, he would order a prisoner to do the task again – and again, if necessary. When that job was done, the day's work was brought: for it had further been decreed by the governor that no inmate, whether awaiting trial or sentenced to penal servitude, was allowed to remain idle: they had either to make mats, sew leather shoes, pick oakum or sift rags and tear them into strips, for which no reason was given.

The younger amongst the forty prisoners who had crossed the concourse with Jem on the previous afternoon were set to tearing rags: two prisoners pulling a small cart went from cell to cell handing out wicker baskets, each containing folded sheets and other old material, which were to be torn into strips, each man being set a quota by weight, a tedious task since there seemed little real purpose to it.

However, it was not sheets and rags which were given to Jem and the older men: they were each handed a measure of oakum, old tarred hemp rope as thick as a man's wrist and as tough as catgut, cut into pieces the length of a man's hand which were to be 'picked,' that is, their fibres were to be teased apart by means of an iron hook fastened by a strap to a prisoner's knee and against which he rubbed the length of oakum. It was hated work, the most hated of all, and for good reason: even though his hands had been hardened by years of manual labour, Jem soon found that his fingernails became broken and his fingers began to bleed, cut by the tough fibres. To ensure that the day's quota weighed the same after picking as before, the guard returned each evening to 'weigh away' a man's 'pickings': failure to meet the quota, with only a minimal allowance being made for dust and waste, would inevitably lead to a man being deprived of his supper or, worse, if he were to fail repeatedly, be dubbed a recalcitrant and put in the dark refractory cells on bread and water. The 'picked' oakum, meanwhile, was sold to the Royal Navy or other ship-builders, where it was again mixed with tar and used to seal the planking of wooden ships.

The new enlightenment of the town's aldermen, however, meant that prisoners were also given other types of work: and, after a fortnight picking oakum, Jem was put to work making clogs, which he did for a further month, then he became a rag-tearer for a month and finally spent a fortnight as a basket weaver. In that way, the first three months passed, with him seated alone in his cell, where, as the system decreed, he ate all his meals, brought to him on a trolley and pushed through the small trap.

Once a day on weekdays and twice on Sundays, the gaol's two hundred and eighty prisoners, less the usual two-dozen or so in the infirmary ward, attended chapel, to be read a chapter of the Bible, to sing a hymn and to utter a prayer for the salvation of their souls: only then did Jem find himself in the presence of the other prisoners, though he was never allowed to converse with any of them and to have attempted to do so would have risked punishment, perhaps a spell in the cold and barren isolation cells. But at ten o'clock each weekday, a bell rang and the warders began to shout: 'Stand to your gates.'

Immediately, Jem would stop his work, stand to face the door, place the cloth-cap upon his head, pull down the peak and, with the cell door already unlocked, step out on to the gallery at the ringing of a second bell at the exact same time as the other prisoners: then closing the 'gate' or door behind him and, in obedience to the warders' commands to 'Face about!' and 'Quick march!' he would trudge in line along the gallery, careful to keep his gaze down at the feet of the man ahead of him while maintaining his distance from him as he descended the staircase and filed along passage to the chapel.

Even the chapel was modelled on the separate system: for, as the prisoners were ushered in, they took their places in a series of cubicles, rows of twenty-two stepped each side of a central aisle, each cubicle divided from the one alongside it by a hinged partition door so that, on entering, each man would close his partition and would not see or supposedly be able to communicate with the man ahead of him or following him. The men entered from the top and filled the places from the first row upwards: consequently, the prisoners who were to sit nearest the chapel wall in each row entered first and the ones whose places were nearest the central aisle entered last: even then, various prisoners in each row seated nearest the aisle were still prevented from communicating with their neighbours across the way by a head-high partition which divided the aisle from top to bottom.

Immediately in front of the pews, two warders sat on elevated seats, with two more occupying similarly raised stations in front of the chapel's organ, so that all four were able to look down into each separate stall to ensure that there were no attempts at communication as the chaplain of the day in the high pulpit, usually the podgy-faced Reverend Hunt, either read to them or berated them in his sermon for their 'depravity and knavery, wickedness and sin,' without so much as a thought as to how much of it was caused by the impositions of him and his kind upon the hungry poor.

When the lesson for the day and the hymn-singing were over and they returned to their cells, even the order by which they left the chapel was controlled by a device consisting of a large rectangular board atop a pole in which two small square apertures had been cut. This was placed in front of the communion table so that all could see it: a warder standing behind operated a length of cord, which, when pulled, forced two wooden discs at the back of the board to revolve, one inscribed with letters around its rim, the other inscribed with numbers. As the cord was pulled each time, so a fresh letter or number corresponding to a lettered row and a numbered cubicle appeared in the slots, starting with 'A' and '1.' Immediately the first figure and letter were shown, the two inmates in the first stalls on either side of the divided central steps pulled their cloth cap peaks down over their faces and, peering once more through the eyeholes, pushed open the partition-door, went back up the steps and exited the chapel, to be followed by the rest, in order and in silent lines, all controlled by the numbered and lettered wheels.

Back in his cell, dinner, which consisted three days out of seven of a pint of meat soup and a half-pound of bread and the other four days of four ounces of meat and a pound of potatoes, was brought to Jem and the other inmates at twelve o'clock. In the late afternoon, at four o'clock, he was allowed one hour's exercise in the yard, during which he and the other inmates, all 'peaked,' walked round and round unceasingly, each holding on to a knot tied in a rope fifteen feet from the one in front and fifteen feet from the one behind, their heads down, trudging in silence till, at five o'clock, the supper bell rang.

Following on from the 'separate system,' inevitably, came the 'silent system,' whereby no prisoner was allowed to communicate in any way, shape or form with any other inmate: naturally, ways around this were quickly devised. In their cells, prisoners rapped on the walls and water pipes with a hard object, a tin plate edge perhaps, using a prearranged common code of one knock for the letter 'A' and two for 'B,' et cetera, that way spelling the words with numbers and in between each word giving three rapid knocks to imply the word was complete before beginning the next. Or they could scratch what they wanted to say on their tin dinner-cans or even talk from cell to cell by shouting up through the water-taps: even prisoners on the tread-wheel managed to pass messages to each other either by their fingers or pointing to certain figures and numbers that have been carved by previous prisoners about the place. Others practised talking through gritted teeth and without moving their lips so that they could converse with their neighbour even while a warder was nearby: in the airing yards, too, whispered asides or remarks could be made behind hands as they trudged round and round.

In the chapel, too, there were always ways of communicating: for instance, a man wishing to pass a message to another on the same row, knowing from experience in which number of stall his friend would sit, would leave a scrap of paper with a message written upon it in that stall as he passed along to his own seat: another might secretly push a letter under the partition door between the two cubicles during the service or put his face close to the stall-door during prayers and whisper his message while pretending to pray. Or he might speak to his neighbour out of the corner of his mouth under the guise of singing a hymn, though discovery, like a breach of any other rule in the gaol, usually meant two or three days in the dark of the refractory cell on bread and water.

EIGHTEEN

AT THE END of the third month, as had been decreed as a part of his punishment, Jem was finally taken to serve his first fortnight on the tread-wheel: that he had not been taken there earlier was due entirely to the new enlightenment of the governor under which all new prisoners, especially if they were not persistent criminals, had to spend their first three months working alone in their cells where they would have time to reflect upon the error of their ways. It also, it was supposed, kept those incarcerated purely for minor misdemeanours, like stealing a loaf of bread or taking a farmer's chicken, away from the influence of the burglars, the robbers, the smugglers and the violent, hardened, long-term and unrepentant criminals in the other galleries.

Eventually, however, the day came when Jem and five others who had stood with him at the bar to be sentenced were taken to a long shed standing on its own in the grounds of the gaol and in which stood the great tread-wheel, the pride of the aldermen of the Court Leet and the law-abiding citizens of Melchborough. To mount the wheel, the prisoners ascended steps at one end, walked along a narrow gallery and waited in silence at their positions till the requisite numbers were arranged on the wheel: then, at a signal, they stepped forward and up on to the first step, their combined weight acting upon the successive stepping boards, set eight inches apart, just as a stream of water acts upon the floating boards of a water-wheel. However, the men did not stand freely side by side, but each climbed the 'never-ending stairs' in a small cubicle enclosed on two sides and so were separated again from their neighbours, while the warders stood behind them to ensure that they did not speak to each other.

In a single minute, he stepped up forty-eight to fifty times, thus lifting his own weight in that time the equivalent of thirty-three feet. At Melchborough, the warders took pride in the fact that the rate was always maintained so in an hour he climbed the equivalent of two-thousand feet, which when multiplied by the six and more hours he actually laboured on the wheel during a ten-hour day, amounted to a daily climb of thirteen-thousand feet.

The continual climbing repeatedly over and over again required great muscular exertion and was exceedingly wearying: Jem, with his limp, found it particularly gruelling and exhausting, though it did not seem to concern the warders overmuch and they seemed to take a delight in watching him climb stiffly up to the steps each morning. Refusal to work on the wheel was punished harshly, as was any other misdemeanour, such as talking to a neighbour, talking back to a warder, displaying surliness, complaining or committing any one of two-dozen minor infringements: a man might receive a blow from the guard or a day in the refractory cell yet again, or both.

Each day on the tread-wheel, Jem trod the wheel-boards for forty minutes in every hour before being allowed a short period of rest: only at a given signal did he take his turn to descend the steps at the far end of the narrow gallery for his rest as another waiting prisoner, already rested, climb the steps at the other end to take his place: that way the wheel was continually kept turning. During his rest, Jem sat on a stool some three yards apart from his neighbour and was still forbidden to speak on pain of extra time on the tread-wheel.

For a man to spend a whole month on the tread-wheel in Melchborough Gaol was not uncommon: some had even been sentenced to spend two or three months of their sentences on it, alternating a week on and a week off. In his weakened state, Jem knew that a man would indeed have to be strong and determined if he were to last unscathed beyond the first fortnight without his health suffering drastically. It was when he returned exhausted to his cell each evening that he first began to despair and to doubt himself: that despair was to grow during his second fortnight on the tread-wheel, even though he passed another fortnight in between tearing rags yet again.

As a young man, he had had a robust enough constitution and, even on his return to Hamwick Dean, despite his war wounds, he had been fit and healthy: but since the enclosures, since he had struggled to earn and had, on some days, gone hungry in order that the children might eat, the lack of food, coupled with his weeks harnessed in the parish cart, had wearied him beyond measure. By then, aged forty-two, he was no longer the man he had been: the lack of food before he had entered the gaol had affected his strength and the work between the shafts of the cart had drained him even more: now he discovered that he was a much weaker man than he had been.

The tread-wheel was also dubbed the 'shin-scraper' by the men who trod its boards, for, if a man did not step lively with his fellows, he would receive a hard knock from one of the revolving wheel-boards: nor was it unknown either for a prisoner to become giddy and to slip and have to be revived with a dousing of cold water. It happened twice to Jem, the first time during his fourth fortnightly spell on the wheel as he was climbing the steps to take his place yet again in one of the cubicles: the second time two days later as he was descending the same stairs. Suddenly, a hazy curtain came drifting down over his eyes and he pitched forward against the back of the man in front: he was revived by the traditional dousing from the bucket and allowed to rest on a stool for a short while, but was still sent back up with the next change of shift.

If anything, it was this very exhaustion which saved him: when he collapsed a third time the next day, again while descending the steps, the prison surgeon was sent for, a tall, slow-ambling fellow, who seemed to react grumpily to any prisoner falling ill on his watch, as if it were an affront to himself and his profession.

'Open his mouth,' he ordered, testily, peering down at a prostrate Jem through his pince-nez spectacles: Jem's lips were prised apart and the evidence was clear for all to see: his gums were swollen and bleeding: and, on opening his jacket, livid spots were found on his skin where the capillaries had been weakened and were haemorrhaging into the tissues. With a great sigh of frustration, the surgeon inserted two fingers into Jem's mouth and pushed and pulled at several of his teeth: all were loose, which drew only a further sigh as he tested each tooth in turn till one fell on to Jem's tongue, forcing him to cough and spit it out.

'Same as the others,' the surgeon said, sighing yet again, though talking more to himself than to those around him, merely confirming aloud his own diagnosis. 'Anaemia and general debility. There's no doubt, he's another. Scurvy!'

At that, he rose to his feet and, with the curt authority of a professional man, ordered: 'Take him to the infirmary. Put him with the others. We'll deal with him there.'

There had been eighteen cases of scurvy in the gaol in the previous year and, clearly, it was still prevalent and increasing since the number now down with it totalled twenty-seven. Jem was simply one of six cases diagnosed that quarter, yet was still treated with what seemed like a sublime disregard of known fact. The warders did not show any emotion, but simply obeyed and Jem was carried out of the shed by two other inmates and not a prisoner on the tread-wheel dared to turn his head to look, or cared anyway.

Scurvy was not uncommon in gaols, whether new gaols or older types: that and insanity brought about by long incarceration, particularly the new-style solitary incarceration, were the two great afflictions of such places. Scurvy, or, medically, *purpura haemorrhagica*, a state in which the blood dissolves and the serum, which is the vehicle for transmitting the red particles, separates and deposits itself elsewhere: thus, the constitution is in a condition of decay: the gums swell and become spongy, the legs are seized by painful cramps and red spots appear on them. It is, or was in the case of Jem and others in Melchborough Gaol at that time, brought on by the want of vegetables and fresh fruit in their meagre diet, and the hard labour which the prisoners undertook for too protracted periods on the tread-wheel on an inadequate diet.

In Melchborough's new gaol, victuals were budgeted for each man supposedly to receive weekly ten-and-a-half pounds of bread, with a pound of potatoes sometimes substituted for each eight ounces of bread, plus seven pints of barley gruel or porridge made from oats and fourteen pints of broth containing one ox-head per hundred prisoners and calculated to equate to ten ounces of meat for each male weekly. An assortment of celery, carrots, turnips and parsnips with a gill-and-a-half or eight ounces of peas or barley were supposed to be tipped alternately into the broth, supposedly a pound per day to every four prisoners. The vegetables were grown within the prison or bought at market and were inserted after the ox-heads had been boiled: but, men being as they are, the full ration was never included and most found their ways into other cooking pots and other tables in the warders' own homes.

Jem lay for three weeks in the infirmary ward, which was simply a large room lit by overhead gas lamps, with the two rows of fifteen low beds down the centre so that the sick lay head to head: it was the only place where the silent system was not enforced. There, the sick were given whatever the infirmary staff, all inmates themselves, thought necessary, including red wine, which, being like blood, was always prescribed for the seriously ill in the hope of reinvigorating them.

Previously, for scurvy sufferers, the Melchborough surgeon had tried a mixture of a compound of bark and 'a weak acid' solution, gargled and then drunk: but it had proved ineffective, though not too injurious to its drinker in that only two of the ten given it had died: the addition of porter to the diet was little better. Then, the surgeon, who also visited the women's gaol in the centre of the town down by the old bridge, had noted that none of the female prisoners, though receiving the same food as the men, suffered from scurvy, apparently being protected from it by the alkaline ley used in their washing work. So a drink of milk was supplied daily for the sufferers in the 'scurvy ward,' as the other prisoners called it, though it may have been the fact that some were well enough to eat the diet of potatoes provided by the attendants. It was not till, in desperation, the surgeon prescribed watercress and lemon juice that the scurvy was cured for a while in those who had been sick and, though it generally yielded to a more nutritious diet, and to tonics and acids, after an interval of a few months, it broke out again.

Fortunately, as a result of his weakened condition, Jem was not returned to the tread-wheel to complete his punishment, but spent the early months of Thirty alone once more in his cell, tearing into strips the never-ending supplies of rags brought to him, though for what purpose he still did not know.

NINETEEN

WHEN THE WINTER of Twenty-Nine to Thirty came, it was particularly severe, worse than any of the previous three, and made worse by the hunger of the rural poor throughout the Eastern and Southern counties. In the Hundred of Hamwyte, continuous frosts beset them for days on end over Christmas and the New Year and it was so cold in the February that the saltwater Langwater at Maydun was again blocked by ice for days on end. Some said they had heard from someone who had learned from someone who had a thermometer that the cold reached ten degrees below freezing Fahrenheit on one day: and someone else said they had heard it was so cold that, when the landlord of the Compasses at Greater Tottle slipped on ice and dropped two flagons of rum which fractured, it froze the rum when it spilled on to the ground.

That Mary-Ann, Jed and Thirza survived was due to chance and the fancies of fashion: for it so happened that, in the capital and certain other lesser cities, it had become an unexpected fashion amongst certain well-to-do young ladies that autumn to wear bonnets plaited from straw and for men to wear straw hats: it was all the rage amongst certain of the younger kind.

In late September, even as Jem languished in the bridewell at Hamwyte awaiting his trial, Mary-Ann and the children had walked the three miles over to Inworth to beg a shilling or two from her friend there with whom she had once been in farm service: it was an act of desperation, and, as it turned out, a fortuitous one: for what she found there was her friend sitting in the half-dark parlour of her own cottage plaiting straw into long lengths, which streamed out behind her like a straw rope.

'All the village women are doing it,' her friend said. 'It is the only money some of us make now. There is little enough work for the men now after harvest A man comes every Monday morning with his wagon to collect the plaited-straw at the Compasses. You plait it into twenty-yard lengths – scores or twenties, he calls 'em – and he takes 'em off to hat and bonnet makers in a place called Luton, wherever that is, and some others go down south of the river to a place called Dunstable. I have heard all the gentry in London are wearing straw hats and straw bonnets these days and they can't get enough of it to make 'em. I can't say what the nobility round here are wearing since I don't see none, but I do hear there's a nobleman up in the north part of the county, a marquis no less, who wears a straw hat to church every Sunday and hangs it on the end of his pew so that the rest of congregation's gentry can get a good look at it and take up with the new fashion. Some of the best makers can get three shillings and sixpence for twenty yards and a good hand can make a score and a half yards in a week, though, of course, the price falls if the work is inferior You might get only tenpence to a shilling for a score of twenty yards, but t'is good money, girl – money anyway. T'is skilled work that comes with practice, but it can be done in the home by both you and your children and will occupy a whole day.'

'One of the local farmers is selling bundles of straw at sixpence apiece from his yard ricks,' went on her friend, 'and Tom Pratt at the Compasses will sell you what sulphur you'll need for the bleaching part of it, as he has got his hand into the business as the place to gather for the pick-up on a Monday morning.' She ended with a shrug. 'It's work and it's money, girl, that's all I will say.'

A means to make money was not to be spurned: so on the way home, Mary-Ann called first at the farm selling the straw for plaiting, where she used the first of the shillings her friend had given her to buy two bundles, a bundle being designated by the farmer as 'as much you can carry, gal.'

Using her shawl and Jed's jacket to contain the straw, Mary-Ann managed to scoop up two reasonably sized bundles, for she did not want to make the two-and-half-mile journey back to the farm more often than was necessary: and if her plan worked out, she hoped to be making the same trip the following Monday with another bundle. On passing the Compasses, she used part of the second shilling to purchase the small jar of sulphur required, which was entrusted to Thirza who was also sent ahead to warn of any small branches ovehanging the narrow lane they took as their route back to Hamwick Dean which might reduce their load by a clutch here and a clutch there. That way, somehow, she and Jed managed to carry the two bundles home without losing overmuch along the way.

Mary-Ann prided herself on being a woman of some dexterity: while she had been sitting with her friend, she had carefully watched how she had plaited the straw, for there were many different patterns to the plaiting: and there and then, to begin, she had tried her hand at the simplest of the patterns: in time, she hoped, she would be skilled enough to work upon some of the more intricate patterns, for the more complex and intricate the plait, the better the price paid.

She began her preparation the moment she arrived back at the 'cottage,' clipping the straw into lengths, as her friend had told her to do, bunching them loosely together, dampening them well and then fuming them over the sulphur placed in a pan so as to bleach them to a clear golden hue. Her friend had also made use of a small 'splitting machine,' little more than a spiked bone head surrounded by cutters and securely attached to a wooden handle: she had lent a spare one to Mary-Ann to get her started since she had two herself. It made the task much easier and, of course, much quicker to do: and a day after she began her work, young Jed presented her with one he had fashioned from an old pigeon's breastbone which he had retrieved from the rubbish at the back of the cottage.

The bone spike was inserted into the hollow stem of the straw and then drawn downwards to divide the straw into even strips: then, holding a bundle of damp, prepared straws under her left armpit as she worked, Mary-Ann would bend her head and pull out three or four of the new splints, moistening them with her own saliva and working them round with her tongue to keep them pliable, the fingers being all the time engaged in plaiting.

There was a drawback, however, as Mary-Ann soon discovered: having to bend forward each time a new straw was required, as the straws were only a few inches in length, soon induced a stiffening of the neck and a stooping habit, while the cramped position of the left arm holding the straw caused her much discomfort. The constant habit of holding dyed straws in her mouth, too, resulted in scratching as the splints of straw were removed and after a few days open sores began to appear at the right-hand corner of her mouth and remained there, for her work was daily. Meanwhile, Jed and little Thirza sat at her feet, clipping the loose ends of straw from the plait, with scissors tied with string around their waists.

News of work where there was good money to be made soon spread around the village and, within a week, a dozen women, including Dick Dollery's wife, Lizzie, and Enos Diddams's Emma and Nathaniel Newman's, William Stubbs's and John Romble's wives, were all engaged in the same work. Caleb Chapman's Wayfarers' now became a second pick-up point for the collection of the plaited straw, not to mention for the lucrative sale of jars of sulphur, while Amos

Peakman, Marcus Howie and Joshua Godwin quickly advertised that they had plenty of straw for sale since the old uses of it for bedding the animals had decreased somewhat since the husbandmen and small farmers who had lost their livelihoods by the enclosures no longer kept the animals which needed it.

There was definitely money to be made: a woman working well and sticking to her task during all hours of daylight could earn as much as a guinea a week on average. However, money engenders greed and some of the women sent their smallest children, some as young as three and four years, to one of the cottages to be looked after by a 'minder,' while they and their older sisters got on with the business of straw-plaiting at home. Unhappily, the children did not play or learn to read and write, but had the New Testament read to them for six or seven hours a day by someone who saw it as her task only to keep the little ones out of the way and also to ensure thay they completed their own plaiting tasks which had been assigned to them by their parents, such as a number of yards to plait, according to their age and the kind of plait they had been taught.

A good child plaiter could plait three yards of braid in an hour and get fourpence for the twenty yards or 'score': for a finer sort of braid, eleven pence was paid for twenty yards. Even the smallest children could earn threepence to sixpence a day employed on coarser work, which for some added as much as a shilling and sixpence to two shillings and sixpence a week to the household economy: and at age seven they could use the instrument to split the straw and earn a shilling a day. Some of the girls of ten years and upwards were even earning a fanciful twelve shillings a week, as much if not more than their fathers and brothers had done in the harvest fields.

The drawback was that it was seasonal work and could be done only in the few short months after the harvest had been gathered-in, till the end of December, for during that time the straw was at its best after threshing: but, it was a fact that, in Hamwick Dean that chill autumn and freezing winter, straw-plaiting put the food on many a family's table, particularly as that summer Titus Broake, Amos Peakman, Marcus Howie and Joshua Godwin had all installed the new threshing machine in their barns and so that autumn far fewer men were employed on that side of the harvest work. Further, the men laid off when the mowing, stooking and carting ended remained idle all through the November, the December, the January, the February and the March, into the April some, and some even during the months which followed.

Unsurprisingly, when the overseer of the poor in Hamwick Dean learned of the money which some of the women in the village were said to be earning, albeit for only a few short weeks, he made a note of their names for the purposes of conducting an inquiry should any of them apply for parish relief. One whose name appeared on Joshua Jaikes's list was that of Mary-Ann Stebbings, said to be earning twelve to thirteen shillings a week from straw-plaiting over the three months from the start of October to the New Year, while her husband was in Melchborough Gaol.

TWENTY

THE BITTER WINTER of Twenty-Nine to Thirty was followed by a wet spring, with rain – sometimes torrential – falling almost daily from April onwards all through the summer, or so it seemed to the men who daily eyed the sky and commented upon the weather every time they met. Indeed, a traveller calling at the Wayfarers' or the Carpenters' Arms or any of the other inns and ale houses of the Hundred for that matter would have found two main topics of conversation amongst those who sat nursing their pots of ale and puffing at their churchwarden clays: one, the fact that the coming harvest was likely to be the worst that any could remember and, two, that, if that were so then, in the coming winter, they faced the real prospect of starvation for themselves and their families, especially as the brief flurry of straw-plaiting by the womenfolk was a thing of the past. Fleeting fashion had decreed that, amongst the ladies of the capital, straw hats and straw bonnets had been replaced by wider felt hats with plumes and feathers: therefore, their services were no longer required.

Worse, at their December meeting, the vestry of farmers had decided that, if it were the case that so many women were earning so much and able to fend for themselves, then the poor rate would stand lowering substantially, which it duly was, so that when those again in need applied for parish relief in the spring, they received even less than before, which had been minimal enough then.

As autumn drew to a close and what could be saved of the harvest was saved, so the threat of wholesale lay-offs again loomed for those who had found work: they, like the rest, faced being idle yet again from November to March, beyond again for some: and this time there would be no extra earnings from straw-plaiting to sustain them as had so many families during the previous winter: Small wonder then that men felt themselves doomed to poverty through none of their own making: the cause of it all, in their eyes, were the new threshing machines which four of the farmers had installed in their barns and which took away men's traditional winter work.

In the good times before the wars against the French, when there had been no threshing machines in the Hundred, the grumblers in the Wayfarers' and the Carpenters' Arms said, there had been upwards of twenty barns in the three parishes employing men in threshing, winnowing and fanning the corn. In a single barn, up to fifteen men would have had employment till the spring: and, if each of those men had a wife and three children, as an average, say, this one employment would sustain seventy-five souls at the coldest and bleakest period of the year without the need for relief. Now threshing machines threatened to make a labourer entirely dependent on relief at the bitterest time of the year.

The threshing machine was not new-fangled machinery: it had been invented more than forty years before in the late 1780s by a Scottish millwright named Andrew Meikle. After two failed attempts at the Houston mill, near Dunbar, East Lothian, Meikle decided to copy from the flax-scutching machine that was used to beat the fibres from flax plants: he constructed a strong drum with fixed beaters that beat rather than rubbed the grain, thus rapidly removing the husks. When he discovered that it worked, he quickly took out a patent in 1788 and began manufacture in 1789 even as, across the Channel, the citizens of Paris stormed the Bastille with their stolen pikes and the women of the city marched on Versailles demanding bread.

Within a few years, a Norfolk man, Charles Burrell, of Thetford, had made alterations to Meikle's machine, adding a double carriage and straw shaker which discarded straw out the back, and was selling his 'improved threshing machine' at a cost of forty-five pounds.

The threshing machine had come into general use in the Eastern Counties after the restart of the wars against the French when a transportable model was developed, worked by two horses, or even two pairs of double-harnessed horses which drove the gears by means of belts. Thus, the smaller farmers could either invest in one or hire one for the harvest period, particularly to compensate for a shortage of labour when so many men were away fighting the French: at that time, even the *County Weekly* had advocated their adoption as a means of preventing waste and reducing labour costs.

Inevitably, the use of such machines at a time of high unemployment, such as that which followed the demobilisation of a quarter-of-a-million men at the end of the war, was questioned and that criticism was continued during the early dismal years of that decade when there were food riots in Norfolk, the Fen counties and many other places. Some claimed that the corn could be threshed as cheap by hand as by machine and declared that such machines ought not to be used where there were numerous poor requiring paid work. The farmers, however, found the threshing machine was such an advance that some willingly spent their lifetime's savings on a single machine which thereafter they hoped to rely on as a dependable source of income should lean years ever come again. For the others who could not afford the forty-five pounds to buy one outright, entrepreneurs soon arose who travelled the country leasing machines to the farmers for the duration of the threshing.

Until the appearance of the threshing machine, threshing after the harvest had been done with a flail, usually on the concrete-hard, clay-daub middle-stead of the barn floor. Using a flail consistently and effectively was skilled work: the ash-handled flail had a swivel on top, with a tough holly or blackthorn swingel, the part that struck the corn, attached to it by thongs, perhaps of snakeskin or eel-skin using a knot of special design. The thresher swung the flail handle over his shoulder and brought the swingel down across the straw just below the ears so that the grains of corn were shaken out without being bruised: part of the skill, as many an inexperienced user discovered was not to crack himself across the back of the neck with it. An experienced hand thresher might get through three quarters, or thirteen hundredweight, in a six-day week. The task was long and arduous and the mainstay of farm work in the dead season: and as such, was often reserved for family men: the new threshing machine which, even if horse-powered, threatened them with unemployment and sure pauperism.

After the threshing by hand was completed, the cavings were sieved from the grain and chaff, the grain being piled at one side of the middle-stead, and a wooden scuppit shovel used to throw it high in the air so that the heavy grains fell farthest away and the lighter ones dropped short, forming a kind of tail: such work was dusty and, invariably, even on the coldest days, the big double doors at one end of the barn and the single door at the other end, would have to be left open to allow a draught to blow through to clear away the detritus.

It was no comfort to men for whom this work had once provided the means of their existence during the long months of winter to learn that the threshing machines could extract ten per cent more corn than they could hammer out by the flail. What galled them further was that work on them could be done by women and children and both Amos Peakman and Marcus Howie were not slow to employ them either in order to save on the higher wages they would have had to pay to the men and 'half-men.' It was to be this fact which took Mary-Ann to, of all places, Amos Peakman's Goat Lodge Farm to work on the threshing machine there in the mid-September of that year: Jed and Thirza went also, for children were also expected to work, otherwise relief would be withheld from the whole family when they asked for it. Even the new middling tenant farmers, the fifty-acre to eighty-acre newcomers such as Angus McCreef, Robert Lenny, William Worden and Henry Cadger, who could not afford to buy a threshing machine outright, were said to be making enquiries about leasing one for the next autumn since their use reduced costs dramatically, their labour costs, that is. Inevitably, from that, other labour-saving devices would follow, chaff cutters and winnowing machines and root cutters, with the poor labourer again being the ultimate loser in the hierarchy of rural life.

As it turned out, in the mid-September, unexpectedly, the clouds over that region of England finally dispersed and the sun shone brightly for a whole week and gave off a fierce heat: all over the county, the last of the delayed harvest was hurriedly being carted, stacked and threshed – using the new and quicker machines. Some declared, half-seriously, that the sun had not given off such heat for years – decades even: variously, the temperature was estimated by its burning of the skin alone as being in the high eighties, perhaps even in the nineties Fahrenheit.

In the airing yard of Melchborough Gaol, in the mid-afternoon of one of those sunny days, Jem was holding on to the rope, walking round and round, keeping his eyes down, when suddenly an unexpected chill came over him, as if a cloud had again passed in front of the sun. There was an inexplicable weakness in him, too: he stumbled momentarily and almost let go of the knot on the rope, but a fierce shout from one of the turnkeys in the tower brought him to his senses. Thereafter, the day was a blur: and that night, as he lay in his hammock, listening to the banging of the other prisoners on the water pipes and hearing them calling out to each other, he felt a great weariness, as if living no longer mattered.

TWENTY-ONE

THAT SAME DAY in Amos Peakman's rickyard at Goat Lodge Farm, Mary-Ann had been working in the hot sun for almost seven hours since the morning start: by then, it was mid-afternoon, the hottest part of the day, with a fierce heat bouncing off the dry earth. The glare off the bleached corn dazzled her, forcing her to screw up her eyes, even though she had fastened a bonnet upon her head to shade her face: from all around came the clanking, grinding, rattling, whirring sounds of a threshing machine.

In between the rains throughout August, Amos Peakman had taken on anyone and anybody in a frenetic attempt to gather-in the harvest, including three roving Irish labourers, who had called at the farm one day simply in hope on their tramp around the district from their camp on Inworth heath. Initially, Mary-Ann had worked as one of the gavellers, gathering and stooking the sheaves as the line of men ahead of them cut the corn, the same as she had done when she had first joined Jem all those years before, albeit this time at a markedly reduced rate of pay. When, after the stooking and carting had been completed and the ricks built in the yard, Amos Peakman had arbitrarily decided he would thresh the over-ripened corn straight away while the weather was bright and hot since he had the machine to do it and that way he could get it to market before others and before its condition deteriorated further. So Mary-Ann and the Irishmen had been kept on when all the others had been laid off, the Irishmen because they had had experience of working threshing machines in other places, so they said, and because he could still pay them less than the village men and Mary-Ann because there was a special job for a lighter woman and she was still cheaper to hire than a 'threequarter' man and, he knew, she would work twice as hard. In that way, Mary-Ann had become the only female hand on the threshing machine in the rick yard and all that week, rather than leaving them at home, had taken Jem and Thirza with her to Goat Lodge, where Amos Peakman had put them to work at sixpence a day gathering up the flints still being turned up by ploughing on his newly enclosed land.

The Irishmen knew their business: they had already completed three of the five ricks and that day were threshing the fourth: so Mary-Ann knew she, too, would be laid off soon, possibly by the end of the week. Nevertheless, she consoled herself with the fact that the work still brought in more than she would be receiving on parish relief, which, since the previous winter and the brouahaha over the straw-plaiting earnings, had been cut twice till it scarcely bought a daily loaf of bread. Though some women had made enough from straw-plaiting to last them and their families into the late spring, Mary-Ann had been forced to go back on the parish in the mid-March. However, she had no wish to rely solely upon the parish if she could avoid doing so, for she knew that, if Joshua Jaikes could have found a way not to pay her any relief at all, he would have done so.

Her task that day was as the 'feeder,' standing on the flat top of the threshing machine to feed the sheaves into the mouth of the mechanism: as each sheaf was pitched across to her from the stack by one of the Irishmen, she would hold it briefly in the crook of her arm while she broke the tie and then expertly spread it in a broad, smooth band so that the beating cylinder caught and tore at the corn stalks like some insatiable monster. Below, the 'tenderman,' the leader of the Irish gang, a man named O'Hare, was busy with his oil-can, staring at the spinning cogs and spindles as if mesmerised by them, ready to oil each the instant his experienced eye considered it necessary. Under the high machine itself, two half-lads from the village, who had also been retained, were leading the four double-harnessed horses round and round the staked gear mechanism which worked the clanking chains and squeaking pulleys to power everything. A third Irishman was raking the ejected straw away from the machine and pitchforking it on to a growing stack: he also helped the 'tenderman' to unhook each filled sack of grain, hook on an empty replacement, and then carry the filled hundredweight-and-a-half sacks into the barn.

As she stood atop the vibrating machine, dust and chaff were blowing into Mary-Ann's eyes, coating her face and drying her lips: the work was monotonous, a matter of stooping and straightening, stooping and straightening again and again, all day under the heat of the sun. All the time she worked, toiling with the same slow, wearisome movements as the others, she found herself thinking of Jem, wondering how he was faring in Melchborough Gaol, whether he was shut in the dim light of his cell, sitting stony-faced as he sewed leather boots and shoes, as she had heard some inmates did. Or perhaps, like her, he was at that very moment out in the same bright sunshine, in the airing yard at some task there, or, since he had been a good husbandman, hoeing the prison's vegetable plots, thinking of her and wondering what she was doing and thinking, too, that in four weeks, just four weeks, by the mid-October, he would be with her again, for his year-long sentence was almost served.

It so happened that, by design and by misfortune, she had not eaten that day: what little food she had in the 'cottage' that morning she had given mostly to Jed and Thirza without eating a bite herself and then had set off for the field with the remainder of it, some dry bread, some cheese and two apples, wrapped in her apron so that she, Jed and Thirza would at least be able to eat when they joined her from their stone-picking for the half-hour break at midday and none would guess at their plight.

As she and the children had settled in the shade beside the barn, O'Hare, who had gone off ten minutes earlier, had returned with two large jugs of home-brewed ale, supplied from Amos Peakman's kitchen, as was traditional since the water in the farm's butts was undrinkable. The gang foreman insisted that Mary-Ann and the half-lads join him and the others in supping both jugs till each was empty: the dryness and the dust, as well as the fact that all the others were sitting happily on the ground some twenty yards from her, chattering away and drinking, had tempted Mary-Ann to cross to them before she had begun to eat her own food, such as it was. She intended, as she stooped to receive the first mug of ale, to have no more than one and then to return to eat her own bread and cheese, which she had left laid out on the apron.

The first tankard of cold ale was drunk solely to quench her thirst and wash the dust from her lips: but before she could return to where Jed and Thirza sat, the gang foreman, pleased to have a good-looking woman in his company, particularly one whose husband, he knew from gossip, was in gaol many miles away and, therefore, 'she might be feeling lonely,' had taken hold of her arm and poured yet more ale into her mug, which she felt obliged to drink as well. It filled her stomach and, therefore, when he bade her to sit with them all while she finished it, she had done so, though still intending to return to where the children sat: the reluctant but welcome second drink had led to a not-so-reluctant third.

While Mary-Ann sipped at the successive pots of ale poured by the smiling foremen, young Jed had his eyes fixed on the food she had left on the cloth: and, though he had already eaten his own, he nevertheless picked up his mother's and, handing the small piece of dry cheese to his sister, ate the bread himself.

Before Mary-Ann could return to where Jed and Thirza were seated, Amos Peakman came striding into the yard, looking at his pocket watch. 'Get them back to work,' he curtly commanded the gang foreman. 'You've had your half-hour. I pay you to work, not to sit drinking. I want this rick thrashed and all sacked up before you leave here tonight. We don't know what the weather will bring tomorrow. We have to get it done today.'

Sheepishly, the men and half-lads climbed to their feet and retook their places on the threshing machine: Mary-Ann followed: Jed and Thirza, too, had got their feet at the first sight of their master and were already scurrying off back to their field so their mother was unable to reproach either of them and, after all, she had left the bread and cheese on the apron and she knew how hungry both were. Besides, the ale filled stomach so it was not so bad.

Well into the afternoon work, the two-half lads, bored by the monotony of their task, thought to enliven it by making the two pairs of horses circle faster: so each took hold of the outer horse's bridle and together they ran with them round and round, laughing as they did so: in consequence, they set the wheels spinning and the chains moving even faster and the vibration of the machine became even greater.

Mary-Ann was stooping to pick up the sheaf forked over to her: she straightened, untied it and then shuffled forward no more than two or three inches to balance herself on the reverberating boards as she fed the straw into the machine: it was then that she first felt a sharp tug at the hem of her dress. Perhaps it was the hunger or perhaps it was the ale she had drunk on an empty stomach, but her reaction was slow: in the next second, almost as if an arm had reached out and seized her, there was a second, stronger tug at the hem: and then a third.

The man atop the stack heard her sudden shriek of agony as her leg was dragged in amidst the flailing machine parts: it was his shout to the 'tenderman' below, coming round the end of the machine, which sent him running to seize hold of the two laughing half-lads, throw them angrily aside and somehow drag the four horses to a halt.

When they reached Mary-Ann, her left leg had been drawn completely into the machine, right up to the thigh: mercifully perhaps, she was unconscious already from the shock of it, for it took them a good five minutes to ease her out. When they did so, they found the lower part of her dress was near ripped off and what remained was saturated and glistening with blood: and when they moved aside the tattered remnants of cloth, they found the whole of her leg had been torn away at the knee: all that remained was the bloody stump, mangled by the rotating parts, covered in dust and dirt and pieces of chaff.

'Holy Mother of God, is she dead?' asked the 'tenderman,' bending over her and crossing himself as he did so.

'She's still living,' said the stack man, hopefully, but already he could see her face was turning pale as the life blood ebbed from her.

As best they could, they lowered her down the ladder and laid her gently on the earth: as they did so, a pool of blood began to form in the dust, for it was still flowing from her mangled thigh and none knew how to stop it.

Amos Peakman was sent for and was none too pleased to learn the reason why the work had stopped and less so because of what it would entail. 'We had best put her on the cart and one of you will have to take her into Hamwyte and let a surgeon see her,' he declared, brusquely, more because it would take up time and time was money.

When one of the horses had been harnessed into a cart, Mary-Ann was lifted on to it, her bleeding leg laid on a bag of chaff to cushion it over the farm's rutted tracks. Whether she was dead at the scene or died during the hour it took to reach Hamwyte, none could say for sure: but she was dead by the time the surgeon, Mr. Topham, looked down upon her, sighed at the waste of a life and drew a sheet over her face.

At Goat Lodge, no one thought to tell the two children working elsewhere on the farm: they would not find out their mother had been 'hurt,' as they were told, till they went looking for her at the end of the day and, on being told she had been taken into Hamwyte, wandered back to their 'cottage' and sat in it alone all night, waiting for their mother's return, till a message was sent back to the parish constable and, through him, Lizzie Dollery and Emma Diddams found them there the next morning, still waiting.

Since she was officially pronounced dead at Hamwyte, an inquest was held there two days later: by then, the last of the threshing had been completed and only the 'tenderman' and the stack feeder attended as witnesses. No mention was made of the ale or the half-lads' prank: the verdict could only be that Mary-Ann's death was accidental, though the coroner's jury did express a hope that 'the farmer upon whose land the dreadful incident had occurred' would take better precautions in future and perhaps employ a more agile lad to do the 'feeding' work rather than 'a woman of so many years': they also asked that some relief be given to the two children, as their father was in gaol at that time.

The Hamwyte coroner, one of its magistrates let out a sigh, almost of resignation: this was not the first death of a woman working on a threshing machine to come before him in his court: in a similar accident the previous autumn in the north of the county, a sixty-three-year-old, who was subject to epileptic fits, had been put on the same flat top of a threshing machine to feed the sheaves into the cylinder when suddenly she had reeled and fallen. Her left arm went right down the mouth of the threshing machine and was crushed and torn out of its socket and she was unconscious with the pain when pulled clear: she, too, died of shock within the day. He knew also of another worker up in the next county, a foreman who had the whole of his clothes, even his shirt, torn from his back when he had been caught in just such a machine: fortunately, one of the men had seen it happen and had been able to stop the machine quickly: had he not done so, the foreman may well have lost his life as well. A twenty-five year-old labourer in the same county, engaged in moving straw from the threshing machine, was not so fortunate when the spindle caught his smock and wound him round and round before the horses could be stopped: he dashed his head at least a half-dozen times on the floor of the barn and, though taken straight away to a surgeon, died within three hours. The jury expressed a hope that the farmer would erect a cover over the spindle.

'To my mind,' declared the coroner with a sigh, almost of resignation, 'there has not been a recent invention by which human calamity has been produced as by the new implement called the threshing machine and this in greater measure arises from the unskilfulness of those employed to work it and who are often ignorant of the powers of its mechanism.'

With another sigh and a glance at his watch, which told him it was almost four o'clock and he had been there two hours almost and ought really to be away in his pony and trap if he wanted to get back home in time for high tea, he gathered up his papers and looked once more towards the jury of shopkeepers. 'Thank you, gentlemen,' he said, slipped off his chair and left the room.

TWENTY-TWO

JEM was seated in his cell tearing rags when he received the letter from Dick Dollery's wife, Lizzie, which was allowed as a compassionate communication to an inmate: it was the first letter he had received in more than six months, not that that was a surprise as inmates were allowed only two communications a year with the outside world: the last had been from Mary-Ann in the April, telling of the straw-plaiting she and Thirza had done that winter, from which she had earned enough to last her till then, though when she wrote it she was having to seek relief again.

Though Lizzie Dollery's letter was written within two days of Mary-Ann's death, it was more than ten days old by the time it was tossed on to the table in Jem's cell by one of the warders.

Dick Dollery's wife was chosen by the others to write it simply because she, too, had completed five years of schooling as a girl and three as a helper to the teacher before falling, as an innocent fifteen-year-old, for Dick Dollery's roguish charms and the steady years of child-bearing which had followed. She at least could write and spell: the letter she wrote, however, she kept simple and factual: '*Dear Jem, I am very sad to have to tell you that your beloved Mary-Ann died last Thursday in an accident while helping Amos Peakman with his harvest. Her dress got caught up in a threshing machine and her leg was badly injured. She was taken to Mr. Topham straight away, but she had lost a lot of blood and had expired by the time she got there. The coroner at Hamwyte said there are too many being hurt in accidents with these machines. Jed and Thirza are with me and Dick and three of ours till you get back. It is cramped, but we can manage. They are well, but miss their dear mother awful, especially Thirza, who cries and it is a job to comfort her. The funeral was paid for by the parish. Dick and myself went, so did Enos and his wife, Nat and his wife and several others so she had a good send-off. She is buried in the churchyard. Thirza laid a posy on her grave and me and some of the others also put flowers on it. Caleb Chapman and his wife were there and provided a funeral tea at the Wayfarers which was paid for by a collection. Rev. Waters read the lesson and said the prayers and did the necessary. We all sang a hymn. May she rest in peace. With great regret, your friend, Elizabeth Dollery.'*

The same cold shadow as he had experienced in the airing yard two weeks before seemed to envelope Jem a second time: then an extreme anger welled up in him as he re-read the letter: according to Lizzie Dollery, Mary-Ann had died 'last Thursday' and it had taken a week for the letter to reach him: an inquest and a burial had been held in the fourteen days since and all the time he had been sitting in his cell, tearing at the rags and wondering how she and the children were coping: how she was managing on parish relief: how young Jed was faring, hoping that he had been able to get work again helping with the harvest or picking up stones: and how young Thirza was faring, too, for, before Jem had been gaoled, her mother had been teaching her to read and to write and do her numbers.

Something happened to Jem in that moment: an anger welled up in him that he had not experienced since he had rushed at the blue-coated French in front of the sunken lane at Waterloo when the 44th of Foot had been ordered forward into the gap left by the flight of the Nassau soldiers: it was anger at being where he was, blaming those around him for the fact that he was there at all: an anger, too, against those damned machines, those infernal threshing machines which had taken the life of his wife.

All that evening, as he lay in his hammock, brushing away the tears which welled up in his eyes before they trickled down his cheeks, the thought came to him again and again that had he been with her, it would not have happened: had he not been in gaol, she would not have had to seek work on Amos Peakman's land and also on his threshing machine, for *he* would have obtained work somehow in her stead. Neither would he have been where he was had Titus Broake not been the one to give evidence so strongly against him, insisting to his fellow magistrates that he was certain that he was one of the poachers, even though no gun had been found in his 'cottage,' and, even if not one of the poachers, by having the two birds in his place of abode he was still as guilty as any who had done the poaching and had viciously shot at three of his men, wounding one of them.

Repeatedly, too, he had reminded the magistrates that Jem Stebbings was already a convicted felon with a grudge against him and a troublemaker also with whom he had already had a run-in. It was because of Titus Broake and his vindictiveness that he had received such a long sentence, Jem believed: and, because he was still imprisoned, his wife had had to seek work to feed his children and, because of that, she had been killed on Amos Peakman's farm.

It was late when the cry of his anguish and his despair echoed along the landing and startled the other prisoners who had completed their own whispering to each other and their tapping of the pipes and were settling down to sleep: but for Jem, in cell fifteen on the third tier, there was to be no sleep that night or the night after or the night after that as the hate and the pain, the memories and the anger, all the emotions which a man feels when he loses the woman he loves and is unable to do anything to assuage that grief except to clench his fists and clench his teeth and screw up his eyes and vow revenge as the inevitable thoughts and memories came tumbling through his brain. Not till the fourth night, red-eyed and wearied, did he finally fall asleep and then it was out of sheer exhaustion at having been awake for seventy-two hours without sleep of any kind.

After that, Jem's spirits sank and sank to their lowest: for a second time, he found himself no longer caring about life.

TWENTY-THREE

A COLD WIND was blowing across the wide gravelled concourse in front of the gaol when at last, on a mid-October Thursday morning, Jem finally emerged from his incarceration and the high metal gates clanged shut behind him: he was at least warmly dressed in a new black surcoat and breeches as well as a pair of sturdy repaired boots, all provided for his release by the prison authorities, his other clothes and footwear having been burned upon his arrival: and, as he had not the means to take a coach and did not want to waste what little he had earned for his rag-tearing and, since, no 'free' carrier passed him, he decided to walk the eight miles back to Hamwyte.

He was within three miles of the town and had paused to cup his hands at a roadside pump to drink some water when he was unexpectedly confronted by a procession of carts and farm wagons, ten in all, coming from the direction of Hamwyte: each cart and wagon was packed with upwards of fifteen or more silent, sombrely staring adults and children. What Jem noted particularly was that the adults seemed mostly to be in their early twenties, some, the women, still in their late teen years, and that there was a preponderance of babes in arms and small children still in the toddling stage.

Clearly, they were all poor country people: their faces were pinched and had the look of the half-starved: the babes and small children were dressed in little more than cut-down rags, while the men mostly wore frayed and patched agricultural smocks: the women, however, seemed to have made an attempt to patch their own dresses and shawls, but really they were little better dressed than their menfolk. They were all perched on bundles and trunks which had been piled on to the carts for seating. At first Jem thought that they must be on their way to market at Melchborough, but then realised that the day was a Thursday and Melchborough's market was held each Friday. What struck him was the sadness showing on many of their faces: there was no air of joyfulness about the procession as one might expect of a company on an outing together: they all stared blankly at the surrounding countryside as if disinterested in it and, though a few turned to look down at Jem as they passed, none made any attempt to acknowledge his own nod of greeting.

It was only by chance that he spoke to them at all: as he waited for the procession to trundle by, a small girl, of no more than three years of age, who had been dangling a rag doll over the side of the last of the wagons near the front wheel, let it fall on to the road. The child immediately let out a wail of anguish and would have jumped out after it and perhaps gone under the rear wheel had not Jem moved quickly to pick it up. A second cry from the girl and a shout from Jem halted the cart some twenty yards on: as the driver turned to see what the noise was about, Jem was surprised to see that he was not above twenty years of age himself and the girl who sat beside him cradling a baby could not have been more than seventeen or eighteen years.

'Is there some fair on hereabouts?' Jem asked, in all innocence, as he handed the rag doll back up to the little girl.

'Gooing to a fair? Lordy, no, friend, we ain't going to no fair! We're on our way to London to take the boat to America,' said the driver in the accent of one from the next county or even the next county after that. 'We're all emigrating. We're all from three parishes up near The Wash, if you know where that is – way, way up. Most on us is from my own village, Tidybridge, though I don't suppose you'd know it by name. The rest is from my wife's village, Fenwell, a couple o' mile away, with twenty-nine others from Marshhanger, which is next on over. We're all part of a benefit club we had up there. There's a hundred and sixty-seven on us, all told, including babes. We're leaving England, brother, leaving for good, for t'is the source of all our misery and we want n'more on it. No labouring man can have a decent life here n'more, not the way things are. There's land in America, virgin land. Why stay here and starve to death when a man can grow food on the open prairie in America, enough to feed his own and a hundred other families? We have a letter from one Marshhanger chap that is already out there – in the State of Kansas – and he says he is rich already and has got a block of a hundred acres that he owns hisself and he hopes to get more afore long. He says, too, the weather ain't that cold there. He says the summer is hotter than in England and his crops grow well. If that ain't enough, he says his spirits are good and his health is much better than it were when he left England and he has no fear of having to goo to the poorhouse either. He says he was a great fool to hisself not to have gorn ten years earlier. Well, we've all sold off our furniture – what we had to sell – and we've quit our cottages and glad to do so and those of us who can't pay our passage has borrowed from the benefit club. Half on us ain't been married too long as you can see – ' He gave a sheepish smile. ' – In fact, some on us only got married in a rush two days agoo so they could join the party as they only take marrieds, excepting the children, of course. Saves a lot o' trouble, that. We've been on the road since midday yesterday. I reckons there'll be a lot more gooing from the counties in this part of the world afore long, the way things have been gooing of late.'

At that point, another man, young like the first, with the same red face and calloused hands of a farmworker, interrupted, though calmly. 'Me and mine are for the State of Ohio,' he said, with the faintest of embarrassed smiles which passed for exuberance amongst his kind. 'I have a friend who has gone already as well and he says Ohio is a great place for growing wheat, too. The land is rich because it ain't never been ploughed afore. My friend says he is about to become a farmer himself and has bought his own farm of eighty-two acres for six hundred and forty dollars in American money, which he says he has saved all hisself from working in a manufactory in a place called New York, which is a city there, I think. He has paid that down on it and is to pay the balance back to the bank over the next five years, he says. In America, a man can better hisself. He can't do that here. All you need is the boat fare and t'is sunnier than England, too.'

'Here, see for yourself,' he added and held out a pamphlet upon which was printed the picture of a sailing ship and under it was the advertisement addressed *'To Emigrants for Boston,'* naming the ship, *'the Ardwell, a barque, two-hundred tonnes, J Kerr, commander, a fine fast ship, sails for Boston on the twentieth. As many berths are engaged, early applications are requested...'*

The first man spoke again, more solemnly now: 'There ain't nothing for the likes of us in this country n'more. The landowners, the rich and the powerful, they run everything and keep everything to theirselves. They 'on't even give a working man the time o' day, some on'em. Our village land was enclosed ten years back. Some lord or other took the lot on it, near enough anyway. It did for us, we being village people, like. There ain't no work on the land n'more for a man that wants to work and what there is the farmers 'on't pay a man a proper wage to do it, a wage what he and his family can live on. So we're off to America. Perhaps thee should come with us!'

It was said with a laugh and a smile, but he did not wait for an answer: the procession ahead was disappearing over the brow of a long, low hill on that undulating road and he did not want to lose sight of them: so, with a crack of his whip, the cart rolled forward again.

As it trundled on its way, several children at the rear called out a sad 'Goodbye, goodbye,' and raised their hands in a weak and somewhat wistful wave: it was as if having their situation explained to them had made them more thoughtful of the great venture upon which they were setting out: the leaving of old England forever.

The emigrants' despair of life in England was not unfounded: lack of regular employment had become a fact of life in the small villages in the arable farming areas of the Eastern Counties: during Jem's incarceration, crop prices had been falling steadily, putting an even greater pressure on the farmers to cut their costs, which many had done by turning to machinery, which reduced the need for manual labourers: in consequence, many rural communities were at breaking point.

Ever since certain disturbances in the north of the Eastern Counties during the December of 1821, parish authorities had seen assisted emigration as a cheap method of disposing of their surplus unemployed long before it became the official remedy: in most cases, the funds advanced were either borrowed from private individuals, the landed gentry supporting the cause, or from country bankers at healthy rates of interest, the capital sum to be repaid by instalments from the rates.

In some Hundreds, it was not unusual for a thousand men and youths to be out of work during the hard winter months, of which six-hundred might have wives and families to feed, the whole numbering four-thousand, all reliant upon relief: the cost per month on the several parishes together might, therefore, be more than nine-hundred pounds, with a further eight-hundred or so pounds spent on outdoor relief. Small wonder then that assisted emigration was a useful method of saving money in poor relief in the short term, rather than an over elaborate method of removing paupers. Small wonder also that, in the twelve months during which Jem had been in gaol, unbeknown to him, there had been a huge increase in the volume of emigration, especially from the two counties to the north, due to the long and sustained depression of agriculture in that region. Widespread cuts in wages, poor harvests and spiralling food prices had placed too great a burden on the impoverished land workers, especially as there was insufficient poor relief to compensate.

North America, that is, the United States itself and Upper Canada, away from the French in Quebec, had become the two favoured destinations for the great number able to leave: the United States, independent for only forty-seven years and anxious to grow, had for years, ever since the Peace, been promoted in emigration pamphlets as 'a country of hospitality which the wild Arab never violates' and where a labourer might raise himself by industry to the level of farmer were he to head for 'the countries west of the Allegheny mountains, that is Ohio, Indiana, Kentucky and Tennessee or the Illinois.' For the depressed arable villages of the Eastern Counties, there was the draw of fertile lands in the Midwest in particular which had been opened up to settlement: assisted and unassisted emigration across the Atlantic from those counties was mounting. Even if the bill for fifty-two people, say, was between four hundred and five hundred pounds for their ship's passage, the parish provided the money and also gave for shoes and clothing to help them go, for it got rid of 'useless and unwanted mouths' and their empty cottages could be pulled down and the freed land incorporated by enclosure into someone's farm and ploughed and sowed for profit..

However, emigrants anticipating an easier pace of life and a chance to better themselves through landownership did not know, of course, that so many were arriving at the principal ports of America that there was little chance of obtaining employment in them and those who stayed in the cities till their money was exhausted often found themselves in distress: those same emigrants often found themselves worse off, facing high living costs, epidemics of disease and scanty employment in the Eastern Seaboard cities.

Jem's wish to see Jed and Thirza again was too strong, however, for him to take up the call of the emigrants: he could not leave them: he also needed to see Mary-Ann's grave in the churchyard: only when he had stood by that and had 'spoken' to her again would there be any easing of his despair: therefore, it was to the churchyard that he went first.

The posy of flowers which Dick Dollery's wife, Lizzie, had given Thirza to lay on her mother's grave had long since withered and the grass had not yet covered the mound of bare earth. For an hour or more, Jem stood there, thinking back over their lives: how he had met her: how she had laughed, how she had smiled and how, sometimes, she would become short-tempered and angry with him, but also how they had loved and made love. The sound of her laughter and the image of her smiling face came to him out of the recesses of his brain: and with those memories came, unexpectedly, the feeling that somehow he had let her down by not being there, by being in gaol.

The same thoughts, the same words had been going round and round in his brain, dizzying him almost, ever since he had received the letter from Lizzie Dollery: that had he been there, had Titus Broake not prosecuted and showed his determination to prosecute, persuading the members of the Grand Jury, then Mary-Ann would never have needed to go out to work – if he had been there instead of on the tread-wheel at Melchborough Gaol: if he had been there...

'It happened all sudden like, before anyone could do anything, we was told,' said Dick Dollery's wife, Lizzie, keeping her voice low and quiet in an attempt at comfort when later Jem called at their cottage and saw Jed and Thirza again and hugged them for the first time in a year, noting how tall Jed, now thirteen, had grown and how pretty Thirza, now twelve, had become and how much she looked like her mother, the girl he had first seen at the Inworth hiring fair all those years before.

'They stopped the thrasher as soon as they could. They was all Irish working it. They said she passed out straight away and wouldn't have felt anything. She was put on a cart and taken to the surgeon at Hamwyte, but she was dead afore they got her there. There was not much he could do. Nothing could have saved her, I don't think, Jem. I was sorry to have to tell you such bad news. The parish paid for the surgeon. It was only a small charge.'

She had died working for Amos Peakman, it was true, but, in Jem's mind, the responsibility for her death lay less with him and more with Titus Broake: he was the true cause of her death and for that he would pay: somehow he would pay...

TWENTY-FOUR

ALMOST THE WHOLE of Hamwick Dean's two hundred or so able bodied men, threequarter men, lads and half-lads were out of work at that time and dependent upon parish relief, which was why the vestry of farmers had cut the poor relief yet again, that month giving out only eight pounds in total amongst them all. It was the same in the smaller Merchant Staplers, where fifty-nine able-bodied men, women, youths and girls from amongst a population of a hundred and ten were without work and in Lower Rackstead, where a further fifty-five of seventy-one able-bodied were in want.

Not that the village and the two hamlets were any different from anywhere else: men and youths were out of work everywhere in the Eastern and Southern regions at that time. Just north of Hamwyte, for instance, so desperate was the situation in one parish that the enterprising overseer of the poor there had successfully contracted with the mayor and Court Leet of the market town for two-dozen of his village's unemployed to walk there every day and sweep the town's streets solely to occupy them and earn their paltry relief, at a small benefit to himself, of course. Not to be outdone, when the owners of a silk mill up in the next county had put up notices all over the district advertising for children as cheap labour, Joshua Jaikes had written to him offering to recruit for him: subsequently, fifteen of the families applying for relief in Hamwick Dean and the two hamlets were told they would have to send their older children there, otherwise their relief payments would be withheld. Amongst those who had gone were three of Dick Dollery's daughters and both Enos Diddams's girls: the anger against the overseer of the poor grew greater after that.

Yet, everyone was still expected to pray to their Maker each Sunday and to thank Him for the breath they breathed, if not for the food they did not have on their tables: and they were still all expected to be in St. Bartholomew's on the very Sunday after Jem returned for Parson Petchey's special 'service of praise and thanksgiving' to God for 'the bounty of the earth,' as he put it, despite the fact that, according to most, it had been the poorest harvest ever known.

Not that Parson Petchey bothered himself with such things: lost in his world, he was more concerned with the wording of his sermons, all the more so since a clergyman friend of the dean of Hamwyte had written to him commenting favourably on his innovation of 'a special service of praise and thanksgiving': the had ridden in his gig all the way from his parish in north Cornwall the year before to stay with the dean, and had heard about the Reverend Doctor's 'special service for the harvest,' which had bolstered his pride no end. The dean's friend had even suggested it might be better if the 'harvest thanksgiving,' as he persisted in calling it, were held nearer to the time of the Harvest Moon, that is, the full moon nearest the autumnal equinox, which fell in the September rather than waiting till the mid-October: and might it not be a good idea, too, to decorate the church with the actual fruits of the harvest?

Needless to say, the Reverend Doctor had politely rebuffed his suggestion: he did not want his church cluttered up with stooks of corn and barley and baskets of apples and piles of turnips and potatoes: his Sunday service of praise and thanksgiving would do as it was, without getting the villagers involved in something more akin to the old Lammas festival, which used to be held on the first of August, before the harvest work began, when loaves of bread made from the fresh wheat crop were blessed at a special service and given to the church as the communion bread. In those days, the days of the old squires, they also held a harvest supper for the whole village in the old black-boarded tithe barn, which stood a short way from Hamwick Hall at the side of the Langridge road: through its massive front doors over the centuries generations of farmers and husbandmen and those who had to pay their tithes had trundled their cartloads of one-tenth produce to be stored.

Parson Petchey had seen to it that it was discontinued soon after his arrival in the village: it was unseemly for men and women to drink to excess and to gorge themselves as they did, particularly in view of some of the debauchery which followed and which he had witnessed with his own eyes: so the village families no longer had a harvest supper and went hungry, but they still went to church on that mid-October Sunday to pray and to sing their happy and hopeful hymns.

Though ending the harvest supper, the Reverend Doctor, of course, still guarded the practice of tithe dues, which in recent years had given way to the payment of money rather than goods or produce as had been given over the centuries. In fact, so fiercely did Parson Petchey, in the name of God and the Church and his friend, the Bishop of Melchborough, guard his 'tenth' that, when some had suggested during the debate on the enclosure petition five years before that the tithes should be abandoned altogether, he had haranged his congregation from the pulpit at two successive Sunday services in true righteous indignation.

'What is owed to God should be given to God,' he had thundered. 'Man cannot bargain with the Lord. He has set his tithe and man must pay it and be thankful for his bountiful harvests! Those who have health and strength granted them and who are permitted this day to sit in God's House to praise and to magnify the Lord, what better reason have they for heartfelt gratitude? A tithe of everything from the land, whether grain from the soil or fruit from the trees, belongs to the Lord. It is holy to the Lord.'

For his sermon that special Sunday, Parson Petchey took as his theme the 'spiritual truth of God's glory and His wondrous works.'

'To the thoughtful mind,' he began, meaning himself in particular, 'to the thoughtful mind, no season in the natural year is more rich in subjects for devout and holy meditation than that of harvest-time. I cannot but think that those of us whose lot it is to live in the country and are engaged in the occupations of a country life have no small advantage over those who live in a town because we are constantly reminded by what we see around us of His great and wondrous works. All the most familiar objects of daily life – the tree, whether it is putting forth its tender leaves in spring or shedding them in severe and yellow autumn – every field in which we see wheat and weeds growing together – every bird taking care of its young – these and many other everyday sights and occurrences in the country impress upon us the spiritual truth of God's glory. How many are the lessons learnt by those who have only recently been engaged in the harvest field? What reliance upon God's goodness and trust in His providential ordering of things? However much the patience of the farmer and his labour is tried by unfavourable weather – however much his hopes are disappointed – still the promise is sure: "While the earth remaineth, seed time and harvest shall not cease." '

As he spoke, Parson Petchey surveyed the rows of pale faces and hollow eyes before him: the number of empty seats around the nave surprised him, though he was unaware of the reason for it: that some, despairing of the Church's Christianity, now refused to enter through its doors. Just as he was oblivious, too, to the fact that amongst them were some who that very day had eaten at breakfast nothing more than their usual fare of mashed turnips and onions and had drunk their usual acorn 'tea.' The causes of those hollow cheeks and glazed eyes he did not consider beyond taking their blank looks to be not people near to feinting with hunger but the simple blind faith of the villagers, his flock, showing through.

Nothing deterred the Reverend Doctor, however. After all, had not he, as God's and Christ's servant on earth, brought back into the House of the Lord the sheep which had strayed and which he had found enmeshed in the thicket of their vices, drunkenness, thieving, fornication and lechery, dissatisfaction with their lot and, from some, aspirations beyond their station? These he had now rescued: even as Abraham had rescued the stray sheep caught in the thicket in the wilderness, so had he. Their admiration for the eloquence of his words was obvious from the way they stared back up at him as he spoke, with mouths open in surprise at the beauty of his text, none moving.

As in harvest time, he continued, all must be activity and diligence and constant advantage must be taken of every favourable opportunity or there would be a danger of the crops being spoiled and the labours of the preceding months ending in disappointment. 'So must the Christian, if he would reap the rich reward promised to the faithful, be ever watchful and earnest, living a life of holy obedience, and maintaining, by ever renewed supplies of grace and strength through the means ordained in Christ's Church, his union, with his Lord and Saviour. And those who have been employed in the fields and who have endured the heat and burden of harvest time have special cause of gratitude to Him who has spared them and blessed the labours of their hands. For in their gratitude to Him who has given of His bounty so freely, might they not forget how during a part of this harvest time, a few of the more aged amongst us were called away from their harvest toil and from amongst the bosom of their companions in labour to their final account while lying peacefully abed ...'

It was a sermon which, he truly believed, could not but have a direct benefit in reminding the villagers of Hamwick Dean how the religion of Christ and the worship of the Church were hallowed in every season and gave a tone to all that they did, chastening their joy as well as soothing their sorrow: and when they reflected upon what an influence the harvest had upon the well-being and prosperity of the country at large, 'how all classes of the community are interested in it, how the burgeoning springs of national industry are affected by it and how scarcity impedes our trade and causes distress and a loss of employment to many,' then they must feel that their rejoicing and thankfulness embraced more than their own more local or individual interests.

Everyone else had risen and filed away – in Parson Petchey's hopes, filled with thankfulness at his words and full of renewed faith – when the churchwardens, Joshua Jaikes and Lemuel Ring, carried the aged Lou Spooner out after the service was over. In actual fact, most were too stupified by everything they had heard to turn and look back, so no one noticed the old man asleep in the corner pew farthest from the pulpit, though, curiously, this time he was not snoring as he had been known to do when he had fallen asleep on a bench in the Carpenters' Arms with his tankard half drunk before him. He was not noticed simply because he had slumped down and was lying full length on the empty seat, that is, till the parson's wife twitched her nose and sent Joshua Jaikes across to detect the source of the smell.

The parish cart was fetched when the road outside was clear, the two churchwardens having to hold their breath as they carried him out: they trundled him back to his hovel of a home by one of the backlanes, knowing even as they did so he would never again have to make the long walk to the church, gasping for breath and supporting himself on a fence or a gatepost or a tree every fifty yards: his next journey would be made on the village's polished funeral cart pulled by four of his neighbours and, since he was so pauperised, the parish would have to pay for yet another burial.

Jem heard of the old man's demise and the parson's sermon from Dick Dollery while sitting in the Wayfarers' again with him and the others, though it was a different Jem, their friends acknowledged, from the one they had known a year previously: more inclined to brood on matters which concerned him, to sit for long periods without talking, sometimes to sit without even sipping at the ale which Dick Dollery or Enos Diddams or one of the others had bought for him. Curiously, the Wayfarers' and the Carpenters' Arms were doing business again: not great business, it has to be said, but some business, as men, having no work to go to, preferred to sit there all day with their fellows and to let what little drink they could afford or what Caleb Chapman would allow them 'on the slate' take away their worries.

They were all sitting there quietly, recalling their memories of Old Lou, when Jem suddenly banged his fist down hard upon the table. 'The old hypocrite of a parson preaches about bountiful harvests while an old man dies in his church of hunger!' he shouted, which caused heads to turn and eyes to widen in surprise, since the outburst was so unexpected. 'He talks about God and yet half the people who sit listening to him are in want and all he offers them are meaningless prayers and pious sentiments!' With that, he staggered out of the door into the yard, as much overcome with remorse as with frustration and anger.

A few put this untypical rant down to a clear derangement of the mind caused by the death of his wife while he was locked up in Melchborough Gaol. 'Poor man,' they thought, 'poor man, he has lost his mind. I never thought to hear a man like him rant so. And him normally so placid and sensible, too! T'is a shame, a great shame. T'is not God who is to blame, t'is them who denies us, them that makes the laws and makes damned sure they are kept. They are the ones to blame, the landowners and the parsons and the rich farmers...

Dick Dollery followed his friend into the yard, where he found Jem standing grim-faced and brushing at the tears which had formed in his eyes: to be truthful, Dick Dollery had his own worries: he had been on the parish since the spring, but like everyone else at the much reduced payment and food was as scarce in his cottage as it was in every other.

'Come on, Jem,' Dick Dollery said, placing his arm around his friend's shoulders and quietly guiding him out on to the road. 'T'will do no good blaming the parson and God for everything that happens. To my way o' thinking, we has to do something to help ourselves because, if we don't, no one else will...'

TWENTY-FIVE

A SERIES of hayricks fired in the middle of the night at Orpington and Sevenoaks in Kent started it all: the ricks were set ablaze at the beginning of June in revenge for a farmer evicting the occupiers of a cottage and then pulling it down. But it was not till the end of August, on the twenty-eighth, that the machine-breaking began in earnest in that same county: four-hundred agricultural labourers descended on farms around Canterbury and destroyed several threshing machines. Next day, two magistrates, with a hundred special constables hastily sworn in and some soldiers, rode out to restore order: some said the labourers were only responding to a misguided comment from one of the two magistrates, made a week or so before, that threshing machines ought not be introduced, so they had smashed those that had been introduced. However, when the magistrate in question turned against them and punished them for it, the labourers took their revenge by firing his ricks, for the magistrate was also a landowner. What were later to be called the 'Swing Riots' had begun.

At the time, the whole of England was unsettled: George the Fourth had died on June the twenty-sixth, to be succeeded by his aging brother, the liberal Duke of Clarence, as William the Fourth. As the accession of a new monarch required a General Election, there would, in effect, be no Government till the election was held: and elections then were drawn-out affairs, the actual voting being held over several weeks: so effectively the country was without government for a time.

Parliamentary reform had long been an issue of contention amongst all the classes, whether for or against it: the prominent Whig, Earl Grey, had some months before made a speech in the Lords on the need for reform, which, amongst other things, would mean doing away with the 'rotten boroughs,' such as Dunwich up in the next county, under the patronage of Lord Huntingfield, which, as a result of coastal erosion, had almost fallen into the sea and by then had only thirty-two people with the vote, yet returned two Members of Parliament: as did Old Sarum, in Wiltshire, under the patronage of the Earl of Caledon, which had only three houses and a population of fifteen. Instead, under Earl Grey's proposed reforms, representation in the House of Commons would be extended to the fast-growing industrial towns of Manchester, Birmingham, Bradford and Leeds, which had populations numbering tens of thousands. Reform would also extend the right to vote to any man owning a household worth ten pounds sterling, thus adding two hundred and seventeen thousand more voters to an electorate of four hundred and thirty-five thousand: therefore, one man in five would have the right to vote. However, for many of the gentry, the idea of allowing the middle-classes to share power with the upper classes was too revolutionary in its aspect.

Parliament had sat for the last time on June the fourth: the election campaigning which followed was dominated by the issue of reform and the normal turbulence of the hustings further highlighted the divisions in the country. Voting lasted throughout July and August: at that time, local returning officers fixed the election timetable for a particular constituency or number of constituencies and, if the seat or seats were contested, polling could continue for many days, with counts and recounts.

At the same time, across the Channel in France that July and August, there had been more revolution to disturb the sleep of the rich landowners of England: in Paris, the overly religious Charles X had been forced to abdicate and had been replaced by Louis-Philippe, the 'Citizen King.' Soon after, in the August, came a second shock when the Belgians staged a revolt against Dutch control of their country. The news of both events was widely reported in the London newspapers: those in power feared that the unrest abroad could spread to England and the great debate on reform and power in Parliament might well be the catalyst for it.

Finally, the election was concluded and, though the incumbent Tory Prime Minister, the old Iron Duke himself, was returned, his party was much weakened when the new Parliament was summoned to meet on September the fourteenth, for a maximum seven-year term from that date.

Meanwhile, all during September, the destruction of threshing machines by bands of men in the district around Canterbury continued practically unchecked: so widespread had machine-breaking become in that one region that a hundred were smashed between the first attack on August the twenty-eighth and the end of October: England, it seemed, was following France and Belgium towards revolution.

Though, from the start, large rewards were promised to informers, including a wise offer to relocate any informer, the offers were not taken up and riot and rick-burning spread steadily. About this time, too, crudely written letters, supposedly signed by a mythical 'Captain Swing,' which was to give the uprising its historical name, started to be sent to farmers, threatening them and their property if they failed to remove the hated threshing machines and raise men's wages.

Some say the name 'Captain Swing' was adopted to puzzle those to whom the threatening letters were sent and perhaps to instill fear by its overtones of hanging: for none knew who 'Captain Swing' was, if he existed at all: though, one suggestion was that the name was adopted from the swingel part of the flail used in the old manner of threshing, but no one knew for sure.

For some, the rising of the agricultural labourers of Kent was the longed-for revolution that would sweep away the gentry just as surely as the revolution in France forty-one years before had swept away the aristocrats there: as one rioter retorted to a magistrate who had attempted to remonstrate with him and his band of machine-breakers: 'This year, we will destroy the cornstacks and the threshing machines, next year we will have a turn with the parsons, and the third year we will make war on the statesmen.'

In previous years, if farm labourers had a dispute with their masters, they might well have set fire to one of his hayricks in the secrecy of night before stealing home, satisfied with their boldness: this time the revolt was more widespread, more violent and more directed. This time, it was joined by village craftsmen such as blacksmiths, carpenters, wheelwrights, cordwainers, rakemakers, bricklayers, roadmenders and foresters, all those, in fact, whose livelihoods were equally as threatened by the deterioration of rural life and the fact that farm labourers had ceased to command what they considered a living wage.

Initially, most threshing machines were smashed on Saturday nights after the inns and taverns had closed: beer, sold at threepence a quart, fuelled the bravado of the men and youths of a village and gangs of between twenty and fifty would descend upon a farm and wreck the hated machine where it stood in the barn.

By the middle of September, the labourers were masters over a large area of the Southern Counties below the Thames: mobs, scoured the countrside for threshing machines to break, forcing all others whom they came across on the farms still working to join them in their rebellion, whether they wanted to or not.

The rounding-up of rioters, however, was left mostly to local magistrates, assisted by bailiffs and other helpers sworn in as special constables, with the militia sometimes in attendance. The magistrates, however, had no proper powers or ability to control mobs of five hundred and more and were more concerned with preventing its spread almost as if it were a contagion: except for calling out the militias, their only other means of maintaining law and order was the unsalaried parish constable. At one place, the gentry themselves turned out to assist a body of thirty-four militia to meet a mob of four hundred and the young son of one of the lesser gentry, who had been roughly handled by the mob, was later observed sitting on horseback alongside a cartload of arrested labourers with his gun cocked, pointed at them and ready to fire. Notwithstanding the fact that the arrests had been made without difficulty or resistance, the officer in command of the militia still felt obliged to write to his superiors of 'the dangers of the situation' and to request fieldpieces be sent: the powers-that-be promptly ordered two pieces of artillery and accompanying soldiers to be dispatched to the area.

As the harvesting got under way, the disturbances became more serious, spreading not only into West Sussex and Hampshire but into Wiltshire and Gloucestershire and as far west as Herefordshire: from there, they went northwards into Berkshire, into Middlesex, then north again into the Midlands counties, across to the Eastern Counties, and then as far north as Lincolnshire and Nottinghamshire, even Yorkshire: county after county was in a state bordering on insurrection.

The troubles in Sussex began early in November: on Wednesday, November the seventeenth, threshing machines were destroyed at Emsworth, Funtingdon and Westbourne and the following evening more damage was done at Westbourne. On November the eighteenth, the rioting reached Hampshire, where a mob at Fordingbridge, under the leadership of a man called Cooper, who rode on horseback and assumed the title of 'Captain Hunt' and was addressed so by his followers, broke the machinery at both a sacking factory and a threshing machine manufacturer. Some said Cooper was a gipsy, others a gentleman, or even the renowned 'Captain Swing' himself: in reality, he was a drunken agricultural labourer from the village of East Grimstead, in Wiltshire, who had served in the artillery in the war. Two months before the riots, his wife had run off with another man and this had unhinged him: to forget his misery, he had first taken to drink and then had joined in the rioting.

At Andover, in the same county, where a foundry was destroyed, the ringleader of the mob was a twenty-five-year-old labourer named

Gilmore, who had also been a soldier, and took it upon himself to enter the room in which the local Justices were meeting and forcefully to entreat with them on behalf of the baying mob outside.

The riots were not confined solely to rural areas: on November the eighteenth, a thousand protesters, led by three members of the Horsham Radical Party, besieged local gentry, farmers and a lay tithe proprietor in that town's church, during which altar rails were demolished for weapons as the men demanded wage increases and tithe reductions. At the town hall, a purely political assembly blamed 'mismanagement' by the Government as the cause of all their ills: employers, whether farmers or master tradesmen, were too impoverished to afford improved wages unless tithes, taxes and rents were reduced, together with the 'total abolition of all sinecures, useless places and unmerited pensions,' while parliamentary reform was 'indispensable.' When sixty-three householders were summoned to become special constables, only four turned out, giving the local Bench – which included the High Sheriff – no option but to lobby for military aid.

London, still without a Parliament sitting at that time, was in a panic and night after night the sky to the south and west of the capital was lit by the red glow from blazing ricks and barns: to those who sat in high places, it brought home the full meaning of mob diplomacy. Such was the climate of fear and suspicion that a man upon the road with a lit cigar was likely to be regarded as a possible incendiary, while a retractable eyeglass, such as Nelson had put to his blind eye at the Battle of Copenhagen, found upon the person of another was mistaken for an air gun used by some rioters to ignite ricks and barns. Further, a traveller innocently requesting directions to a farm found himself having to explain his presence to a troop of armed special constables, who suspected him of being the actual 'Captain Swing.'

There was terror everywhere amongst the landowners: indeed, so alarmed about likely revolution was the old Duke of Buckingham when the uprising spread into his county of Hampshire that he removed cannon from his yacht in the Solent and positioned them at his house. 'This part of the country is wholly in the hands of the rebels,' he wrote to the Government. 'Fifteen-hundred rioters are to assemble tomorrow morning and will attack any farmhouses where there are threshing machines. They go about levying contributions on every gentleman's house. There are very few magistrates and what there are are completely cowed. Something decisive must instantly be done.'

However, with a thousand labourers to every soldier and most soldiers in London, where the Tower was fortified, the county magistrates and gentry were more or less left to their own devices. Some troop movements were made: thirty soldiers went in a hired conveyance from Portsmouth into Sussex and a company from Dorset sailed into Southampton by steamboat, but, in doing so, left that county ungarrisoned. Elsewhere, the pace of the revolt was almost too rapid for it to be quelled. At Wilton, in Wiltshire, a mob was led by an eighteen-year-old, named John Jennings, who declared that he was going to break the machinery at a woollen mill 'to make more work for poor people,' while another cloth factory at Quidhampton was attacked in which one of the leaders was a seventeen-year-old, named John Ford.

Sympathy for the labourers' cause was widespread in all the affected counties and came from many quarters, particularly from the smuggling fraternity, for that was still a common practice in the coastal counties and it was from them that the agricultural labourers sometimes found their natural leaders, men outside the law who had learned audacity and resourcefulness and had a habit of common action. Sympathy also came from some of the more enlightened, more altruistic clergy: at one place, some men stopped a coach and found a bishop riding in it: the men brusquely demanded money and, to their surprise, the bishop gave it to them without protest. Though he recognised several as being from the very town in which he lived, he made no attempt to report them to the special constables patrolling the place, as others might have done, but the next day called twenty of them to his palace and set them to properly paid work, clearing and tidying the grounds, rebuilding a wall and trimming bushes and the like, then opened the doors of his palace and handed out food and other necessities to those in the town who were distressed.

The rising, meanwhile, had continued westward into Dorset and Gloucestershire, then back into Buckinghamshire, where, in addition to the usual agricultural workers breaking any threshing machine they came across and demanding higher wages, there were riots in High Wycombe and attacks were made on the recently installed machinery at several paper mills along a three-mile stretch of river between Loudwater and Chepping Wycombe. Paper mills were also attacked at Colthrop, in Berkshire.

News of the events south of the Thames and west of the capital trickled through to Hamwick Dean, first via the coach drivers and passengers from London arriving at Hamwyte and then to the village by the wagoners. On hearing of the happenings, the men in the Wayfarers', the Carpenters' Arms, the Bull at Merchant Staplers and the Green Man at Lower Rackstead grumbled that all they, too, required to make their lives tolerable again, and nothing more than that, was a minimum wage of two shillings and threepence a day in winter, which would give them thirteen shillings and sixpence for their six-day week, and two-shillings and sixpence a day in summer when the work was longer and more arduous and more necessary, which would give them a weekly wage of fifteen shillings. Yet summer long, all through the harvesting, those that had been lucky enough to find work had at the highest received no more than seven shillings and fourpence threefarthing a week from Titus Broake, who had arbitrarily set the rate, being a magistrate and thinking his word always binding, with which the three other large farmers, Amos Peakman, Marcus Howie and Joshua Godwin, also being magistrates by then, had concurred and which, too, had been followed by the ten other small farmers who now existed in the district following enclosure, farming sixty or seventy acres and none employing more than seven or eight men, half-men and boys and laying them off when there was no work just as the others had always done.

Like so many, there were amongst the inhabitants of the villages in the Hundred some who were as near to starving as any could be and still be breathing: it showed in their haggard faces, was manifested by their thin frames and their ragged clothes, by their barefoot children, by the cowed manner of the older labourers and the determined anger of the younger men.

The people were at the end of their tether: the price of wheat, which during the first bad harvest in Twenty-Eight had risen to its highest level in eight years, from sixty-shillings a quarter in the September to seventy-two shillings a quarter by the October, had remained high – and, consequently, so had the price of bread – too high for many even to purchase a loaf on some days: people who had once been proud of their independence were now reduced to utter destitution.

TWENTY-SIX

WHO SENT the five letters signed by 'Captain Swing,' or just 'Swing' in two instances, in that first week of November, the greater majority of the inhabitants of Hamwick Dean never knew, though there was one man who suspected he knew, but had no actual proof, not having seen them being written, not knowing the hand of any of the writers or having seen them in the possession of anyone either. However, no one ever asked Seph Kettle, the landlord of the isolated Shoulder of Mutton, standing in a dip on a lonely stretch of the Maydun-to-Wivencaster road: indeed, no one even discussed the matter with him since he had so few customers, so he was never in a position to tell and, therefore, kept the secret to himself and spent most of his time making the beehives he sold which kept his body and soul and his thin wife's body and soul together.

What he might have said, had he been asked, was that he was surprised one evening to find seven men from the village, who did not normally drink in the Shoulder of Mutton, enter his ale house, which as usual was deserted, order their ale in a two-gallon jug and then disappear into the small snug at the back which they asked him to open up for them and which was so rarely used he had not lit a fire in it for a full six-month even though it was November by then: and before they closed the door, they even requested that, if he wished to enter, would he please knock first and would he also not let anyone else go near. It was all very conspiratorial and he suspected some act of sedition was afoot and, in view of the news he had been hearing from other places, he was not surprised that men should be acting that way, especially as they were all agricultural workers whom he knew by sight.

Had he entered the small back room without knocking soon after they had closed the door or had he peeped in through the small windowlight above it within five minutes of their starting, he would have seen six of them, Dick Dollery, Enos Diddams, Nathaniel Newman, John Romble, William Stubbs and Thomas Judd, all seated around a table, with a lantern burning over the middle of it, the jug of ale already half empty and the six swallowing their ale and watching as the seventh dipped a pen into a capped inkwell which they had brought with them and slowly wrote out a letter. He might even have known that the seventh man was Jem Stebbings, just out of Melchborough Gaol, whose wife had been killed in a terrible accident while working on a threshing machine a few weeks before and who might well, were he a seditious type, have a score to settle with a few in the village whom he was not prepared to name.

'You're the only one amongst us who can write a good hand,' Dick Dollery had declared in asking Jem. 'Will you write the letters to Broake and the others for us? Of them all, Broake's the one we need to put right.'

'Aye, gladly. For Mary-Ann,' replied a grim-faced Jem, who had always been proud of the legibility of his hand, learned during his five years of schooling in the village's Dame School, before he had gone on to the land with his father.

'Won't they recognise your handwriting?' Thomas Judd asked, concerned.

'I can disguise it,' replied Jem. 'The handwriting should be as different as we can make it so they will think the letters have all been written by different people. T'is a pity all of you can't write.'

'I can write a bit,' Nathaniel Newman said, indignantly. 'I was taught by my old mother. I'd be willing to write one of the letters.'

'Jem's best at it,' said Dick Dollery. 'He had schooling. Best leave it to him. We're only sending five.'

'I'd still like to do one at least,' protested Nathaniel Newman, a little petulantly. 'My writing en't that bad.'

'I can write a bit, too,' said Thomas Judd, eagerly, not wanting to be left out: then after a pause, he sheepishly admitted: 'Well, I can print after a fashion. I mayn't be as good as Jem here, but I could write one. T'will spread the confusion better if they are all by a different hand rather than just the one no matter how you disguises it.'

'Aye, he's right,' nodded Enos Diddams. 'T'would be better if they all looked different, like.'

That was the simple truth: if each of them could have penned a letter apiece, then it would have widened the area of complicity, especially as there were not many amongst the farm labourers of Hamwick Dean who could write: and those that could barely did it legibly: and if later the new parish constable, Ephraim Simms, the grocer, who had taken over at the last Easter vestry from the cooper, Elijah Candler, were ever to pursue the matter of who wrote the letters, the number who would fall under suspicion would be small enough as it was and almost a give-away if all written by a single hand.

So it was decided that Jem would write three of them, Nathaniel Newman would write one and, if he could manage it, Thomas Judd would attempt to print the third in readable capital letters. The first of the letters, which Jem wrote with his right hand, but in an untidy fashion, with the lettering itself sloping backwards and three deliberate spelling errors, was to 'Squire Broake' because he was the worst of the landowners and because, more than anything, they resented his unchallengeable authority and the sway he held over every aspect of their lives. *'This is a warning to all who seek to lord it over their fellow man at which you are the meanest and the blackest,'* Jem wrote. *'If you do not pull down your threshing machines on your farms and raise the poor mens wages on each and give to the marryd men two and sixpence a day and for the single men two shillings and threepence and all agreed with the justesses we will burn down your barns and you in them. Ignore me at your own peril. This is the only notis from Captain Swing.'*

The second letter, to Parson Petchey, for his arrogance and his un-Christian, uncharitable manner, he wrote entirely with his left hand, this time attempting to disguise his writing by making the lettering almost childishly large and untidy yet again. The third, to Amos Peakman because, as well as the matter of Mary-Ann's death by his threshing machine, he had become even more arrogant and uncaring than he had been before, typified by the way he had laid off the men and women that autumn without a thought or concern for them or their families: the letter to him, Jem wrote in a normal hand, though with a certain carelessness, as if the writer had never mastered the basic principles of script and writing in straight lines. When he passed the letters around, there were broad smiles and chortles of delight, for these were the ones who had ill-used them the longest.

Nathaniel Newman and Thomas Judd then took it in turn to scratch out their single efforts, which took as long to write as it had taken Jem to complete his three, including thought on how to disguise one from another. Both then read his effort aloud, but in a low voice in case Seph Kettle was listening and with obvious difficulty since neither had had any schooling: Nathaniel Newman had started work in his father's forge at the age of seven and Thomas Judd, to put some food on his widowed mother's table, had become a bird scarer at the age of six, then a gleaner after the harvest and a boy cowherd, as poorly paid as all children were, but at least earning something which helped before he had been apprenticed as a cordwainer. His mother had also taught him to read and write, after a fashion.

Nathaniel Newman's letter was for Marcus Howie because he, like Peakman, was a bullying, bustling uncaring master who was never satisfied with anything that was done and also because he owed the blacksmith money for the repair of a horse rake and was refusing to pay the full amount, saying the repair was poorly done. Thomas Judd's letter was for Joshua Godwin because three years before, when the bad harvests had set in, he had colluded with the others to lower wages from eleven shillings a week to seven shillings for married men and only five shillings for the single threequarter men and half-men. The same smiles, nods and murmurs of approval greeted their efforts as they were passed from hand to hand: the letters had been started almost in a jocular fashion: now there were a few pursed lips of apprehension: for now they needed to summon the courage to deliver them.

The following night, soon after midnight, three shadowy figures crept through the churchyard alongside the parsonage and, after surveying the scene to ensure that all was still and discerning no movement or light in the darkened house, one of their number forced his way through the privet hedge with no concern whatever for the damage he might cause, crept across the recently scythed lawn up to the high-arched front porch, thrust a roll of paper in the crack between the edge of the door and the frame and hurriedly retreated.

Parson Petchey's new housemaid found that letter the next morning when she went out to polish the doorknocker and took it to the parson's wife, who handed it to the parson: *'The poor of this parish are many and desperate,'* it read. *'They are reduced to beggars. They want bread and meat not sermons. Their true rights has been taken from them. If the callous wrongs inflicted on them by the likes of you and others of your kind are not soon righted to the satisfaction of the many, if the yoke of the tithe which keeps you in luxury is not lifted, if the relief paid is not raised and if the overseer of the poor Joshua Jaikes is not soon gone for good from this parish, great trouble will befall you. Mark my words. – Captain Swing.'*

The new housemaid was immediately scolded by the parson's wife for finding the letter and upsetting the Reverend Doctor for the whole of that day, as though she had written it herself: and when summoned by Parson Petchey to account for it and asked if she had seen the person who had delivered it and, if not, why not, she was scolded a second time for not being alert and told to get up earlier the following morning for no other reason than the parson and his wife had realised that someone had crept up to their home, like a common burglar, and thrust the insolent missive into their doorway. Not that the villagers knew anything of this or the letter: only those who perpetrated the deed knew of the parson's consternation, till the next Sunday when the parson gave full vent to his feelings from the pulpit yet again.

The letter to Amos Peakman at Goat Lodge was similarly half-pushed under the gap in his door in the dead of night so stealthily by whoever did it that there was not even a single bark from the yard dog, which was kenneled by the gate, so that no one would be able to come through it unless he let them, which might have led a shrewder brain than Amos Peakman had to realise that the dog was probably wagging its tail at the lanky, blond-haired figure who stole across the yard to perform the deed and threw it a rabbit's leg to chew.

'Sir,' the letter declared, 'Your name is writ down amongst the black hearts in the black book. Ye have been the blackguard enemy of the people on all occasions. Ye have not done as ye ought. Ye have turned men from their rightful work and ye have reduced their relief. If thy threshing machine is not broke by you, we will break it for thee. This is to advise you and the like of you to make your wills. Beware of me. – Captain Swing.'

To Marcus Howie, who had similarly laid off ten of the village's labourers at the end of the harvest work, Nathaniel Newman's letter read: 'We are fifty and unighted against any force that mite oppose us. We will give you a week to destroy the threshing machine in your barn. If it is not done by that time, we shall commence our labours. You will see your ricks on fire before we leave your premises. Signed on behalf of the whole, Swing.'

The letter to Joshua Godwin, which had taken Thomas Judd fully two minutes to scratch out in uneven capitals, was delivered two days later and, like the recipient, was short and brusque: 'Mr Godwin, mind your yards be not afire if ye act as ye do, dam you. We will have thy thrashing mashine broke and good money paid for our wages or else. Be warned. – Swing.'

In most places, local issues themselves were sufficient to spark the threatening letters being sent to unsympathetic landlords, landowners and clergy: such as the need for a living wage and continual employment, cuts made suddenly in poor relief for those who were forced to go 'on the parish' and the setting of harsher conditions of qualification for what meagre relief was doled out by the overseer as the numbers without work increased sharply and the drain on the poor rate mounted alamingly. Other factors, too, played their part: higher cottage rents set by absent, uncaring landlords at Michaelmas and resentment at the influence which the parson exercised in the village, especially on the matters of tithes and social status: in Hamwick Dean that November, it all added to the incendiary mix.

The grumblers in the Wayfarers' and the Carpenters' Arms did not know it, but the smaller farmers, like Angus McCreef, William Worden and Robert Lenny, who had set up since enclosure in Hamwick Dean, Richard Shadwell, John Dicker and Henry Sweetapple at Merchant Staplers and Jonathan Hartless, Thomas Crawley and Thomas Templeton, of Lower Rackstead, were themselves in dire straits at that time, barely able to pay their own high rents to the owners of their land and barely able either to meet their tithes to the Church, which along with the many taxes imposed upon them were the reasons for their distress. They, too, had had to lay off men who, in previous years, they had employed over the long months of winter as an act of charity: as a consequence, they, had begun to consider ways to reduce their costs and leasing one of the new threshing machines from the new machinery agent in Wivencaster, which would cut the numbers required on their farms and, thus, their wage bill, was the only answer that they could see for the future, knowing full well it would force yet more men and their families 'on the parish' in the years ahead.

TWENTY-SEVEN

'SQUIRE' BROAKE,' as it happened, was not at home when the letter signed 'Captain Swing' was pushed under the main door of the Hall in the depths of the night: instead, he was asleep in his town house in St. John's Wood in London, as befitted the newly elected Member of Parliament for Hamwyte: for, that summer, he had been persuaded by certain affluent gentlemen in the town to put himself forward – for the Tories, naturally – in place of the aged and doddering Sir Benton, who was retiring. It had been a momentous week.

Parliament had not met since the fourth of June and much had happened at home and abroad since then, especially in France and Belgium. Sir Titus Broake, as he had now become, knighted by the King that summer, with the support of his good friend Sir Gentry, had taken his seat on the Tory benches in the Commons on the previous Tuesday, October the twenty-sixth, and had sat somewhat bemused through the election of the Speaker. After that, he had spent the next two days with Sir Gentry being introduced to fellow Members in the House itself, in Sir Gentry's club and at various eating establishments and had returned to the Hall only on the Friday to see what concerns Heginbotham and Trott might have. On the Monday, the first of November, he had returned by coach to London so that he might join the other Members of the House of Commons at the bar of the Lords on the Tuesday, the second of November, to listen to His Majesty King William's Address at the opening of the session.

He had been somewhat irritated by the House procedure when, on their return to the Commons, the Speaker had informed them that he had procured a copy of the new King's Speech and, to prevent mistakes, he would read it again 'for the satisfaction of the House' – the whole thousand words of it: he had found himself somewhat bemused by the long discussion upon points in it and, except for the novelty of hearing the Members debate obscure points, had not been much interested.

There had been some small discussion on reforming Parliament – doing away with the 'rotten boroughs,' redistributing the seats to the more populated industrial towns, thus, getting rid, too, of the 'placemen' who were in Parliament as a reward for the political support they had given an elected official, voting annually for Parliament – but, as a newcomer, he had been content to sit and to listen to others and then to retire to the club

The only thing that had drawn his attention during the early part of the sitting on the following day, Wednesday, November the third, when matters arising from the King's Speech were still being addressed, had been a petition from numerous persons confined for small debts in the Marshalsea and the Four Courts in Dublin, complaining of the state of the prisons and the abuses concerning the recovery of small debts. 'Damned cheek!' he had thought. 'They should not have got into debt in the first place!' After that, Sir Robert Peel, the leader in the Commons, had spoken at length on the rather dull subject of the Management of Public Business, the import of which Titus Broake had only vaguely understood.

It was sometime later that a Mr. Maberly had risen to enter his protest against what he termed 'the very extraordinary Speech we have heard from the Throne – extraordinary,' he said, 'because I think that nothing could be more extraordinary than for the Ministers to put into the mouth of his Majesty a Speech which omitted all mention of reform and of reduction of taxation – the two topics which agitate the whole empire, from one end of it to the other.'

Members lolling on the benches sat up at that and the whole place livened up: and even Titus Broake had found himself murmuring his agreement when Lord Eastnor, replying, observed that it was not inconsistent for the King to omit any recommendation of reform in his Speech from the Throne, for such a recommendation, he believed, had never been made in a King's Speech during the past two hundred years: and, with respect to reform, he believed few of those who advocated it were agreed upon the sort of reform that was necessary. As far as Titus Broake was concerned, his side had won that round and he cheered and waved his order paper with the rest of them.

The sitting on November the fourth was memorable to Titus Broake only for a Mr. Hume's advice to Ministers concerning 'a cause of great public alarm, and by that means of great loss of property to individuals.'

'It is feared,' the Member said, 'from the tone of the King's Speech with respect to Belgium, and of the explanation which Ministers have offered of that Speech, that they mean to plunge this country into a war, the consequence of which must be most ruinous.' He was satisfied that they had no such intention, but still he felt, in common with many intelligent persons in the House and elsewhere, that it was impossible for any man to say where our 'conference, for the tranquillity of Belgium' would end. After that, a Member had requested leave to bring in a Bill for doing away with the necessity of taking the Oath of Abjuration on the acceptance of Civil Office and of the Oaths taken by the Members of that House before the Lord Steward, which had caused him to yawn, and he was still yawning when a Member proposed something about copies of treaties being provided in the House by the printer on the country's relations with foreign powers, particularly with Belgium and Holland.

The following day, however, the Friday, he was somewhat confounded by the buzz at the club: everyone seemed to be discussing what the old Duke of Wellington had said two days before in reply to a speech on the Address by Earl Grey, one of the main Whig advocates of parliamentary reform: the feeling everywhere seemed to be that the Old Duke, in making an uncalled for declaration against reform, had committed a momentous blunder when the feeling throughout the country generally was in favour of reform and his speech was being condemned by friends and foes alike.

Sir Gentry was almost apoplectic: 'In three minutes,' he complained bitterly, 'the Prime Minister has done more for the cause of reform than the Whigs have been able to achieve in a year! He has united all reformers and given the Political Unions the battle cry they needed. He cannot remain! His fate is sealed! I can scarcely conceive of an act of more egregious folly.'

Word had got round, too, that the Duke had been hissed by certain of the public and had been hit by a stone thrown at him and such was the concern in the metropolis of the rising anger amongst the labouring classes that several Members said they had heard shopkeepers say they were considering arming themselves.

The Old Duke's 'blunder' had occurred on November the second when he had risen in the Lords to reply to Lord Grey's remarks on the Speech from the Throne: he had somewhat snidely declared in part that he had never read or heard of any measure up to that present moment which could in any degree satisfy his mind that the state of the representation of Parliament could be improve. He was fully convinced, he said, that the country possessed a legislature which 'answered all the good purposes of legislation,' and that to a greater degree than any legislature ever had answered in any country whatever. Indeed, he would go further and say that the legislature and the system of representation possessed the full and entire confidence of the country. The representation of the people at the present contained a large body of the property of the country in which the landed interest had a preponderating influence. Under those circumstances, he was not only *not* prepared to bring forward any measure of parliamentary reform but he would at once declare that, as far as he was concerned, as long as he held any station in the government of the country, he should always feel it his duty to resist such measures when proposed by others!

Immediately, there had been a furore in the chamber: as he sat down, Wellington had whispered an aside to the Earl of Aberdeen, his Foreign Secretary. 'What can I have said which seems to have made so great a disturbance?' he enquired.

A somewhat crestfallen Aberdeen had replied: 'You have announced the fall of your Government, that is all.'

Talk of reform, of doing away with the 'rotten boroughs,' of universal suffrage, annual elections and ridding the House of 'placemen' was everywhere, Titus Broake had found: a person could not sit with five or six Members taking coffee before someone mentioned it: some in his party were for it in a moderate form, he knew, while others were rigidly opposed: to Wellington, reform, radicalism and revolution were all the same thing.

Events had gathered apace after that: on the Thursday, the fourth of November, the Earl of Winchilsea had declared in an attack on the Duke in the Lords that the best and only security was to be found in doing ample justice to the people and in relieving their distress, and for this purpose, an inquiry should be instituted into the condition of the great body of the agricultural labourers, who were loyal and faithful, but suffering very greatly. He could not restrain his 'astonishment at hearing the declaration made by the noble Duke the other evening, relating to parliamentary reform. The noble Duke thought our present legislature so perfect that he stated that, if he had to form a legislature, he would create one, not equal in excellence to the present, for that he could not expect, but something as nearly of the same description as possible. He could give nothing more perfect, more capable of satisfying the empire, than the present Parliament...'

Later, the earl had urged that an inquiry ought to be instituted into the situation of the labouring classes, that their lordships might give them effectual and speedy relief. If that passage of the noble Duke's speech which related to parliamentary reform had been framed with a view of conciliating and gaining the support of the high-minded noblemen with whom he himself was usually united, he could tell the noble Duke that he might as well attempt to take high heaven by storm! The country was in such a situation, that it required the most efficient men in the Administration. The present Ministers were not in possession of the confidence of the country, and other individuals placed in their stations must rescue the country from danger.

Those opposing reform were concerned that a Bill would create a division in the legislature between rural and industrial interests, divided geographically by a line between The Wash and Severn. The scene would then be set for a struggle between classes and economic interests and, as one Member had said: 'The field of coal would beat the field of barley, the population of the manufacturing districts was more condensed and would act with more energy, backed by clubs and large assemblages of people, than the population of the agricultural districts. They would act with such force in the House that the more divided agriculturalists would be unable to withstand it, and the latter would be overwhelmed.'

Titus Broake, therefore, was concerned that county Members like himself would, in future, be unable to maintain and protect landed interests without the help of Members for closed boroughs – the 'placemen,' who were the 'true protectors of the landed interest': reform, too, might lead to a campaign against the Corn Laws. In fact, it was the very petitions to Parliament for repeal of the Corn Laws, coupled with demands for the reform of Parliament, which had led to his accepting a request from certain dignitaries in Hamwyte to stand in Sir Benton's stead.

The possible loss of any influence he and other county men might have had exercised Titus Broake's mind more than anything else that evening in the club: like so many Tories, he feared that, in a Reformed Parliament, the country squires like himself would not be able to stand against the active, pushing, intelligentsia who would be sent from the manufacturing towns. With the Crown and Lords weakened as independent working features of the Constitution, nothing would be able to challenge the power of a Commons elected by the 'sovereignty of the people.' Once the principle of breaking down the traditional structure of government in deference to popular demand was admitted, then it mattered little, in his opinion, if on the first occasion a decent moderation, as some in his Party were prepared to allow, confined the additions to the electorate within the half-million mark. It was the first step which marred all. On those grounds, Titus Broake joined Sir Robert Peel in opposing the Reform Bill.

Hopes of a settled government to deal with the crisis were dashed when, on November the fifteenth, division amongst Tory Members led to Wellington's government being defeated in a vote in the Commons and the Prime Minister tending his resignation to the King on November the sixteenth. Two days later, on the eighteenth, William the Fourth decided to ask the sixty-six-year-old Earl Grey to form a government, the first predominantly Whig administration in twenty years. It marked the end of a fifteen-year period of political paralysis for the earl – he having earned the direct animosity of the late George the Fourth for opposing a Bill to secure the King's divorce from the odious Queen Caroline.

The new Prime Minister declared that his first act would be to form a Cabinet committee to produce a plan for parliamentary reform: however, true to an aristiocratic tradition, he gave high positions in the Cabinet to his son, his three sons-in-law, his three brothers-in-law, as well as his nephews, though he did bring in two merchants, making one Secretary to the Treasury and the other Vice-President of the Board of Trade.

TWENTY-EIGHT

IN HAMWICK DEAN, Titus Broake's long-suffering wife considered the letter pushed under the Hall door important enough, in view of the disturbances south of the Thames of which she had heard, to forward it by Caleb Chapman's post office in the Wayfarers' to her husband in London. It took twenty-four hours for Jem's letter to reach Titus Broake, from collection at the Wayfarers' by the Hamwyte post boy on his pony, then via coach from Hamwyte to London and further delivery on to St John's Wood. Two days later, a seething 'Squire Broake' was back in Hamwick Dean, conferring with Parson Petchey and the three other main landowners of the area who had also received missives, namely Amos Peakman, Marcus Howie and Joshua Godwin.

Just as no one knew for sure then who had sent the letters, though many guessed at the names of at least three of them, so no one knew who it was who crept across the graveyard alongside the parsonage the next night when the Reverend Doctor was again sitting in his study, with the three candles burning, one in a holder on the table before him and two in a candelabra above his head, writing out another sermon. As he leaned back in his chair, pen still poised, and read the words he had written down, with the usual pride at his own eloquence, so a single pane in the upper window of the study shattered and, before he could even move, a pistol ball had cut in half one of the candles on the candelabra and embedded itself at the end of a two-foot-long furrow across the ceiling.

Parson Petchey was on his feet in an instant, heading for the door and the safety of the inner passageway, his face white with fear: and just as there was no doubt in his mind that some dastardly coward, skulking about in the night, was out to murder him, so there was no doubt in his mind either that, had he not leaned back at the exact moment the ball shattered the window pane, it would have struck him in the head. The good Doctor was not to know or to appreciate that the perpetrator, being a good shot and rewarded with a medal for being so by the old Volunteers, had, from the dark of the graveyard thirty yards away, aimed not at him but at one of the candles well above his head and had expertly cut it in half. The shot was fired simply to let the parson know that there were some outside in the surrounding darkness who did not fear him, who detested him and his ways and his sermons and who would happily see him dead and buried in his own graveyard.

The new parish constable, the grocer Ephraim Simms, had not wanted to be elected in the first place: he had hoped the task would go to someone else, but those present at the Easter vestry meeting, the other traders and the farmers and property owners who could vote, had said 'It's your turn, Ephraim. We've done our share' and so had voted him into the post.

What irked Ephraim Simms, as all others before him, was that the position was unpaid and the incumbent drew only what expenses he incurred and then only to amounts that a begrudging vestry would sanction: even then he had to wait a fortnight or more for them to be paid back to him. He was already out of pocket as it was: the expenses, in his opinion, were never enough to cover the loss of time and the effort he spent, or was supposed to spend, on investigating complaints. So far, in the seven months since his election, he had taken part in the removal back to their own parishes of a pauper family who had suddenly appeared in the village from somewhere up in the next county and had tried to build a hut in Captain's Wood: the vestry certainly did not want the expense of keeping them to fall upon their poor rate and, by default, upon himself and others. Secondly, he had had to waste a further day-and-a-half chasing after and apprehending an apprentice shoemender, young Will Harrington, who had left his employ at Tom Brady's shop without reason and had been caught heading for goodness knows where: the youth himself did not seem to know when questioned, just saying that he wanted to get away and see the world. Ephraim had found him sleeping under a hedge four miles out of Hamwyte on the Melchborough road and had given him a ride back to Hamwick Dean on his pony and had managed to convince the shoemender that the youth had run off to see a girl he had met at Melchborough fair rather than bother with charging him with a misdemeanour and having to waste more time attending the next petty sessions at Hamwyte to give evidence. Besides, he had enough to do in his grocery shop on The Street without having to chase after men and youths who flouted laws which they said were 'made by the high-ups against the interests of lowly countryfolk who have lived here for generations and now are treated like serfs in their own country.'

Ephraim Simms had viewed the letter which the parson had brought to him in the hope that he might recognise the hand which had written it, but, not being much of a writer himself, with only four years of formal schooling in the Dame School, the new parish constable had to admit that he could not identify the writer and when he took it across to Caleb Chapman, who was more likely than anyone to know, he claimed that he could not recognise the hand either since it was such scrawly, uneven writing.

As far as the writer or writers of the other threatening letters were concerned, he was not fooled, but did not see what he could actually do about it, being one man against a possible half-dozen or even 'fifty,' as the letter to Marcus Howie stated. He would go through the motions of an attempt at detection, of course, and had already noted, but kept to himself, that the writing on the letters to Titus Broake and Amos Peakman, like the writing on the parson's letter, had to be by someone who had been schooled fairly well, even though on two of them it was shaky, as if written with the left-hand rather than the normal right-hand as a means of disguising it. Further, it had also been pointed out to him that the words '*unight ...mashines... justasses... marryd... mite ...notis*' were misspelled, which otherwise he would not have known. Whoever it was who had sent them, he had heard that they had been toasted, as had the shooter, in the Wayfarers' and in the Carpenters' Arms, and in Merchant Stapler's tiny Bull Inn and the Green Man at Lower Rackstead and the Compasses on the Greater Tottle road. 'To a brave man, a braver man than I,' some said, not knowing or caring even if the shooter stood amongst them: they had already tipped their pots in the self-same toast to those who had sent the letters.

On the matter of the shooting, it had been with some trepidation that the grocer-cum-constable had answered the summons to the parsonage and had listened to Parson Petchey's account of the ball which had missed him 'by inches' when clearly, Ephraim Simms could see from a rough estimation of its trajectory from the shattered window pane to the start of the groove, that it had passed fully five feet above the seated clergyman's head. Either the perpetrator was a bad shot that he should have fired so high or he had done so deliberately and so was intending neither to kill nor to wound, though he did not say so to the parson since that would have been to provoke even greater indignation at a perceived lack of sympathy for 'the victim of this outrage.' Instead, he simply recorded the Reverend Doctor's losses, a shattered window pane, a candle cut in two and a groove in the ceiling which would need replastering: and, of course, to note his own expenses of time, exactly one half-hour, and of his travel, four-hundred yards exactly from the door of his shop to that of the parsonage.

Of course, he had promised Parson Petchey that he would make thorough enquiries, as a good parish constable should: but, being a wise man and mindful of his trade and the fact that whoever had committed the deed was in possession of a gun, most likely a bird gun, he quietly forgot this promise in the days which followed and, in conversation with Caleb Chapman and the other shopkeepers, intimated he thought it 'a burglary attempt gone wrong' and the work of one of the itinerant gangs who were abroad on the roads at that time, travelling from place to place, because the numbers of crimes always increased when they and others like them, didikais and gypsies, were in the area. There was a gang of them camped on the far side of Inworth heath so it might well have been one of them, he suggested to Caleb Chapman, who, thankfully, did not disagree, though he did not agree with it either, but just let out one of his usual incomprehensible throat-clearings. One thing he was certainly not disposed to do and that was to take on rebellious and violent men with guns, whether he knew them or not: and to attempt to arrest any of them alone was more likely to earn him a blow across the back of the head with the nearest weapon handy to the assailant or assailants. Meanwhile, as he reported to the vestry, he was 'still looking as best he could' and would make his report in due course.

TWENTY-NINE

OTHER EVENTS, however, were to distract him from his intentions: for the very next day a notice announcing a meeting one week hence between all middling farmers of the three parishes and a deputation from the day-labourers, to be held in the Wayfarers' on Saturday, November the twentieth, and attended by an 'impartial' magistrate from Hamwyte, who would act as a mediator, was nailed to the doors of St. Bartholomew's, St. Cuthbert's at Lower Rackstead and St John's at Merchant Staplers. The farmers clearly feared that the disturbances raging through the counties south of the Thames and to the west and north of the capital were about to reach the Hundred of Hamwyte. The notice was also put up in the hostelries of all three places for those who sought solace at one but no longer did so at the other, for there were some in all three who had ceased to care for their faith and regarded it all as a great lie perpetrated by those who wished to keep the 'lower order' subservient to themselves.

Such was the smaller farmers' concern that, late one afternoon three days before the meeting, when Enos Diddams was caught pausing to stretch his aching muscles while digging a channel to drain water from a flooded field on William Worden's leased acres along the Merchant Staplers road, the new farmer, rather than rebuking him, addressed him instead respectfully by his first name, gave out an embarrassed cough and, almost as one conspirator might do when approaching another, then looked about him as if to ensure that no one was within hearing distance, even though they were both standing in the middle of a hedged eight-acre field.

'I have heard all about the talk that is going on in the Wayfarers' and the Carpenters' Arms,' said Farmer Worden, who was one of the hardest-hit of the newcomers. 'I just want thee to know, Enos, that me and the other tenant farmers would be willing to look favourably on a demand for a raising of the wages we pays, which I know is all you talk of in the Wayfarers' and the other pot houses, but we would need something from thee in return. I know we ain't been here long, but we would be obliged, if you and any of the others are contemplating a bit of action of your own like them south of the river, if you would see your way to getting a little off the tithe or else we can't afford anything more. Do that for us and we'll look at what you ask more sympathetic, like. You have my word on that.'

When Enos Diddams reported it that night in the Wayfarers', Dick Dollery and the others refused to believe him.

'T'is true, I tell'ee,' protested Enos Diddams. 'He told me plain as day. I tell'ee, the likes of Henry Cadger, Will Worden, Bob Lenny, Tom Crawley, John Hartless, Pete Sparshott, Dick Shadwell, John Dicker, Henry Sweetapple – they are all with us on this. They all want their tithes and rents reduced. They and the others are not mad enough to refuse our requests. If we do as they want and ask for something off the tithes, then Will Worden promises they will pay the wages we ask, but they can only do it and carry on doing it if their rents and tithes are reduced.'

The men trusted the smaller farmers: for amongst them there was an obvious sympathy for their fellows which had manifested itself in the likes of Henry Cadger on the old Glebe Farm and the other newcomers, Angus McCreef, William Worden and Robert Lenny, included deliberately creating work to employ some of the day-labourers of the village and the two hamlets during that year. Though each was a great deal poorer than the likes of Titus Broake, Amos Peakman, Marcus Howie and Joshua Godwin, they had deliberately retained gangs of men and lads to sow their corn, peas and beans by the more laborious dibbing method instead of by a horse-drawn drill, and then had chosen to hand-flail their corn and barley in their barns, just to give a lucky few dozen work throughout the winter when, in other Hundreds throughout the county, the high rents and tithes were forcing smaller farmers like them who could not afford to buy threshing machines outright to lease them. None of the middling farmers in Hamwick Dean, Lower Rackstead or Merchant Staplers had yet brought in a machine, but everyone suspected that each was thinking of leasing one for the next harvest, knowing that by that they could save more of their corn than they had been able to do during the previous two harvests and, at the same time, drastically reduce their labour costs since other costs were already dragging them down.

Unfortunately, they could not employ everyone and Jem, being in gaol then, was not one of them: neither was Dick Dollery nor John Romble, the wheelwright, who had lost much of his business since enclosure and was trying his hand as a day-labourer whenever he could as were Thomas Judd and William Stubbs as a matter of necessity.

'Henry Cadger has said the same thing to me of his own free will,' declared William Stubbs, who had not thought to mention it earlier and now was surprised to discover someone else had been approached in the same way. 'He said that, if we are going to protest that our wages are too low, then we should demand the tithes and rents be cut, too. He told me they are too high and they benefit only the parson and the lord of the manor. He told me plain as day that we should all go to the tithing meeting and dinner and demand it. He said if there were enough of us standing outside supporting the other farmers, they would use that as an excuse not to go in at all.'

The tithing dinner, which annually was attended by all the farmers, Titus Broake, Amos Peakman *et al* included, and others who received the tithe payment – excepting Parson Petchey, of course, who would not attend such functions as a matter of course – was not set till the second week in December: and that was too long a wait for some: there was no guarantee either that, even by waiting, they would achieve anything: and they brooded upon what might be done for several minutes.

It was then that Jem spoke for the first time. Since his return, his companions had found him morose, reticent and despondent: whereas once he had willingly joined in every conversation, now he spent long periods listening, brooding, doodling in the beer spills on the table, no longer challenging their thinking as he once had with his sharper mind: it was as if his thoughts were permanently elsewhere: hovering over the mound of his wife's grave in the churchyard, in Dick Dollery's view, though he did not say so aloud.

'If you want to change things,' he said calmly, with a determined set to his face, 'then you must act as a body. Go in a body to the rector and demand an abatement of all the tithes and rents. Unsettle the parson and any others who take it all.'

'McCreef, Worden, Lenny, Shadwell, Dicker and the rest are all good men,' declared Nathaniel Newman, nodding in agreement. 'They'd pay you the wage if they was able, but they just en't able at the present. Times are hard for them, too, what with the level of tithes and rents they has to pay. Their own rents is too high and Petchey 'on't let them off their tithes or reduce them.'

'Then he'll be first,'declared Enos Diddams. 'He's still got two hayricks in the meadow alongside the parsonage. They'll make a nice blaze.'

'We ought to burn out the lot of them,' growled Dick Dollery, 'every last straw stack, Peakman's, Godwin's, Howie's and Broake's and all.'

'T'is the new machinery we should smash,' grumbled the morose-faced John Romble. 'The sooner we do that deed round here like they are doing down in Kent and other places, the better it'll be for all of us.'

'We have to do something,' said William Stubbs. 'They have slashed the poor rate till a man and his family can hardly survive. If we do nothing, they will beat us down again on wages next year as well.'

'I tell thee one thing, brothers,' declared Dick Dollery in a grim tone, 'I would do anything rather than live again through such a winter as the last and, if that means that we must smash all the threshing machines in this parish and anywhere else, then so be it, brothers, so be it.'

'Aye,' chorused the others, nodding agreement. The 'Swing Riots' had reached Hamwick Dean.

THIRTY

THE AFTERNOON of the farmers' meeting, the road outside the Wayfarers' was so full that it seemed the whole village had turned out, from the oldest grandfathers and grandmothers able to hobble there on sticks to the youngest babe-in-arms carried there: not a house in the village had a body left in it lest they were abed and unable to walk. True to their word, all the middling incomers from Hamwick Dean, Henry Cadger, Angus McCreef, William Worden and Robert Lenny, joined Peter Sparshott, while five farmers came from Lower Rackstead, including, surprisingly, the larger tenants Silas Kempen and James Allen, while, similarly four came from Merchant Staplers, Thomas Godbear unexpectedly amongst them, too. In consequence, many had come from those places to swell the numbers to eight-hundred all told, so that the yard and The Street in front of the Wayfarers' were thronged more than they had ever been, even allowing for the Whitsun fair held there since Tudor times, but of late abandoned because no one could see a way by which they would derive any cheer from it. So many had not gathered together since the first of the enclosure meetings five years before: indeed, there were so many that they blocked Mr. Able's driveway, all facing the inn, with a low buzz of talk circulating amongst them.

The labourers of Hamwick Dean had long since realised, ever since he had spoken at the enclosure meeting that in Jem Stebbings they had found a natural leader, one who was used to common action and who had long since learned that audacity and resourcefulness sometimes paid worthwhile dividends. So it was that Jem again found himself at the front of the great throng, huddled in a circle with Dick Dollery, Enos Diddams, Nathaniel Newman, John Romble, Thomas Judd and William Stubbs, discussing what they might ask of the farmers, based upon Enos Diddams's and William Stubbs's startling news.

'You was always good at talking,' Dick Dollery declared with a grin, almost relishing the irony of the fact that the one upon whom they had called to be the spokesman for the village and the two parishes had only recently returned from gaol.

'Remember,' Jem warned them, somewhat embarrassed by their faith in him, 'remember, our fight is not with the tenant farmers. It is with the likes of Titus Broake and the Parson and the Peakmans, Howies, Godwins and Jaikes of this world.'

For that reason, Titus Broake and the three other principal farmers of the neighbourhood did not attend the meeting: indeed, when Peter Sparshott, out of courtesy, sent one of the half-lads he employed with a note to the Hall, informing Titus Broake of their intention to hold the meeting arranged in the Wayfarers', the lord of the manor had gone back inside the Hall and reappeared with a single-barrelled gaming gun, cocked and ready to fire, which he threatened to do if the poor lad did not get off his property and be damned quick about it: which the boy had done, of course: and, since Titus Broake deemed it unnecessary to attend, so Amos Peakman, Marcus Howie and Joshua Godwin deemed it unnecessary to attend as well.

Parson Petchey also did not attend, even though he was entitled to do so as a magistrate still at Hamwyte and still also the resident landlord for the Church's acres: he would not have been welcomed by the farmers had he done so, since he and his Church were considered the cause of half their troubles, though to his wife he declared that he felt it better to leave such matters of adjudication on labouring wages to an impartial mediator, a brother magistrate from Hamwyte, whom he had recommended to the farmers so as to 'legitimise proceedings.'

'When I had Glebe Farm, I paid at least twelve shillings to any whom Mr. Jaikes hired,' he boasted somewhat pompously to his wife as they sat at dinner the evening before the meeting. It did not occur to him that the other employers of labour in the three parishes had funded that wage bill through their tithes: besides, he had two sermons to write for the Sunday, which were far more important than a mere meeting between farmers and labourers over rates of pay.

Mr. Able, however, did attend, at the request of the farmers and the labourers alike, and was looked upon kindly as he came hobbling up, leaning heavily upon a stick, for he was then in his sixty-second year, frail and in poor health, having only recently recovered from a chest infection brought about by a fall on his driveway one evening when returning to his home from a sojourn in the Wayfarers'. He had lain unconscious for a good half-hour before he had recovered himself enough to reach his front door and pull on the bell: there were hopeful smiles upon the faces of many that, with him as a referee, there was a chance at least that some agreement might be reached.

However, less affability was shown towards the next arrival, the 'impartial' magistrate from Hamwyte, one Aloysius Grimwade, a portly man, with mutton-chop whiskers, a gold chain across his front and a face flushed red from too much good wine and too many portions of roast beef: When he rode up astride a bay mare, perhaps not unnaturally, there were more than a few half-hearted souls who bowed their heads and turned away, as if fearing to be recognised and remembered for being there by a magistrate who that year alone had gaoled thirty-eight poachers.

However, the men and women of Hamwick Dean, Lower Rackstead and Merchant Staplers who stood on the road outside the Wayfarers' were there peacefully that day, without weapons of any kind: no cudgels or pitchforks, hedging tools or other sharp-bladed instruments. Jem and Dick Dollery and Mr. Able had inisted upon that: they were there solely to discuss their distress with the farmers of the immediate district who deigned to attend and so waited patiently.

It was as the crowd parted that Jem, Dick Dollery and the five others stepped forward and calmly handed up to the Hamwyte magistrate a letter which Jem had written the previous evening in the Wayfarers'.

'We would be obliged, your honour, if you would read this out to the farmers on our behalf,' said Jem, acting as threir spokesman. 'It is a request for a deputation of six of us to meet them in the Wayfarers' and put our demands face to face so that they might be discussed, proper like.'

'I will give them your letter, but I am here to listen and nothing more,' was the magistrate's sharp retort as Jem and the others stepped back and allowed him to ride on around the back of the inn to stable his horse.

When, an hour or so later, Henry Sweetapple came out it was to request that Jem and Dick Dollery only appear before them: and, as the two men entered the bay-windowed parlour, some of the farmers from the two hamlets, not knowing either particularly well, regarded both coldly as if they were the arbiters of some impoverishing imposition to be made upon them. Jem, however, met their eyes with a steady gaze: he had stood times enough before supercilious captains, indifferent lieutenants, hot-headed ensigns and shouting sergeants not to be put off by their hostile stares.

Calmly, Jem raised his hand for quiet. 'Most of you know me and I hope you will know that I am an honest man,' he began, a comment which drew wry smiles from those in Hamwick Dean who did know of his recent history, 'so I will do you the courtesy of speaking honestly before you. Our demands, we consider, are not unreasonable – we ask only for a living wage and for constant employment. You all know that our talk these days is all about wages and the reduction in wages which have fallen on us. The truth of the matter is, the poor single man is got down to six shillings and a man cannot live on six shillings a week, for it is not living, but a long starving. I know that some of you say a shilling and eightpence a day should be enough for a married man with a family. Some of you have said you are prepared to go to two shillings a day, and think that sufficient. We have a different view. We, the labourers of these three parishes, intend to have from Michaelmas to Lady Day two and threepence a day for married men – that's thirteen and sixpence for a six-day week – and from Lady Day till Michaelmas, we will have two and sixpence, which is fifteen shillings a week. And, for them that has over three children, we want an extra one and sixpence a week. Likewise, all single men are to have one and ninepence a day. Further, we intend to have the rents of our cottages lowered to as reasonable a level as we decide is reasonable and being fair in doing it. That is what we intend to have before we leave this place and, if there is no alteration agreed, we shall proceed further accordingly to what we have decided, for we are all at one on this and we will keep to each other.'

The threat implied in the latter words was clearly evident in view of events elsewhere and, though it drew a low mutterings from amongst several of the farmers, no one rebuked him outright for having said it: indeed, they began to pass comments amongst themselves when they noticed that Jem's hand was raised for quiet: he had not yet finished speaking.

'We want, too,' he continued, noting the surprise on the farmers' faces that there was yet more, 'we want, too, an end to winter unemployment and a promise that none of you will be following others in the use of the threshing machine, bought or hired, not just yet – not when men are hungry and their children cry for the want of food.'

The three larger farmers, Silas Kempen, James Allen and Thomas Godbear, eyed each other uneasily: since others in other places were importing threshing machines, each had been considering hiring from an agent in Wivencaster come the next harvest, for, as yet, none had yet bought his own: indeed, the agent had already visted their farms to discuss terms for the following year: their desapproval at Jem's demand showed on their faces, but they remained silent and heard him out.

Jem, meanwhile, continued: 'They are a curse to us and are to blame for men being laid off all winter and forced to go on to parish relief. I am not a fool. I know in my head that one day we shall have to accept them for what they are and what they do and they will appear on almost every farm, but now is not the time At this moment, the men outside are not prepared to listen to reason, let alone consider what progress has been made in farming, especially if they never share in any of it and have no likelihood of sharing in it.'

He paused again to allow his words to sink in, noting how farmer eyed farmer, unsure of how to react to these demands, none wanting to be the first to give away his own feelings: Silas Kempen and James Allen shuffled their feet uncomfortably and Thomas Godbear sniffed and rubbed at his nose.

'Mindful of all that we have asked of you,' Jem went on, 'we have agreed amongst ourselves to do as some of you ask of us – we have decided we will ask also that all tithes and farm rents be reduced, too, for it is the rents and tithes that you pay as much as the threshing machines which have brought us all to this – '

Nods and smiles greeted that announcement and for the first time the farmers seemed to relax and the general air of hostility to abate: except, that is, for the Hamwyte magistrate, who puffed out his cheeks and blew in exasperation at each and every request he heard. However, since he was there as a legal referee, with no actual input himself, he knew that he would have to bow to the farmers if they agreed to meet the men's terms, which was the cause of his frustration. Beside him, with his stick placed between his knees and his chin resting upon his hands, Mr. Able sat smiling kindly, almost in admiration of Jem, Dick Dollery thought.

As Jem and Dick Dollery went out again, a silence fell over the whole company of farmers: none wanted to be the first to say anything: all shifted uneasily upon their chairs and inspected their pots of ale, studied the puddles on the tables and even the chips in the flagstones of the floor rather than catch the eye of another of their number.

Though, the awkward silence lasted only five seconds or so, it irritated Mr. Able. 'I know that I differ from many of you gentlemen in many of my opinions and I may be wrong in what I say,' he declared, banging the heel of his stick down upon the floor, 'but I state it to you just the same. We all agree that it is time that we had tithes and taxes done away with and the only way to stop what is happening elsewhere from spreading here, I say, is to run before the evil. Let the magistrate here and the vestry men amongst you agree to raise the wages to what the men demand and you will stop the riot and incendiarism which plagues other places from spreading here.'

Surprisingly, a number of the farmers were nodding their heads in agreement.

'We has no objection to raising the wages of the men to what they ask,' declared Richard Shadwell, who had been elected the farmers' spokesman. 'We realise that the wages of the men are low and that their cause is a just one. What we ask in return is that they goo to the parson and get the tithes reduced, for it is the tithes and the rent we pay our own landlords that are forcing smaller farmers like us that can't afford to buy these machines outright to lease them. None of us here yet has a machine, but I have to tell you I myself am thinking of leasing one for the next harvest, just in the hope that I will have a better harvest than the last and save on my costs. There may be others amongst you thinking the same. Were it not for the great want to reduce costs, I would have no objection to keeping men on to flail the corn in my barn all winter. T'is done as well by that method as it is being threshed by a machine in my opinion.'

Again none dissented from what he said and, though they talked for a half-hour more and drank another round of ale as well, the matter at hand was settled eventually with a chorus of 'Ayes' and only two 'Nays', but for the most part with smiles and sighs of relief that they had come to a form of agreement. Tankards were drained and they followed Mr. Able as he shuffled out into the yard, where a chair had been placed just outside the door: the old lawyer was carefully helped up on to it, supported by Richard Shadwell and Thomas Allen, as the waiting villagers all came surging forward, eager to hear the result of the farmers' deliberations, hoping that for them an auspicious day had dawned and the beginning of a new era had begun.

'At a meeting held this day at the Wayfarers' Inn,' Mr. Able read, in his now quavering voice, 'of the farmers, to meet the poor labourers who delegated the following – one, Jem Stebbings and, second, Richard Dollery – to meet the gentlemen this day to discuss the present distress of the poor, it was resolved that – ' He paused briefly to allow any hub-bub amongst the crowd to die away. ' – it was resolved that the gentlemen agree to give to every able-bodied labourer with wife and two children two shillings and threepence per day, from this day to the first of March next, and from the first of

March next to the first of October the gentlemen agree to pay the same two shillings and sixpence per day, and the men are to have one shilling and sixpence per week with three children, and so on according to their family – '

Mr. Able broke off as loud cheers erupted and people jumped up and down and clapped their hands above their heads: there was much back-slapping and smiles all round: a great 'hurrah' went up and poor Mr. Able, enfeebled as he was, had his back slapped by fifty muscular hands before he reached the safety of his driveway again. Some of the farmers were laughing and smiling, too, and, it was true, some were near to tears as well: the women were less reticent, they were mostly all crying and the children were staring in wide-eyed wonder at the antics of their elders, for some even linked arms and danced in skipping circles around the inn yard and out on to the road.

THIRTY-ONE

THE MATTER of the wages settled, the next reform in the new era was to be the parson and his tithe: but not till after the Sabbath. The tension built all Sunday: all knew that there was a conspiracy about the place, though no one actually stated anything: people just sensed that something was about to happen: indeed, that it must happen as a consequence of all that had gone before. However, nothing was likely to be done that would interrupt the observance of the Lord's Day and which might reflect badly upon those planning to carry out any deed, whoever they were. The villagers went to church as usual, though the congregation was noticeably smaller: they sang their hymns as usual and said their prayers as usual and, when they left at noon, the men went off to their respective ale houses as usual and the womenfolk and the children went back to their cottages as usual, since it was cold and rainy and not a day for standing around gossiping.

Originally, tithes were payments in kind, such as crops, wool, milk and the like, comprising an agreed proportion of the yearly profits of cultivation or farming, and made by parishioners for the support of their parish church and its clergy. In theory, tithes were payable on all things actually arising from the ground and subject to annual increase – such as grain, wood, vegetables: secondly, all things nourished by the ground – the young of cattle, sheep, for instance, and animal produce such as milk, eggs and wool: thirdly, they were payable on the produce of a man's labour, particularly the profits from mills and fishing. Such tithes were termed respectively predial, mixed and personal tithes.

Tithes were also divided into great and small tithes: corn, grain, hay and wood were generally considered great tithes and all other predial tithes, together with all mixed and personal tithes, were classed as small tithes. It was common, but by no means universal, for the great tithes to be payable to the rector or parson of the parish and the small tithes to another of the parish's clergymen, the lower status vicar: for at the dissolution of the monasteries, not only much Church land, but in many cases also the accompanying rectorial tithes, passed into lay ownership. These tithes became the personal property of the new owners or lay impropriators, such as the lords of the manor or squires: men such as the old Darcy-Harprigg squires and now Titus Broake.

From early times money payments began to be substituted for payments in kind, a tendency further stimulated by enclosures, particularly the parliamentary enclosures of the previous century, one object of which was to get rid of the obligation to pay tithes. This could be done in one of two ways: by the allotment of land in lieu of tithes, or by the substitution either of a fixed money payment or of one which varied with the price of corn (hence the name 'corn rents' applied to payments in lieu of tithes). The limits of the land allotted, or of the land charged with a money payment, were generally delineated on a map attached to the Enclosure Award: in Hamwick Dean, the great tithes were paid to Parson Petchey, the others to Titus Broake as lord of the manor.

That Sunday evening, the landlord of the Wayfarers' noticed, somewhat peculiarly, that Dick Dollery and Enos Diddams were absent from his bay-windowed room and he was puzzled by it, especially as the absence of one was generally a precursor of trouble of some kind, a point confirmed later when it was reported that two figures had been observed high up amongst the branches of an elm tree overlooking the parsonage well after midnight as if spying upon the hook-nosed parson to ensure that he did not attempt to depart in the night.

The following morning, Monday the twenty-second, at nine o'clock, as Parson Petchey trotted out of his gate in his gig and turned right towards the church, intending to enter and to kneel before the altar as usual to say his prayers for the day, as usual, he was surprised to find a group of six labourers talking together by the church gate, as if waiting for something or someone. In normal times, he would have expected the men to have been at work, but these were not normal times: even so, he would have expected them to step aside and allow him to drive his gig on to the verge, but this time not a man moved: not one of them removed his hat and not one came forward either to help him to dismount and tether his horse to the iron gate as they had always done in the past out of courtesy and deference. Instead, they simply turned their backs on him and continued their huddle: their lack of respect to their better was guaranteed to incense Parson Petchey and it did.

'What are you men doing here?' he demanded in his usual imperious tone, as if hoping by it to set them walking off somewhere else.

'We're waiting for a friend and, while we're doing so, we're discussing the news from other places,' said Dick Dollery, calmly, turning to face the rector, 'particularly what the labourers like us are doing in those places and why they're a-doing it.'

The Reverend Doctor had been informed by his warden and overseer, Joshua Jaikes, of the outcome of the meeting between the labourers and the farmers and the part the leader of the seditious rabble gathered outside his church – namely Dick Dollery – had played in it, along with that ungrateful felon, Jem Stebbings.

'I trust you men are not conspiring together intending to follow the incendiarism of others in other places,' declared the parson sharply, his head tilted down as he eyed each in turn over the top of his spectacles. 'It is a capital offence to burn down a man's barn and his stacks. I trust your conduct will be quiet now that you have got your wage rise?'

For once, Enos Diddams, Nathaniel Newman, John Romble, Thomas Judd and William Stubbs met his gaze quite openly and there was no embarrassed shuffling of feet or lowering of heads. 'There is some of us who thinks we have been quiet too long, Parson,' Enos Diddams replied, darkly. 'As for what thee hopes, thee will know of that all in good time. If thee truly wants to know what we are a-doing here by thy churchyard gate, I'll tell'ee – we're discussing how much we ought to have off thy tithe, that's what we're a-doing.'

Parson Petchey gave out an astonished laugh: that mere village labourers should even deign to discuss the tithe he received was an insult to him: and for them then to have the nerve to tell him so to his face, well, that was sheer insolence!

'If my income was to be reduced, I could not do the good I am in the habit of doing,' he snorted, somewhat pompously, and with that strode off towards the porch without so much as a backward glance, though his face was taught with anger.

'We'll have thee, tithes and all, Parson, and we'll stuff them up thy arse before this day is out,' Dick Dollery growled as he watched the Reverend Doctor disappear into the darkened church.

When Parson Petchey came out after a half-hour upon his knees praying to the Lord, the six had gone: three hours later they were amongst a crowd of three-hundred thronging the parsonage driveway and spreading on to the lawn as Jem, Dick Dollery, Enos Diddams and the others of the newly formed 'People's Committee' strode up the whitened stone steps, entered the gloom of the arched porch and tugged long and vigorously on the cast iron door pull: they could hear the bells ringing loudly inside so there would be no excuse for Parson Petchey not to answer.

'We know thee are home, Parson,' Dick Dollery called out. 'We know thee are in there so it en't no use trying to hide from us. Come out, we want to have a word with'ee.'

'Kick the door down and drag him out!' a voice shouted impatiently from the back of the throng, which was a somewhat foolhardy suggestion in view of the fact that the arched oak door stood eight feet high and was well studded with large iron nails, precluding any such possibility and more than likely would have exhausted an axman attempting to break through it.

'Put a stone through his window. That'll bring him out.' This time it was a woman's voice, again from the rear of the crowd.

Clearly others were thinking like Dick Dollery, that the Reverend Doctor was most probably hiding behind a curtain in the hallway or lying full length under his bed or locked in his study: he was. in fact, standing upon the stairs peering down at them through the landing window and at the same time motioning his trembling wife and two maids back up the stairs.

'Come out or we'll come in and get thee!' shouted a second man's voice from amongst the crowd.

Such calls, Jem knew, would do only harm if they were heard by others less sympathetic to their cause. 'We'll have none of that!' he cried, turning on the two men and the woman: he was determined that the meeting with the parson would be a peaceful, if not an amicable, one, though behind him the crowd considered his approach too lenient and there was an angry stirring and muttering.

'If I am to be your spokesman, we do as I say,' declared Jem, addressing them. 'I aim to put our case without causing anyone any harm. And that includes the parson and his wife and any others in the house. We are not here to make trouble. This is a peaceable protest and it will stay that way!'

Then turning back to the door, he shouted in as loud a voice as he could, while still remaining intelligible, so that those inside would hear and understand: 'Doctor Petchey, we ask you please to come out, sir, and to hear what we have to say, that is all. We are not here to harm you or anyone in your house. We are here to talk to you – to make a request on behalf of ourselves and the farmers. You have my word on that, sir. No one will be harmed. No one.'

Dick Dollery's lips curled in a sneer at Jem's use of the 'sir,' but he said nothing: had it been left to him, he would have used, 'Come out, ye old devil!' or 'ye old bugger!' and not apologised for using either.

THIRTY-TWO

AS IF THE PARSON had been waiting for just such an assurance, immediately there was the sound of bolts being drawn back and the thin face with its shock of white hair, vulturine eyes and hook-nose peered through the gap.

'What do you all want? Why are you here? Do you know you are trespassing?' was the Reverend Doctor's response on seeing Jem standing in his porch and three hundred others filling his driveway as far as the gate and covering part of his lawn. His use of the word 'trespassing' was deliberate, hoping to cow them by suggesting they were in the wrong in the eyes of the law even when just standing there.

Jem turned slowly and regarded those behind him. 'No one is trespassing, Doctor Petchey,' he said, calmly. 'As you can see, most are standing on the driveway as a person is allowed to do when visiting a place so there is no trespass in that and the rest are standing on your lawn and the only likelihood I can see is that they are flattening a few blades of grass so I don't think there is much to be gained by accusing them of trespassing, is there? And, as to why we are here, Doctor Petchey, I think you know full well why we have come. I have been elected as their spokesman and we are here because we have promised the farmers we will get a touch off your tithes. We want a lowering of the tithes, not only here, but in Lower Rackstead and Merchant Staplers, too, and, while we are about it, we reckon you should pay more to the poor rate.'

'And who is going to persuade me to do that?' demanded the parson, feigning amusement and, at the same time, opening the door wider.

'Why us,' Dick Dollery, standing beside Jem, answered him, 'all of us who are standing here and we 'on't be leaving till we have done it.'

'You are in a dream, man,' declared Parson Petchey testily. 'I will not submit to any reduction in the tithes, certainly not by force.'

Here Jem laid a hand on Dick Dollery's arm to prevent him from saying anything further which might antagonise the parson even more than he had and cause him to slam the door shut. 'The farmers have undertaken to raise our wages and we have undertaken to reduce the tithes,' he declared calmly. 'The tithes must be reduced severely and we reckons three hundred pounds a year should be enough for you and your wife for your keep.'

The parson protested straight away: 'That is preposterous! You as their spokesman should know that I can do nothing about reducing the tithe. The greater part of it goes to His Grace, the Bishop at Melchborough for the general good of the Church. There is nothing I can do to alter that. You must know that. What I take is for my living and to pay the curates.'

'Aye, we know what goes where,' Jem replied, again quietly. 'We know the Church takes the best part of it and that Titus Broake takes a cut of it, as well as a few others. We know what pittance you pay your curates, just as we also know you take five hundred and fifty of it just yourself, which is a deal too much, in our view.'

The Reverend Doctor reddened: the continuing calmness of his manner and the determined look upon his face deterred any attempt by the parson to dispute the figure.

'You are a man of the cloth, Doctor Petchey,' Jem went on. 'I ask you how, in all conscience, you can justify taking five hundred and fifty pounds from the tithes each year for yourself when there are people in this village, in all three of your parishes, who don't earn one fiftieth of that all year and at this very moment have been put out of work and don't just have hunger to contend with this coming winter, but are faced with the prospect of actual starvation and all for the want of a decent rate of relief, which the vestry has reduced twice this year and is talking of doing again, so I am told.'

'I have contributed as much to the poor rate over the years as any other landowner in Hamwick Dean, Lower Rackstead and Merchant Staplers,' protested Parson Petchey, stretching his neck so as to lift his head even higher in the manner of the haughty when they wish to emphasise a point, which was a peculiar habit of his during all his sermons.

'Ah, but they don't take five hundred and fifty pounds out of it every year as you do!' Jem reminded him a second time. 'That is what we are here to ask you, parson – to reduce the tithe you take from the village by at least two hundred and fifty pounds a year. We think that three hundred is quite enough for a man to run a parsonage that has only a wife to keep.'

Parson Petchey blanched at the suggestion. 'Two hundred and fifty pounds! No, no, I couldn't possibly do that,' he exclaimed, with a dismissive wave of his hand. 'What you ask is impossible, utterly impossible. I have servants to pay, the maids, the cook, the gardener and his boy.' It was bad enough that he should have to suffer the indignity of having to discuss his finances with a common labourer, albeit one who was accompanied by three hundred of his own parishioners: but this man had only recently returned after serving a term in Melchborough Gaol for poaching, for goodness sake!

On hearing his refusal, several at the front of the crowd let out cries of anger and began a general push forward towards the steps. 'Burn the place down!' shouted one hot-head, again from the back of the crowd, while another cried: 'Give us what we want, parson, or it will be the worse for you!' Yet a third threatened: 'We'll take the payment in goods right now if he won't give in. There must be three hundred pounds worth of summat in there!'

Jem whirled upon them and shouted for them to stand where they were: he was their spokesman: they had elected him and he would do the talking! Though he well knew the law would look upon them as a mob whatever they did, while he was in charge, he was determined they would be disciplined.

Turning back to face the white-faced parson again, he said quietly: 'It would be in your interests to find it possible to do what we ask, Doctor Petchey. I should give a little thought to it if I were you, but do not be too long about it, mind, for, as you can see, they are not in the mood for delays and I do not know how long I can hold them off or stop them from doing something foolish. They have come for a purpose, Doctor, and that purpose is to get you to reduce the tithe and in particular the amount you take from it as your year's wages. They want it cut and they want you to sign a piece of paper to say that you will do it and they want you to do it today!'

'That sounds very much like a threat, Stebbings,' the Reverend Doctor declared with a sudden truculence and an unexpected defiance. 'Am I to understand that you will resort to violence if I do not accede to your wishes? If there is any lawlessness here, I will hold you entirely responsible for it – as you say, you are their spokesman, their ring-leader.'

'I make no threat to your person, Doctor Petchey,' Jem told him carefully. 'What I am saying is that there are three hundred people standing on your driveway and your lawn, all your parishioners, who are here to ask you to reduce what you take out by two hundred and fifty pounds and for you to reduce the tithes. For if you do that, and if you will put it in writing that you will lower the tithes, the farmers have promised they will pay the men the higher wages they seek. We have their word on that, signed and sealed. That is why I urge you to heed the sense of what I say as their spokesman.'

It was at that moment that Parson Petchey saw Nathaniel Newman at the front of the crowd and became incensed again at what they were asking. 'If I reduce the tithes for the farmers,' he declared vehemently, 'I shall also have to reduce them for the tradesmen of the village. I see Mr. Newman, the blacksmith, there and Mr. Cobbe, the cordwainer. Mr. Brady, the shoemaker; too, is amongst you – ' He continued to scan the heads of the crowd. ' – and several others I see, who are also tradesmen. Mr. Romble, the wheelwright, who is a carpenter mostly, and Mr. Jolly, who earns his living making rakes, and you, Andrew Norris, you are a baker, and William Hoskins is the butcher, all whose tithes would also be reduced, even though they are self-employed and do not pay wages to labourers as others do. Small wonder they are here – it is to their benefit if the tithes of the farmers are reduced as theirs will be reduced also and they will be much better off for it.'

'We pay the poor rate to support the labourers the same as the rest,' shouted Nathaniel Newman, taking a pace forward, which forced the parson to take a step back.

Thinking the parson was going to renege on any promise or weakening that he had hitherto shown, several in the crowd began chanting loudly in unison, 'Reduce the tithes! Reduce the tithes!' 'Cut your share! Cut your share!' while above all the others came the angry voice of Dick Dollery at the front of the crowd, exasperated by the parson's arguing: 'Take less, Petchey, or we'll have thee, one way or another, we'll have thee!'

It was almost with a sniff of disdain that Parson Petchey acknowledged his defeat. 'Very well,' he said, again stretching his neck in a haughty manner. 'Faced by a mob, I find that I am in no position to resist. If that is what you want, I will write a letter and sign it and I will abide by it and, at the same time, I will write to the Bishop, advising him of my intention to reduce my share of the tithes by a hundred and fifty pounds a year – '

'Two hundred and fifty,' Jem reminded him, seeing the craftiness of the man.

'Come now, let us be sensible about this – ' Parson Petchey began.

'Two hundred and fifty,' repeated Jem, calmly.

'Two hundred and fifty!' the hook-nosed parson wailed. 'A highwayman never robbed a man of so much on a single day!'

'Two hundred and fifty, you old skinflint,' Dick Dollery shouted, coming up two steps to shake his fist under the Reverend Doctor's nose.

Perhaps having been reassured by Jem that he was safe for the moment, Petchey glared back at Dick Dollery with same disdain. 'And if your wages for a year were cut in half, could you live on them, Mr. Dollery?'

It was a foolish remark to make to a man who had barely eaten in three days. 'Two hundred and fifty is not half. Thee still has plenty to live on,' Dick Dollery bellowed angrily back, thrusting his face close to the parson's: in fact, so angry did he appear that Jem feared he might strike at the cowering clergyman. 'Right now, I am living on a lot less than half a wage. I am living on nothing – nothing at all at times and my wife and three girls that is still with me are as near to starving as anyone can be without actually a-dying from it.'

'Come, come, surely you exaggerate?' protested Parson Petchey, but even he recognised in the vehemence in Dick Dollery's tone there might be a semblance of truth in what he said or a man would not act so outraged at another's throwaway remark.

'You have me at a disadvantage,' the Reverend Doctor added with a shrug. 'Very well, two hundred and fifty it will have to be. I will have Mr. Jaikes write out an agreement and deliver it to you.'

'Not to me,' Jem told him. 'Post it on the church door so that everyone can see it. That way you will be making your promise to the whole village, not just to me.'

There was another anonymous shout from the crowd: 'How about giving a bit more to the poor then, Parson?'

'I already give enough to the poor rate,' the clergyman snapped, irritated by this fresh demand.

'I live on a shilling a day with a wife and five children to keep,' the anonymous voice shouted back: all eyes turned to the speaker: it was Shadrach Hodge, the most regular of all drinkers in the Carpenters' Arms.

'I have standards to maintain,' declared the parson, somewhat petulantly. 'As the rector of this village, as a Doctor of Divinity and the Lord's representative on this earth, it is reasonable, is it not, that I should maintain a living as befits my position? Standards must be maintained.'

Jem answered him with a shrug. 'If that is what you believe, Doctor Petchey, then so be it,' he said simply.

The reply only incensed the clergyman all the more and he did not see the trap into which he was about to plunge. 'But I do,' he insisted, 'I most certainly do, at all costs.'

'T'is the relief the parish gives, little as it is, that the people of this village relies upon to keep body and soul together,' declared Jem, coldly, irritated that the parson should proclaim such self-interest so blatantly, 'and now we learn that even that is to be cut to the bone. Men are out of work and their families are near to starving and yet you are not prepared to consider any increase in your contribution to the poor rate to help the starving from the five hundred and fifty pounds a year you take out of the tithe! T'is nought but taking bread from the mouth of a starving man. What kind of a man of the cloth are you, Doctor Petchey, that you would do that? What kind of a man are you indeed?'

All Parson Petchey could do was to gulp at his own foolishness and declare with a flourish of the hand to dismiss them as if they would just vanish by his doing it: 'Be gone all of you. I will have no more of this. You have extracted more than your pound of flesh from me today.'

The significance of a Shakespearean metaphor on greed and avarice was lost on the labourers and their wives, none of whom had ever seen a proper play, saving the Mummers at Whitsun, let alone seen a drama by the Great Bard himself.

'On your head be it then, Doctor Petchey,' said Jem, adding: 'I will have the farmers witness the agreement before it is put up on the church door. I hope for your sake that it will satisfy everyone.'

Parson Petchey had never been spoken to in so insolent a fashion before and did not take kindly to it. 'Be warned of one thing, Stebbings,' he said coldly, 'as the leader of this lawless mob, I will hold you personally responsible for whatever mischief they do in this parish or any of my parishes. Be assured of that. It will be laid at your door. I will see to that.'

Jem smiled. 'I would not expect anything else of you, Doctor,' he said. 'Now I must bid you good day, for we have other business to attend to.'

With that, he touched the brim of his hat and turned away: the old parson could only watch him and the others disperse, seething with anger at the indignity he had suffered, made all the worse by the cheers and backslapping which greeted the malcontent felon,

Stebbings, and his obvious lieutenants, Dollery and Diddams, as they descended the whitened steps and made their way towards the gate.

'Well, we have dealt with the parson,' said Dick Dollery, rubbing his hands gleefully. 'Next, we'll tackle Titus Broake and the others.'

The arrival of the 'unwashed mob' and their threatening demands had so horrified the parson's wife that she had fainted and, when the Reverend Doctor went back up the stairs to the bedroom, he found her being fanned by one of the maids, who had had to apply smelling salts to revive her. The poor woman was bemoaning how far removed was Hamwick Dean, with its ungrateful 'peasantry,' its mud and its smells and its wickedness, from the genteel world to which she had belonged as a girl, when she had travelled with her mother to sojourn for two weeks amongst the silk-gowned and muslin-gowned young ladies and the stiffly formal gentlemen at the many balls and assembly hall concerts in the spa towns of Bath and Cheltenham and other places.

Unhappily, after she and the Reverend Doctor had married, all that had been not so much forbidden her as considered *infra dig* by him: God and Jesus and Oxford had been his daily sustenance till he had got it into his head to come to the depraved place where they now lived!

THIRTY-THREE

IT SO HAPPENED that on the day of the farmers' meeting at the Wayfarers', before Jem and Dick Dollery had gone back out into the yard, Jem had read out one further request, really a declaration of intent, upon which they wanted the farmers' agreement not to intervene and the magistrate's agreement that he would not deny them their wish to carry it out.

'We also request,' Jem had declared calmly, his eyes fixed upon the Hamwyte magistrate, 'that the permanent overseer of the poor of this and the neighbouring parishes, namely Joshua Jaikes, be directly discharged and that, in case we are obliged through misfortune or affliction to seek parochial relief, we may apply to one of our neighbouring farmers or tradesmen, who would naturally feel some sympathy for our situation, and who would be much better acquainted with our characters and claims. This is what we ask at your hands – this is what we expect and we sincerely trust this is what we shall not be under the painful necessity of demanding it in a different manner.'

'I cannot agree to that,' the startled magistrate had declared. Then, after a pause for thought, he had added quietly with a dismissive shrug: 'But neither can I prevent you doing it.' After that, he had said no more.

So it was, before the villagers had dispersed to their homes and before the farmers went back into the Wayfarers' to discuss the import of what they had agreed amongst themselves, Mr. Able also read out an addendum to everything else that had been agreed.

'It is further resolved,' the lawyer had called out, as shouts of 'Quiet!' and 'Silence!' rippled through the throng in the Wayfarers' yard, 'it is further resolved that no objection shall be raised if the poor of this parish and the adjoining parishes of Merchant Staplers and Lower Rackstead, by their own action, see fit to take the present overseer of the poor, Mr. Jaikes, out of the parish to an adjoining parish, there to take their leave of him in such place as they decide, but, in so doing, to treat him with civility as befits an officer of the parish'

'Aye,' Dick Dollery had shouted, gleefully punching at the air with a clenched fist. 'we'll treat him with the same civility he showed to us, especially you, Jem. It's time we had an end to these permanent overseers. Drive them from the parishes, I say. Let us be done with them once and for all.'

That was two days previously: now, having dealt so effectively with the parson, the moment to deal with his 'appointee,' the hated overseer of the poor, was at hand. As the mob streamed away from the parsonage and headed for Joshua Jaikes's cottage on Forge Lane, Jem and Dick Dollery again found themselves at their head: it was almost as if the villagers had appointed the two as 'captain' and 'lieutenant,' as Parson Petchey had surmised since they seemed always to act in concert.

'To Jaikes's! To Jaikes's!' they all shouted: and each time, the cry went up, it was followed by a great cheer.

At the overseer's gate, the crowd halted: and, while Dick Dollery and Jem went up the short path to bang upon his door, others began calling for Jaikes to come out: however, only the frightened face of his wife appeared at the window, to be hurriedly withdrawn when the people saw her and began shouting even more angrily.

'Come out, Jaikes, we want a word with'ee,' Dick Dollery shouted directly through the door, still hammering upon it with his fist. 'Come out, ye old skinflint, because if we has to come in, it'll be all the worse for thee.'

Eventually, after much shouting, a white-faced Jaikes opened the door and stood there almost trembling and near to weeping. 'Go away,' he cried in a desperate voice. 'Go away or I shall have the magistrates on you. You will all be up in court before the beak if you do not.'

His pitiful attempt at defiance was greeted with laughter and jeers, for the mob were heady from their victory over the parson and determined upon their business: what to do had lready been decided. The parish cart was wheeled out from the back of the cottage to a roar of approval: everyone knew what it was for: Dick Dollery and Enos Diddams were grinning broadly at the prospect and even Jem managed a smile. Without further ado, Jaikes was seized by a half-dozen pairs of hands and carried kicking and shouting out on to the road, where he was forcefully backed between the cart's shafts and the harness looped over his shoulders and around his waist and forehead. Then several of the heavier women, urged on by their friends, lifted their skirts and climbed aboard the small cart, only five of them, but enough to make Jaikes strain at the harness as the men behind gave it a push to start it rolling. Then they stood back to jeer as the near weeping overseer hauled his cargo of heavyweight passengers out of the lane and up The Street, which was lined all the way by revellers, who laughed and cheered and catcalled and jeered his passage through them. Here was the revenge for which they had all longed. Indeed, some would have thrown rotten fruit at him had they any to throw, but in straitened times, it had all been eaten or was used for other edible purposes and not to be wasted on the hated overseer of the poor: instead, Dick Dollery uprooted a sturdy roadside sapling and passed it to one of women at the front of the cart and she happily busied herself flicking it out over Jaikes's ears as he bent to his task, though several times, inadvertently, she did it a little too enthusiastically and left three red weals across his cheek.

Only one man went back as they set off: Jem Stebbings. 'There's no need to worry, Mrs Jaikes,' he told the overseer's weeping wife, 'we have no grudge against you. No harm will come to you. Our argument is with your husband. They are going to run him out of the village and they won't want him to come back. I'm sorry for you over that, but the people have had too much of his ways. They're only getting their own back for all the slights they have suffered from him over the years. It is no more than he deserves, as you well know. I will see to it that no real harm comes to him, but the villagers are determined he has to go and go he will – '

At which point the tearful women burst out: 'I told him he should be kinder to people, I told him he shouldn't do some of the things he did, but he was too arrogant. I am a good Christian. It weren't right many of the things he did, but he would do them. Said it was his job to do it so they did not cheat the Poor Law. Well, he's paying for his sins now. I just don't want him to come to any harm, that's all.'

'He'll come to no harm,' Jem assured, her again and set off after the crowd to ensure that his word was kept.

What they did was to take Jaikes to the parish boundary between Hamwick Dean and Lower Rackstead, forcing him to drag the cart the length of The Street and along the ridge-top road: there, they unharnessed him, rolled him in a large puddle by the roadside, laughed at his distress and his soaked condition and gave him his orders.

'Bugger off, Jaikes, and don't come back!' Dick Dollery advised him, swinging at him with his boot to send him on his way. 'Don't thee ever set foot in Hamwick Dean again or we'll do a sight more to thee than we have done this day!' He accompanied his words with a deliberate motion of throat-slitting: there were some who believed he meant exactly that.

As Jaikes set off along the ridge-top as fast as his bowlegs could take him, the whole crowd, men, women and children alike, formed a line across the road to prevent him from returning: only when his disconsolate figure had disappeared around a bend did they drift back towards the village, though some of the sturdier youths remained with their eyes fixed upon some particularly large flints stacked at the side of a field from the children's picking, hoping that Jaikes would try to return and they could use them against him.

What he did eventually was to go across country to the 'impartial' magistrate, Aloysius Grimwade, at Hamwyte, to protest at his 'disgraceful treatment': but for once the magistrate decided that he could take no action against a whole village, which is what Jaikes said had turned on him. He simply told the deposed overseer to try and contact his wife by some means other than going back and, further, to be sensible and look for a position elsewhere, perhaps up in the next county. He had heard there was a vacancy for a poorhouse master at Witchley: perhaps Mr. Jaikes would be better off trying for that: he would give him a reference and it was quite a way away from his present troubles, was it not?

Needless to say, none of it pleased Joshua Jaikes and he left the magistrate's house seething with indignation.

THIRTY-FOUR

NO ONE expected that Titus Broake would blithely agree to increase the wages of any labourer whom he hired simply because others had agreed to do so, even less that he would bother himself with differentiating between winter and summer payments to his own disadvantage. That he had returned to the Hall on the Saturday and was still there on the Monday was a surprise to many, for, in the few weeks since he had become the Member of Parliament for Hamwyte, he had, it seemed to the villagers, preferred to spend the greater part of his time in London, leaving the running of his estates to Heginbotham, and they had expected that he would have gone back to his townhouse in St. John's Wood rather than remaining amid the grey gloom of the countryside in late November.

Four village youths, lying atop a straw stack from which they had a view of all comings and goings, took it in turns to keep a daily watch on the Hall, from early morning on the Monday till late evening on the Tuesday – thus, it was known to Jem and the others that the lord of the manor was still at home when that afternoon three worried-looking visitors arrived at the Hall, namely Amos Peakman, Marcus Howie and Joshua Godwin.

The watchers on the straw stack and those to whom they reported – Jem, Dick Dollery and the others of the 'People's Committee' – were not to know that when, somewhat forlornly, the three farmers broached the subject of the signed agreement between the other farmers and the men – 'agitated by that radical troublemaker and felon Jem Stebbings,' as Amos Peakman put it – they were given short thrift by the lord of the manor.

'What you do is your affair,' he had retorted. 'I don't consider myself to be bound by what is decided by others. If you agree to what they ask, then you will have to live by it. I have not agreed to anything and nor will I.'

If truth had been told, it was no surprise to anyone either that Amos Peakman, Marcus Howie and Joshua Godwin should make it known on the Wednesday by way of Ephraim Simms, the parish constable, that, as the lord of the manor had no intention of paying higher wages, then neither had they, irrespective of what the parson had agreed regarding the tithes. It was just a sadness that they should become so insensitive to the poverty of their fellow men as to follow the lord of the manor's lead: for, when all was said and done, after Titus Broake, they were the three other largest occupiers of land in the parish. All three had a threshing machine in his barn, while Titus Broake had invested in two of them, both of which he kept in his barn at the Hall, had employed, not the local men he had employed formerly, but Irish labourers from the same band as Amos Peakman had used and who had set up a camp on Inworth heath. It was a matter of some contention to the men who sat in the Carpenters' Arms and the Wayfarers' that they saw what little work there was now taken from them by 'bloody Papists from the bogs of Ireland!'

What concerned Jem and the others who sat in the Wayfarers' on the Wednesday evening, drinking to their success over the parson and the overseer and discussing what to do next, was that if, in the weeks and months ahead, the four largest landowners of the parish still refused to pay the higher wages, then one could not blame a smaller farmer, who had agreed to pay them, asking himself the question: 'Why should I pay if others do not?' And reasoning, too: 'It means my costs will be all the greater when I am the one who can afford them the least.'

'We shall have to make 'em pay,' declared Dick Dollery, with a determined sniff. 'We have sent 'em the letters, let's act on 'em. If they 'on't pay of their own accord, then we shall have to help 'em make up their minds. T'is only right that Broake, Peakman and the others should pay as well.'

None dissented: indeed, there was a chorus of agreement: so, it was perhaps no surprise that on the morning of Thursday the twenty-fifth, with a rime of frost covering the gateposts, ice upon the puddles and the pale disc of the late November sun struggling to disperse an encircling grey mist, upwards of two hundred and fifty men, women and older youths, the sixteen-to-eighteen-year-olds, that is, some with heavy staves as clubs, some with hammers, axes and iron bars in their hands, some with pitchforks and billhooks as if expecting a battle, were to be found gathered on The Street outside the Wayfarers', wrapped and huddled against the cold, waiting as their breath rose in clouds above them.

The reason for their wait was soon signalled by the sound of a bugle being blown in the distance as, eventually, through the curtain of mist came a hundred other men, women, youths and girls, the combined contingents from Merchant Staplers and Lower Rackstead, sent word to attend the previous evening and now marching together behind the tattered square of a home-made 'Tricolour' tied on a broom handle and held aloft by a gangling youth who was almost dancing in his exuberance. Everyone let out a cheer as they arrived, as if they were all Revolutionaries themselves and it was forty-one years before and the start of the Revolution and they were the citizens of Paris about to storm the Bastille fortress: except the 'Tricolour' was fashioned from irregular strips of red, blue and yellow cloth and, therefore, not a 'Revolutionary Tricolour' at all.

When greetings had been exchanged and the noise of the cheering had died down, Jem addressed them, standing on a table taken from the Wayfarers', albeit again with the reluctant permission of the landlord, who looked down at the assembled mob from the window of his bedroom, unwilling to join them on their enterprise in view of his past status and nervous of the outcome, for their sakes, not for his own.

'Brothers and sisters,' Jem began, speaking now as their 'Captain,' for that was how Dick Dollery, Enos Diddams and the others had begun to refer to him, 'the other farmers have agreed to pay two and threepence a day in winter and two and sixpence a day in summer. We want the same from Titus Broake, Amos Peakman and the others and we are determined to have it. We want, too, an end to the use of those infernal threshing machines, which are to blame for you being laid off all winter and forced to starve on parish relief. It is not only us in this village who are asking for it, it is happening all over. The working man is rising up – rising up as he should have done long ago. We are not alone in what we do. It is a countrywide movement to better the wages and conditions of the workers and we in Hamwick Dean, in Lower Rackstead and Merchant Staplers, we are a part of it – an uprising of the common man against the tyranny of the landowning classes!' Loud cheers greeted this: staves and hammers were brandished and the youth with the 'Tricolour' waved it wildly above his head: under his oratory, they were warming to their revolution.

Jem waited till the noise had subsided, then continued in the same strong, steady voice: 'That is what we are about, brothers and sisters, We know what we have to do. We have to smash the threshing machines. Smash them all! T'is all because of the new machinery that we are in the state we are in and the sooner we do the deed the better it will be for the all of us. Are you ready, brothers? Are you with us, sisters?'

'Aye,' chorused three hundred and fifty voices, raising fists and weapons on high yet again. 'We're with you Captain. We're with you.'

Why should they not be? After all, had not one of the Hamwyte magistrates himself been overheard a fortnight before at a tithe audit in a village to the north of the town, reiterating the comment of a magistrate in Kent, reported in the London papers, saying that he, too, thought threshing machines should be banned from all farms in the county for taking away men's winter work and causing all the trouble that was abroad in the south of England? And was it not rumoured also that the new King was sympathetic to their cause as well?

'Let us go then!' Jem cried, leaping off the table and pushing his way through the throng to take his place at their head. 'To Broake's first, to the Hall and then to Peakman's.'

That they should start at the Hall was almost taken for granted, since the lord of the manor was the most hated of them. As they moved off, the youth with the 'Tricolour' ran on ahead and waved it as if drawing them to follow him: some of the youths behind took up a chant which they professed they had heard was the cry of others in other places. 'Bread or blood!' they shouted. 'Bread or blood!'

Alongside Jem, Dick Dollery was carrying a heavy hammer and around him were grouped Enos Diddams, John Romble, Nathaniel Newman, William Stubbs and Thomas Judd, all suitably armed with iron bars and hammers themselves.

At the window of the Wayfarers', Caleb Chapman watched them go with a sad shake of the head: and, as the yard emptied, he went down to retrieve the table and then quietly closed the door of the inn, knowing full well what they were about and knowing full well, too, that no good would come of it.

THIRTY-FIVE

TITUS BROAKE was also looking out of an upstairs window as a long stream of angry humanity came pouring down the hill towards the old Hall: grim-faced, he watched as the white-painted five-bar gate leading up the long drive was swung open and a noisy, shouting mob streamed through.

'Damned peasants!' the lord of the manor muttered to himself and, recognising several at the front, added in the same angry undertone: 'I might have known that damned villain Stebbings and his footpad companions would be behind it.'

With that, he left the window and, despite the pleas of his wife, hurried from the house to join his equally grim-faced bailiff, Heginbotham, standing at a second gate leading into the yard where the outbuildings were situated.

'Rabble!' snorted Titus Broake as he joined his man. 'Rabble! That's what they are. They need teaching a lesson they won't forget.'

'Had I not best go for help, sir?' Heginbotham suggested, nervously eyeing the approaching mob.

'We'll see what they want first,' said Titus Broake firmly, not one to be panicked. 'Then, if they cause any trouble, we'll fetch the constable.'

The bailiff did not reply: at least the mob had the sensible Jem Stebbings at their head, he thought to himself: he had long suspected that the former soldier had told the truth about the two pheasants, but he had said nothing: it was not his place to contradict his master. He had always thought that the malcontent Dick Dollery alongside him was the more likely culprit: and, for the love of God, what was that fool youth doing waving a French Tricolour? Did he think this was a revolution or something?

Beside him, his mud-brown lurcher, bewildered by the villagers' loud chants, let out a low growl, unsure whether to begin barking its warning in earnest, eyeing its master, awaiting his signal.

Titus Broake, however, had no such doubts. 'You are wasting your time here,' he shouted as the villagers came to a halt some twenty yards from him, signalled by Jem's raised hand and a shout from Dick Dollery. 'I do not give in to extortion, nor do I fear any mob. You are trespassing on private property. Leave my land immediately, all of you, or I will send for the parish constable and have the ringleaders arrested and put in gaol.'

The threat only drew a laugh from those at the front of the crowd who heard him, particularly from several Lower Rackstead youths who had forced their way to the head of the column to be with their Tricolour-carrying comrade. 'Ephraim Simms couldn't arrest his own shadow,' one of them sniggered.

'Ye'll not see Ephraim Simms this day,' said Dick Dollery, tightening his grip on his hammer. 'He's shut his door and he 'on't be coming out till all this is over, if I am any judge.'

'Wise man,' said Nathaniel Newman alongside him, who held a five-foot iron bar. 'This is village business. It en't anything to do with him. This is between us and you, Broake.'

At that point, Jem went forward a few paces so as stand clear of the crowd and held up his hand to quieten the noisy, chanting youths behind him. 'We are not a mob,' he said in as calm a manner as the situation allowed, determined to maintain some decorum, but knowing that behind him there were many who were in no mood for any discussion between them and 'Squire Broake,' seeing it as merely an unnecessary delay: they wanted to get on with the business at hand, smashing his machinery. So did he, for Mary-Ann's sake, as the first act of his revenge for her death: but that would be done anyway: meanwhile, he would seek to extract as much as he could from the despised Northern incomer.

'We are here to state our case as reasonable men,' Jem went on, which only induced a curl of the lip from the lord of the manor. 'We have come about the wages you pay. We have come to ask you to increase them to what we and the other farmers have already agreed.'

From an inside coat pocket, he took out the sheet of paper upon which were written the resolutions agreed with the other farmers and which each had signed. 'This is what we intend – ' he began.

'I don't give a damn what you intend!' Titus Broake interrupted, harshly. 'You'll not get any satisfaction here. Nor will I be coerced into it by a village rabble. So be off with you! Get off my property!'

Some might have surged forward there and then had not Jem again held up his hand to deter them: instead, he calmly read out all that had been agreed with the other farmers and, as he did so, much to the discomfort of Titus Broake and his henchman, Heginbotham, each resolution was greeted with a noisy cheer from the villagers, particularly when Jem demanded that all cottage rents, raised over the past two years by the likes of Titus Broake and others, be lowered.

'That is what we intend and ask you to sign before we leave this place,' Jem concluded, folding the paper and repocketing it. 'If there is no alteration agreed, we shall proceed accordingly, for we are all at one and we will keep to each other.'

'I'll sign nothing of the sort! I'll be damned if I will!' Titus Broake shouted vehemently back. 'And as far as the wages I pay, I pay the men what they earn when they earn it and I'm damned if I will pay them any more!'

'Then we should like the keys to your barn, if you please,' Jem requested, still politely. 'You have two threshing machines in it and we aim to end their use today.'

'Go to the devil, the lot of you! You'll get no damned key from me!' exclaimed Titus Broake: and then, as if irritated by the whole business and wishing to have done with it, he stepped back from the gate and added sharply: 'Do your worst, but remember, there will be a reckoning for all this, Jem Stebbings, there will be a reckoning.'

'T'is not our day of reckoning, t'is thine,' a sneering Dick Dollery infomed the lord of the manor and, with a wave of his hand, he motioned the eager men and youths forward with a cry of 'Come on, lads! To the barn! To the barn!'

In an instant, master and bailiff were forced to one side: they could only stand and watch as the whole crowd streamed through the gate into the broad yard. It was at that moment that Heginbotham's lurcher began to bark wildly at finding itself suddenly surrounded by a forest of legs: the terrified animal began snapping at passing ankles and would have continued to do so had not one of the Lower Rackstead youths struck it viciously across its hind quarters with his stave, which sent the poor animal howling off into a corner of the yard, where it continued to whimper for sometime after.

The barn reached, its padlock was prised off and the doors wrenched open: and there stood two of the hated machines. Almost in a fury, as though the machines were some monstrous beasts which had been cornered and had to be destroyed, the men and youths surrounded them and began swinging their hammers, axes and iron bars: and so overwhelming was their fury that, as one man struck his blow, so a half-dozen others jostled with each other to follow him, till the barn rang to the sound of iron striking iron and the splintering of wood, all to a background of cheers and shouts from those inside and the multitude still outside. Jem struck for Mary-Ann, Jed and Thirza and himself and Dick Dollery, Enos Diddams, Nathaniel Newman, John Romble, William Stubbs and Thomas Judd and all the others struck for themselves and their families.

The two threshing machines, like all others, were largely made of wood, the metal parts being only the rotating drum and the iron bars of the stationary 'concave,' so it was not too difficult a task for men armed with hammers, axes and iron bars to smash them. Only when the two machines lay splintered and broken and their iron parts bent and twisted upon the floor of the barn did the men and youths, their fury spent, pause to survey the wreckage: and only then did the enormity of their action strike home. Nervous smiles appeared on the faces of some and others exchanged anxious glances at those alongside them, as if to ensure that they were not alone in what they had done and it was some form of mitigation of their action that others had done the same. Yet others, less bothered by guilt, began to look about them to see what else could be destroyed: a turnip cutter, a grinding stone and various implements, scythes, reaping hooks, pitchforks, hayrakes were all pulled from the walls of the barn and left either broken or bent upon the hard, dirt floor so as to be unusuable.

Though a hundred or so had been able to crowd into the barn to witness the destruction, the greater number had been forced to remain outside, all the time being peered at by the frightened faces of Titus Broake's wife and young son from behind the curtains of the manor house bedrooms fifty or so yards away. Broake himself had also retreated to the house to watch from a parlour window, powerless against such a number: however, he had not given up and at that very moment Heginbotham was crossing a nearby field towards the village on his way to fetch the parish constable. Curiously, the grocer's shop was closed, which was unusual for a start, and no matter how hard the bailiff hammered on the door, no one came to answer it, not even Ephraim Simms's wife and children, for by that time the parish constable was halfway down to the hill towards Hamwyte in his gig, with his wife and children beside him, ostensibly off to the haberdasher's, but in reality ensuring he was well away from the place while all the action was happening. Curiously, he was followed soon after by Caleb Chapman in his pony and trap, almost as if the two had conspired to be on the road together.

Jem, Dick Dollery and the other members of the 'committee' were pushing their way back through the encircling crowd some forty yards from the barn, accepting the plaudits and the back-slapping for having accomplished their mission, when suddenly a loud shout went up behind them. People began to cheer wildly and, when Jem turned to look, to his horror, he saw the flickering light of flames in the barn's dark interior and smoke beginning to filter through a small hatch opening at one end.

'No! No fires! No fires!' Jem shouted above the cheers as he and the others turned about and began to force their way back through the throng: but such was the disorder, their progress was difficult: at the first shout of 'Fire!' the whole crowd had surged forward to get a better view of the blaze and had formed a solid phalanx around the barn's open doors.

'Burn the place down! Burn the place down!' some were shouting, happy to see the flames: for, to them, burning the barn was simply an extension of what they had already accomplished, another blow against the hated landowners, who, by their avarice and their indifference to the plight of the labourers and their families, had made their lives such a misery.

To Jem, however, while it was one thing to break-up the hated threshing machines as one who had more cause than most, it was another thing altogether to commit arson: that was a thousand times worse: breaking a threshing machine, he well knew, was a felony which likely might earnb a man a few months in the House of Correction at Steadleigh, but arson to property such as a house or a barn or a place of manufacture was likely to be a hanging offence if caught.

By the time he, Dick Dollery and the others had managed to reach the front, those who had been inside the barn were all scrambling out though the wide-open doors as the heat of the blaze began to hit them – that is, except for the Lower Rackstead Tricolour-carrier and a brown-toothed, smirking simpleton with spikey dark hair: they were standing just inside the door, making no attempt to leave, almost jigging with delight and applauding the growing conflagration. It was quite clear to Jem and Dick Dollery who had set the blaze: no sooner had he and the others quit the barn, having smashed up the threshing machines, than the Tricolour-carrier had improvised a flaming torch from a piece of sacking soaked in an oil and, handing it to the simpleton, had persuaded him to toss it on to a pile of straw at one end of the barn.

'What in God's name did you do that for?' Jem roared, seizing the Tricolour-carrier and hurling him to the ground, as much to get past him as to punish him. 'We came to smash up the machines, not to put the place to the torch.'

The youth, who had fallen upon his elbow, let out a howl of pain, dropped his flag and clutched at his injured arm. 'It wasn't me, it was him. He did it!' he whined, pointing at his simpleton companion. There was no time to argue, however: the straw was well alight.

'Get water! Get water!' Jem shouted to the throng still staring somewhat stupified at him, bewildered by the sudden change from euphoria to alarm. 'We need buckets to put the fire out. We need water. We must save the barn. We did not come here to burn down the barn.'

Ignoring the fierce heat and the choking smoke, he seized one of the broken pitchforks off the floor and began frantically dragging the burning straw towards the open doorway some fifteen yards behind him. Such was the heat being given off, however, he could only rush quickly forward, skewer as much of the straw as he could, then retreat hastily, dragging what he had gathered with him. By that time, the others had formed a line under the direction of Dick Dollery and he was able to push each flaming pile quickly along the ground to his friend, who had similarly snatched up a broken pitchfork: he, in turn, pushed it on to Enos Diddams, the next in line, and he to John Romble and that way, using whatever came to hand, they were able to pitch all of the burning straw out into the yard.

The fact that the barn was built of brick, with only its interior posts and roof cross-beams made of wood, helped their cause: however, in one corner, where the straw had been piled the highest, the flames had taken a hold on the timbering forming one of a series of byres and was licking at two of the upright posts supporting the cross-beams: if the cross-beams caught, there would be no saving the place as it would sweep along under the roof fanned by the draught from the doorway.

Fortunately, some had realised the urgency of acting: as the last of the burning straw was heaved out into the yard and Dick Dollery and the others were stamping upon eveything else, three men appeared lugging heavy pails of water: they had taken them from the milking parlour nearby and dipped them into a cattle trough in the yard so that at least there was water to hand.

As quickly as he could, Jem climbed up on to the lopsided remnants of a farm wagon, the wheels and boards of which they had smashed only minutes before, and, taking the first of the pails which one of the perspiring men handed him, he pitched its contents as high as he could up the vertical post at the flames even then licking at one of the cross-beams: but such was their height much of the water fell short. Dick Dollery, who had taken one of the other buckets, also climbed up on to what remained of a broken wagon ladder to pitch a second pail of water at the junction of the upright and the cross-beam where the flames were at their fiercest, but again much of it fell uselessly to the floor and the flames persisted: the third pail thrown by Jem also fell short.

'More water, more water,' Jem shouted, which sent the three with the buckets dashing back out into the yard to the cattle trough: once again, they came hurrying back, even as many of their comrades, realising the wantonness of the act, streamed out through the yard gate, heading for the road back to the village, not wishing to be seen in the vicinity of a burning barn.

Again the contents of each pail were hurriedly pitched upwards at the flames: fortunately, this time Dick Dollery was able to reach higher than Jem: his second pail doused the flames licking along the cross-beam and the water cascading down the upright post extinguished most of the lower flames. The next pail of water thrown completed the task, soaking the lower part of the post again and putting out the fire altogether. As a precaution, however, a further three pails were thrown over the smouldering timbers to soak them and to ensure the fire did not re-ignite.

Outside there was a sudden burst of cheering: not for Jem and Dick Dollery and their brave action, but sarcastically for the unexpected reappearance of the lord of the manor, who had seen the smoke and the sudden activity and had come rushing from the Hall.

'That was a deliberate attempt to burn down my barn,' Titus Broake shouted as Jem and Dick Dollery and the others came coughing and spluttering out of the pall of smoke drifting from the barn doorway.

'Your barn is saved,' Jem told him angrily, as he stood in the centre of the yard, bent double to gather his breath and rubbing at his watering eyes. 'We did not come here to burn your barn. We came for the purpose which we have carried out. Nothing more.'

'Someone set it alight,' snapped Titus Broake. 'It did not catch fire by itself. You are their leader so you must be held responsible. All this will be laid at your door when I tell the magistrates. I have had truck with you before, Stebbings. You will rue this day.'

With that, while the rest of the men and youths and women streamed away towards the road, Titus Broake stamped off into the barn to ensure that the fire was throughly dampened down.

A fuming Jem, meanwhile, was some way up the drive, anxious to catch up with the Tricolour-carrier and the simpleton and give both 'a kick up the backside,' but, by the time he reached the centre of the village, they and the rest of the Lower Rackstead youths were nowhere to be seen.

In fact, they had hidden themselves behind some outbuildings with a few of their friends till the furious Jem, Dick Dollery and his companions had passed: then they made their way to the Hall porch and began banging loudly on the front door knocker till it was answered by a maid, to whom they made the demand that the lady of the house, who they had seen watching from an upstairs window, come down to speak to them. Their object was to demand two guineas 'for the work or else!' Titus Broake's sudden return from the barn thwarted their plans and they all scurried off at his approach without receiving anything.

THIRTY-SIX

THE VILLAGERS' DAY, however, was not yet finished: indeed, it had just begun: Titus Broake's threshing machines were only the first they intended to demolish: there were three others in Hamwick Dean alone which had to be smashed, including for Jem, the one which had killed Mary-Ann. So, from the cross-roads guidepost at the top of The Street, they headed out along the ridge-top road to Amos Peakman's farm down Goat Lodge Lane. Jem had recovered himself by then and his mood and that of the others was still one of grim determination: at Goat Lodge, he would take revenge for his loss.

They found Amos Peakman standing at his gate, with his faithful black-and-white border collie at his side.

'I've been expecting you to come, especially you,' replied the farmer matter-of-factly, but, other than that, he made no other reference to Jem's recent misfortune. Instead, he stood his ground, which took courage when faced by a mob of upwards of three-hundred still, all armed with staves, hammers, iron bars, axes, scythes and pitchforks, and with a few women amongst them ready to screech their hate into his ears.

'Did you receive a letter?' Jem asked him, bluntly, feeling he had no cause to be polite to the man, 'a letter from Captain Swing?'

'Aye, whoever he damned well may be,' replied the farmer with a contemptuous snort. 'I treated it like I should. I burned it on the fire.'

'He is our leader,' said Dick Dollery, which drew smirking laughter from those around him.

'Captain Swing! Captain Swing!' chanted several of the mob gleefully, mostly those at the back who were unseen, at the same time brandishing their staves and hammers in the air.

'Well, I don't know him,' Amos Peakman retorted. 'I've never heard of him.'

'He's here amongst us all! We're all Captain Swing together,' shouted a small man, one of the Merchant Staplers contingent, well hidden amongst the crowd.

'You may well be,' snorted Amos Peakman, unfazed, 'but I don't take kindly to letters threatening the destruction of my property. I suppose it was your lot who rousted the parson and Jaikes the other day.'

'Aye, it was us, so thee knows what we're about,' Dick Dollery declared forcefully. 'We have just done Broake's place and now we intend to do thine. Off to the barn, men!'

'Do your worst!' Amos Peakman cried contemptuously. 'You'll answer to the law eventually, the lot of you, and I shall be there to watch when they stand you over the drop at Melchborough Gaol. I'll make sure of that. Now do your worst. I won't stop you.'

With that, he, too, stepped back and swung open the gate to allow them through, staring hard at each face as the men and youths passed, as if determined to remember each of them, which forced some to pull scarves and kerchiefs up over the mouths and noses and others to look away.

However, Amos Peakman's reference to hanging had annoyed some from the Lower Rackstead contingent, who did not know him: before he realised what was happening, he found himself seized and, despite his struggles, was swung backwards and forwards and, with a 'One, two, three!' was pitched feet first on to the midden heap nearby: and, before he could climb to his feet, willing hands were shovelling the foul-smelling dung on top of him with their pitchforks.

Jem, Dick Dollery and the majority, meanwhile, had trudged off to the barn: the padlock was levered off and cast aside: once inside, all realised that Jem must strike the first blow for this was the very machine which had killed his Mary-Ann: vengeance demanded it: and they held back for that. So, again taking a sledgehammer from one of the men, Jem raised it above his head and brought it crashing down against the machine's side, without knowing it splintering the wood at the very spot where Mary-Ann's blood-soaked dress had brushed against it as she had been lowered to the ground and left its stain. As he stepped back, so others pushed their way forward and set about beating the iron work of the threshing machine to pieces and destroying the boards and stage, which, knowing what they did of Mary-Ann, they did with an extra vigour.

By the gate, a laughing crowd still surrounded Amos Peakman and would not allow him to crawl from the dung heap: each time he tried, spluttering with rage, they pushed him back: one man against a hundred was really no contest. Eventually, Jem and a perspiring Dick Dollery had to go to his rescue: they returned from the barn to find

Peakman sitting atop the dung heap, his head in his hands, almost weeping from the indgnity of what he was being made to suffer.

'Let him go now,' said Jem, 'he has had enough. He will not be so keen to get rich on the backs of our labour after this.'

'We can get some money out of this old skinflint before we goo,' Dick Dollery said hopefully: and at that, as if the suggestion were a command, several of them seized Peakman a second time and frog-marched him across the yard to his house. They took the precaution of marching him inside before releasing him and there demanded he pay them for all their effort in breaking his machine.

'Two pounds is the price,' declared Dick Dollery, holding out his hand expectantly. Surprisingly, though still near apoplectic with rage at the indignity inflicted upon him, Amos Peakman complied, taking the money from a bureau drawer and almost throwing it in Dick Dollery's face.

'Look, brother, we are two pounds the richer,' the lanky labourer crowed, jingling the coins in his hand on rejoining Jem, 'and not a peep of a protest from him. Give it to us as meek as a lamb, he did. We'll drink well tonight.'

However, no sooner had they begun to walk away than the door was pulled open and Peakman appeared shouting angrily after them from the safety of the porch, complaining bitterly at the way they had treated him and vowing every possible kind of retribution of the law would be brought down upon them for it. By then, of course, none cared: they had completed their task: the threshing machine lay in bits in the barn and pieces of his turnip cutter were scattered about the yard and two ricks in the field alongside were well ablaze.

What made it worse for the farmer was that his wife and his unmarried daughters had witnessed his humiliation from an upper window: throughout it all, they had screeched hysterically at the treatement of their husband and father, so much so that it had been heard above all the commotion and, in desperation to silence their noise, one of the men had thrown a stone and broken a window pane above the wife's head, showering her with glass and causing a wound to her scalp which now bled profusely and only caused more shrieking.

It was not what Jem had expected and it dispirited him to see how much the men and youths, when in a mob, resorted to base instincts: all he could do was call out for them all to come away. 'The job is done here. We have two more to do today,' he cried as they exited on to the road.

From there they marched on to Marcus Howie's farm at Smallponds along the Merchant Staplers road, where, they went straight to the barn and where a row broke out amongst some of the men and youths as to whose turn it was to break the threshing machine, which Jem settled by allowing thirty who had not yet had the chance to swing their hammers, axes and iron bars to break it and whatever mechanical implements were nearby: that done, he led them up to the farmer's front door and banged loudly on the knocker. Howie's invalid wife answered it, leaning on her stick.

'Is the master here?' Jem asked politely, not wanting to appear too aggressive to a woman with a twisted foot: he knew most likely that her husband was not, for he had not made an appearance while they were smashing his threshing machine and, indeed, the figure of a man had been seen making off across the field behind the house and many thought it must have been Marcus Howie himself, but the gloom was too deep for them to be certain at that distance.

'He is not,' Howie's wife answered boldly. 'Why do you disturb us? Have you not done what you came to do?'

'Aye, we have done that,' Dick Dollery interrupted, but more sharply 'and now, if you please, we will have some beer and a sovereign from you for our effort. That will satisfy us and then we shall leave you.'

'I have no money to give you,' Howie's wife answered sharply, as if challenging men whom she knew to defy her. 'I won't give you money, but, if you are civil, I will give you beer.'

'Beer then, ma'am, if you please,' Jem replied, taking off his hat.

At that, Martha Howie called out to her sixteen-year-old daughter, Lucy, who was loitering in the darkness at the far end of the hallway so as to be well out of sight of any leering youths and men standing on their front lawn. Cheers greeted the pretty daughter when finally she appeared on the front step with a great pewter jug and a half-dozen tankards: each tankard was filled in turn and each man and youth drank a swallow from one before passing it to another.

However, it took the farmer's attractive daughter several returns to the house to fetch more ale to satisfy the demand: unfortunately, as she passed nervously amongst them, refilling the pewter tankards as each was emptied, several of the youths took the opportunity to fondle her rear, while others contemptuously reached out to cup her breasts and one even went behind her and gleefully hoisted up the back of her skirts to reveal her long underdrawers.

'Damn you! Stop that!' Jem shouted, pushing in amongst them and roughly shoving the latter youth on to his back. 'She is a young girl. Keep your damned hands to yourself or you will have some of us to reckon with.'

Fortunately, some of the older men, who had daughters of the same age, rose to their feet from where they were sitting on the grass ready to support him and that proved enough of a deterrent to force the youths to slip away, though some did remember to mumble a sheepish apology for their behaviour. However, the poor girl's humiliation had been such that, reddening with shame, all she could think to do was to scurry back inside to hide her face, though she did give Jem a look as she passed him as if to say, 'Thank you' for what he had done.

Following that, the mother slammed the door shut in disgust and ignored the shouts of those who wanted it opened again: with no prospect of more beer being brought, the mob began to drift towards the gate and back on to the road: they still had one more farm to reach that day.

They arrived at Joshua Godwin's Milepole Farm at midday and went straight into the barn, where they broke his threshing machine in the usual fashion, also his winnowing machine and two seed drills: and some of the mob, noting Dick Dollery's success at Howie's farm, went up to the house to demand beer, food and money. Joshua Godwin himself opened the door, with his three young sons standing beside him, their eyes blazing angrily at the indignity being inflicted upon their father, while his white-faced wife and their two maids watched anxiously from the windows above.

'This is all I have in the house,' Joshua Godwin said, almost apologetically, handing over two sovereigns: he did, however, have cheese and bread and a dish of butter as well a firkin of home-brewed ale, which he allowed two of the men into the kitchen to carry out: then he quietly ushered his sons back along the passageway and closed the door. His humiliation, however, was not yet over: as the mob streamed away, having eaten his food and emptied the firkin, one of the Lower Rackstead youths, knowing that he was not known to the farmer, waited till the rest were out of sight, then went back, knocked on his door yet again and, when Joshua Godwin answered a second time, held an iron bar over the startled farmer's head and threatened to split his skull open if he did not give him even more money.

'Give me some damned money or we'll come back in the night and set fire to your house and you in it,' the youth threatened: the frightened farmer had to borrow half a sovereign from his maidservant to give to the youth before he would leave.

Jem, Dick Dollery and the greater part of the throng knew nothing of this: they were well on their way back to the village by that time: marching all over the parish and smashing up threshing machines, wagons, turnip cutters, grindstones and other implements was thirsty work and the Wayfarers' was the obvious place to celebrate their success.

As they approached, several of the youths ran on ahead and banged so loudly on the door that poor Caleb Chapman's wife had no option but to open it: as soon as she did so, two hundred or more pushed past her into the large bay-windowed parlour, overflowing into the taproom and the vault. Immediately, the demand was for a barrel of ale to be rolled out and tapped: the younger element, elated by the ease of their success that day, wanted free drinks to be given to everyone till the barrel ran dry, but Jem instructed Dick Dollery to hand over the two sovereigns he had received from Joshua Godwin and, when it was learned that one of the youths had gone back to threaten Joshua Godwin again and extort even more money from him, he was quickly upended and the money which fell out added to the kitty. The youth then was unceremoniously kicked up the backside and pitched out of the door into the front yard to join the others who could not gain entry: as far as Jem and the 'People's Committee' were concerned, asking and receiving was one thing, demanding with menaces was another.

When Ephraim Simms and his family finally returned from Hamwyte and trotted past the inn, it was to ironic cheers, for many guessed why he had made himself scarce: the same cheers greeted Caleb Chapman on his return to assist his harassed wife.

Bolstered by the ale, the company that evening was cheerful and proud: the whole place was the merriest and the friendliest it had been in a long time. Back slapping and much boasting were the order of the evening: and it was long after midnight when the lanterns were finally extinguished and the landlord and his wife were allowed to go to their bed.

All in all, everyone reckoned it had been a good day's work.

THIRTY-SEVEN

SO WHY the men of Hamwick Dean, having achieved their own ends, should take it upon themselves to march all the way to Inworth the very next day to help the men there to secure higher wages as well, when they were always their deadly rivals, was beyond the comprehension of many: but march there they did on a freezing November morning, more than ninety of them, and while there, joined a mob from another village in demolishing the hated Inworth poorhouse and so set in motion a train of events which was to have dire consequences for several of them, Jem amongst them.

The General Workhouse Act of 1723 had enabled single parishes to erect a workhouse if they wished so that they could enforce labour on the able-bodied poor in return for relief: most places, like the vestry at Hamwick Dean, rented a couple of small cottages for the purpose, somewhere to put the fatherless families and old widows. By the war's end, however, through neglect, they were so delapidated that even the vestry agreed they ought to be pulled down before they collapsed upon their luckless inhabitants. Then, in 1819, an Act to Amend the Law for the Relief of the Poor was passed, which provided for either the enlargement of a village's poorhouse or the building of a new one: such were the times in the Hundred then, with pauperisation increasing rapidly, that the representatioves of a dozen parishes south and east of Hamwyte decided to combine and to build a new and larger poorhouse at Inworth, this one to serve Inworth itself, Hamwick Dean, Merchant Staplers and Lower Rackstead, the estuaryside villages of Gledlang, Salter, Cobwycke and Cumvirley, plus Greater and Lesser Tottle, Beckenden and Foliot Magna.

The various parish authorities realised that there were considerable savings to be made by placing their pauper families together, even if they were just wives and children deserted by their husbands and fathers, which they often were, rather than each village vestry supporting them as paupers within their own homes and having to pay their rents and provide them with clothing and food, especially the sick and elderly paupers waiting to meet their Maker. A Board of

Guardians was established, comprising a clergyman or a landowning farmer from each parish, subscriptions were received from the various vestries and from certain philanthropic landowners and other parties, particularly in the eleven parishes where it would not actually be located, and a building was erected on donated land alongside the Wivencaster-to-Maydun high road, close by several junctions: thus, it was central to all and easily accessible to every poor unfortunate who was forced to trudge there. The building contained three wards of thirty beds each on the ground floor, one ward for elderly and infirm males and young single males thrown on to their particular parish, one similarly for females and a third for sick and distempered children, with, on the top floor, five reasonably-sized rooms, which were designated as 'family apartments,' comprising a daytime living area and a bedroom large enough to sleep five if they all crammed together.

The master was William Mussett, a gangling, stooping, thin-faced, round-shouldered, former navy coxswain, regarded as being particularly obnoxious and harsh to the poor of the villages: in one incident, he had chained two of the more lunatic inmates to the wall so that they could not get out and wander abroad. The day the news got out, three guns, loaded with pellets, were discharged into his bedroom at midnight and, although the clothes and furniture of the bed were pierced and torn by the pellets, neither he nor his wife were harmed: the only evidence for the Inworth parish constable and the Justice to investigate was the ladder left at the window and three figures seen running away towards the wild expanse of the heath.

Of all those in Hamwick Dean who, by the misfortune of their circumstances, had been forced to seek sanctuary in the Inworth poorhouse 'apartments,' none despised the place more than Enos Diddams: in the previous March, while Jem had been incarcerated in Melchborough Gaol, he had been unable to pay his rent after the money from the straw-plaiting had all been spent and, when the Hamwick Dean vestry refused to pay it for him, he had been evicted from his cottage by the same assistant collector from Hamwyte who had evicted Mary-Ann and her children. With his wife, he had been forced to trudge to the new poorhouse at Inworth, where they had spent several miserable weeks before their 'escape' in the early summer back to Hamwick Dean.

There, in the poorhouse, poor Enos had suffered the petty rules, orders, byelaws and regulations of the place, enforced with an unsympathetic hand by William Mussett. For example, the rules, which were read out monthly to a parade of inmates in the rear yard, decreed that any person sent there by the parish authorities, who was capable of doing any work, was to be employed by the master in some labour 'best suited to their strength and capacity.' For him, that had proved to be back-breaking work in a clay pit on the heath, when his labour was hired out to the owner more to the benefit of Mussett than himself, and he spent five dreary weeks digging out the thick, glutinous clay which lies all across that region, made more glutinous by the spring rains, shovelling it on to a cart to be transported to a brickmaker's yard at Wivencaster.

'Such poor persons as who are able to work,' the rules decreed, 'shall be called up by ring of bell and set to work by six in the morning from Lady Day to Michaelmas and by eight from Michaelmas to Lady Day; and continue until four in the afternoon from Michaelmas to Lady Day, and from Lady Day to Michaelmas till six in the afternoon. And if any such poor person shall refuse or neglect to do such work as shall be allotted him or her, or wilfully spoil the same, or depart from such house without leave from the master, or shall be guilty of any disorder or disobedience to these rules and orders, the master shall reprove such person for the same, and punish him or her by confinement or alteration of diet, as the said master shall think fit. And if such person shall be guilty of the like offence a second time, the master shall complain thereof to the Visitor of such house, who is hereby authorised to order the punishment of confinement to be increased to such degree as he shall think fit.' What that meant was incarceration in the same House of Correction at Steadleigh as Jem had once languished, for a period not exceeding two calendar months and not less than one calendar month.

Mussett, of course, not only kept meticulous accounts of the household goods, the linen, the furniture and the utensils provided and a record also of the materials bought for work and the goods made from them, but he also recorded daily everyone's demeanour and respectfulness towards him, even their thankfulness or, mostly, lack of it, all of which he laid before the Guardians at their monthly meeting, and before the Visitor, one of the local Justices, whenever he went to the house.

He would prowl the apartments once a day to ensure they did not waste fuel by keeping fires burning unnecessarily, since fuel cost money and detracted from his budget, and neither were candles to be kept alight once the sun was up and nor were they to be lit before sundown: all candles and fires had to be put out at bedtime, which was set at eight o'clock between Michaelmas and Lady Day and nine o'clock between Lady Day and Michaelmas.

'The fortunate dead,' as he called them, were at least quickly removed by cart and decently buried as soon as was convenient, their clothes and goods being delivered back to the Guardians and passed on to anyone else seeking a shirt or a smock or a dress or a pair of worn shoes: at least the parish to which the dead belonged paid the funeral charges.

Nor was any poor person permitted to go out of the poorhouse, or anyone permitted to enter it, without the permission of the master. However, what irked Enos Diddams the most was that no liquor was allowed in or to be drunk there, without the permission of the said master. For Enos, the restriction on his drinking was worse than having to attend divine service at the nearby church twice every Sunday, which was why he fell foul of the regulation which stated that any who, in the opinion of the master or the Visitor, was thought improper to continue longer there, could be dismissed from the house, which eventually he and his family were.

'I was never so glad to see Hamwick Dean again,' Enos Diddams told his friends when he finally sat in the Wayfarers' once more, having obtained waged-work digging drainage channels for William Worden, which enabled him to pay rent on one of the village's empty cottages in which he was then ensconced.

'The damned place should be got rid of,' he declared: for so long as it was standing, he, like other poor unfortunates who had wound up in its wards and apartments, feared that his circumstances might again become such that he and his kith would have to go back there.

It so happened that as they sat in the Wayfarers' that evening, drinking to their success of that day, three men from Inworth, having learned what they had achieved at the meeting with the farmers and of their activities that day, had walked the three miles to the village to ask for the support of their rivals. The farmers of their village, along with the parson and some of the lay impropriators of the tithe, were meeting for their annual tithing dinner at the Anchor Inn at noon the next day, the Friday, and the Inworth men hoped, if a large enough assembly were gathered outside, they might agree to meet a delegation and be persuaded to discuss the matter of their men's wages, particularly if it were put to them in a reasonable manner by someone who had done it elsewhere.

As soon as they entered, the three were recognised as Inworth-ites and roundly jeered by their fellows, in a good natured way, of course.

'We wish to see the Captain of your crew,' declared their leader, a giant of a man named Abbott, fully six-foot-four in height, standing in the middle of the bay-windowed parlour and looking about him with a determination that challenged any Hamwick Dean man to make any remark about him being from a rival place.

Abbott was a widower with seven children, a tinman and knife-grinder by trade, who, like Jem, had seen service overseas during the war in the Buckinghamshire Regiment and had been wounded in the head, which meant that even a small amount of drink affected him and his temper. However, when he shook Jem's hand, he did so in a manner that told everyone that he considered he was parlaying with an equal, a former soldier like himself.

'The men of Inworth have sent me to ask if you, as the Captain of your crew, would oblige us with your presence tomorrow morning at ten o'clock,' he declared, boldly, seating himself at the table where Jem sat with Dick Dollery and the others, while his two cohorts stood behind. 'We would like you to be there with us to meet the rector and to go into a meeting between us and the farmers and do the parlaying with them on our behalf as to what wage settlement they can make for us. I am told you have made a good fist of it here in Hamwick Dean and that you have got the tithe reduced. We were hoping you might be able to help us to convince our parson, Mr. Coleman, the same as you have convinced your parson, to take off some of his tithe. He has six hundred and fifty a year for himself, but we think he can exist on far less than that. Our farmers are the same as yourn and say they would pay us more if they were not so crippled by rents and taxes and the tithe. That's why we have come to you. We would like you to get the farmers to raise their money and get the same terms as you have been given, if that be achievable. I have had word others is coming from other places, Salter and Cumvirley and the like, to support us in a show of strength. We want as many there as we can get. The farmers usually has their tithing meeting from eleven onwards and the dinner at one o'clock. There's a fair bit o' drinking afterwards and it normally goos on till the evening.'

'I will gladly come,' said Jem, 'and I will bring the letter I wrote out and gave to our meeting to show to your parson and the farmers. We would be happy to support you tomorrow so long as you are buying the ale tonight!' It drew laughs from those around, but Abbott responded by doing just that.

So the following morning, Jem, carrying the agreement with the farmers in his pocket, signed and sealed, along with the letter that the reluctant Parson Petchey had written agreeing to a reduction of his tithe, set out alone for the prearranged meeting with Abbott and his two cohorts and the Inworth parson, who would be waiting for him at the maypole in the centre of the village at eleven o'clock. Dick Dollery, meanwhile, was given the task of persuading as many Hamwick Dean men as he could gather to put aside their natural rivalry with the men of Inworth and take to the road in support of them. It would be a simple matter: they would march over to Inworth in the mid-morning and join the other villagers on the green there to add their support: after that, they hoped, there would be free ale by way of a celebration at the village's two ale houses, the Ship and the Anchor.

Inworth, astride the Maydun-to-Wivencaster turnpike, was a bigger village than Hamwick Dean, with a population of some eight-hundred then, and a total of adult males, including boys, lads and half-men, of just over three hundred. When Jem arrived on the green in the centre of the village, a crowd of some six hundred men, youths, women, girls and children had already assembled by the maypole: a number of the men gave Jem curious looks when the giant tinman and knife-grinder went forward to welcome him and to escort him through the throng.

'He is the Captain of the crew at Hamwick Dean and he has come from there to help us in our cause,' the giant Abbott shouted, though the news was greeted with only a desultory muttering from the Inworth villagers, while one of the women petulantly demanded to know why it needed a Hamwick Dean-ite to help them.

'Hold your bloody tongue, woman! He is helping us because I have asked him. That is why,' was Abbott's rough answer.

At that moment, the Reverend Coleman came up, bringing good news: the farmers and the lay impropriators were willing to meet a small delegation led by Jem and Abbott and to hear them so long as they conducted themselves peaceably and their demands were not too extravagant or foolish. While they stood talking, yet more came up: two-hundred together from two villages to the north of Inworth, all welcomed with cheers and shouts, so that by the time Jem and Abbott and his two cohorts went into the meeting along with the Reverend Coleman, there were upwards of eight-hundred souls milling about the village green and its main street. In fact, the whole central green at the crossroads was a seething mass: and, when told that a number were on their way from Hamwick Dean and two hundred or more others were marching from Salter, Cumvirley, Lesser Tottle, Beckenden and Foliot Magna, the villages to the southeast, 'to show comradeship with their fellows in Inworth' – and the latter, in turn, of course, to ask for similar support when they, too, made their demands of the several farmers in their villages – some who could count and add gleefully speculated that there might well be more than twelve hundred or more standing soon outside the Anchor Inn and rubbed their hands and chortled with delight.

As it turned out, the meeting between Jem, the giant Abbott, the parson and the farmers was contentious and dragged on past noon, delaying the start of the farmers' dinner, which put no one in a good mood. Discussion was heated and pacifying words were needed several times from the Reverend Coleman before the meeting finally agreed that the rector would give up a fifteen per cent share of the tithe he received, as would two other lay impropriators present, and, in consequence, the farmers would raise the labourers' wages in line with those suggested by Jem. In addition, several of the farmers promised that they would seek to employ the men to sow peas, beans and grain seed by dibbing, as others were doing elsewhere, and they would also return to hand-flailing the grain in the barn, which would give a good proportion of the villager men and youths employment through the worst months of the coming winter into March.

Handshakes were exchanged to seal the bargain, though the parson thought his tithe reduction excessively steep and sniffed at the 'severity of the terms,' as he called them. Nevertheless, the paper detailing the agreement was drawn up and signed by all and given into the possession of Samuel Chaplin, the innkeeper, for safe keeping and, as a gesture of goodwill, the seven farmers there each put a pound into a pot to be shared out amongst the labourers as beer money. Then they all went outside and climbed up on to a wagon before the assembled crowd: even the Reverend Coleman stood with them as the terms of the agreement were read out, chaffing at the indignity of the reduction, but seemingly accepting it.

The news that the farmers had contributed to a barrel as a gesture of goodwill was particularly pleasing: it was as the crowd was cheering and clapping Abbott as he drew the first fill of ale that two women came hurrying past, one carrying a bundle of linen sheets, the other some pillow cases.

'The Salter mob is breaking up the poorhouse!' one shouted. 'Everybody is taking what they can get. There's good pickings there if you hurry.' Then, bowing her head on seeing the rector, as if that way she would not be recognised, she scurried on past.

As was to be expected, there was a sudden surge away from the wagon and the inn, even by the men who might have been expected to stay to drink: in no time at all the crowd upon the green had halved and several hundred figures were streaming along the narrow lane towards the poorhouse, some gleefully shouting to each other as they went at the prospect of what they were about to witness.

'This is not what we bargained for,' cried one of the farmers, angrily. 'Our rates will double to pay for any damage that is done. You must stop the damned fools! This will cost us money we can't afford.'

'T'is none of my business what a bunch of Salter-ites does,' said the giant Abbott, shrugging. 'Besides, the damned poorhouse will be no loss to anyone. There 'on't be a man, woman or child round here that can say they'll miss it.' With that, he jumped down off the wagon and, as if to make his point, ambled leisurely after the figures running on ahead, sipping from his tankard as he went, as if to say, 'I will go and watch and take my time getting there, but I will do nothing to stop it.'

Desperate, the Reverend Coleman turned to Jem. 'You must stop them, Mr. Stebbings,' he pleaded. 'If you have any influence with these men at all, I beg you to use it now and stop the destruction of the poorhouse. You must stop them – for their own sakes! No good will come of it, no good at all.'

'I'll do what I can,' was Jem's reply as he jumped down: but so many were already streaming away ahead of him towards the scene of the destruction that they blocked the narrow lane and his progress was necessarily hampered. Worse still was the shock when he got there to see that amongst the wreckers were his friends, Dick Dollery, Enos Diddams, Nathaniel Newman, John Romble, William Stubbs and Thomas Judd, along with a dozen others from Hamwick Dean who should have been with him on the green.

THIRTY-EIGHT

HOW THIS had come about was that, when Jem and his friends and the Inworth trio had raised their tankards in a toast to each other's good health, Dick Dollery had spoken up. 'Thee'll want more than one man from Hamwick Dean to support thee,' he had said. 'especially if thee has any trouble and we has to smash a few turnip cutters and fire a few ricks to persuade 'em. We can't let they Salter-ites and Tottle-ites get a march on us, can we? T'is short notice, but if I can't bring fifty or sixty from this village, then I would be a poor fellow indeed. I'll round 'em up tomorrow, early like, whether they wants to come or not. We are all in this together. The labouring man needs to stand together on this and show people that he won't be done down ever again. What say thee?'

A chorus of 'Ayes' was his answer: and after that, they discussed what terms Jem had put to the farmers at the Hamwick Dean meeting which could be put to the Inworth farmers, though at that early time none knew whether the likes of Angus McCreef, William Worden, Richard Shadwell, John Dicker and the others actually would pay what they had promised, for farmers in other places, who had promised the same or similar, had been known to have lapses of memory over what they had promised and what they had agreed and signed to do.

The next morning, while Jem had been on the road to Inworth, the sound of a trumpet being blown loudly and persistently had summoned the men and youths of Hamwick Dean to their normal gathering place outside the Wayfarers': the trumpet-blower was Dick Dollery. By ten o'clock, the fifty he had promised the giant Abbott had actually grown to ninety-eight in total, though, peculiarly, such was the grumbling of many that an observer might have thought that many had been pressed into answering the call rather than being there of their own free will: at least a half-dozen who had been given flail work in the barn of one of the four middling farmers claimed that they had been called from it and threatened when they had argued that they would prefer to continue there rather than do anything to help the despised Inworth-ites.

As it was, there was not a man or youth left in the place between the ages of sixteen and forty when finally the long column marched up The Street and turned along the ridge-top road towards Inworth, with Dick Dollery striding along at its head, blowing his trumpet to announce their passage all the way to the larger village, followed by John Romble and Enos Diddams holding up a banner between them with the words 'Bread Or Blood' painted on a tattered piece of canvas fixed between two poles, and Nathaniel Newman, William Stubbs and Thomas Judd striding along behind, each carrying their weapons as before.

When they had all gone, there was throughout the village an eerie silence which frightened the younger children who had thought the noisy progress of the mob great fun at first: only they and the women and old men remained. Curiously, this time, the women did not wave the men off and there was no banter between them, no cheers or shouts of support from the onlookers as they departed along the ridge-top road, just an apprehensive silence as if sensing something, such as ill luck or that there was an unnecessary foolishness about their mission.

It so happened that, en route to Inworth, the Hamwick Dean contingent called in at the Green man at Lower Rackstead to recruit a few more 'volunteers,' which took time, of course, since it necessitated going round the cottages and farms to swell their numbers, while Dick Dollery and the other members of the 'People's Committee' sat in the ale house gratefully accepting the offer of a 'free firkin' which the landlord rolled out. In consequence, when Jem and the giant Abbott were inside the Anchor negotiating with the farmers, the parson and the others, they were reluctantly forming up on the road again, still with a mile-and-a-half to go.

Instead, approaching from the south was another contingent numbering two hundred or more, all armed the same with hammers, iron bars and staves, bent upon a different mission altogether: these were the Salter-ites, and those from Cumvirley, Lesser Tottle, Beckenden and Foliot Magna, who had also heard of the tithing meeting and were determined to use the gathering together of so many to suit their own ends. Debouching on to the Maydun-to-Wivencaster high road west of Inworth, a mere half-mile from where the poorhouse stood, they did not turn towards the Anchor Inn, where the villagers were all gathered, as one would have expected, but went left towards the poorhouse and halted by its gate.

The leader of the Salter-Cumvirley mob, a tall, robust, blustering thirty-five-year-old named Thomas Sack, whom everyone called by the nickname 'Tater,' accompanied by a half-dozen others, then marched straight up to the front door and banged loudly on the knocker.

William Mussett, the master, had an hour earlier stood amongst the gathering outside the Anchor, simply to listen to the comments of those there and to gauge their mood: under the current unsettled and riotous climate, he suspected that something might happen, but what he did not know. However, fearing more for himself from the Inworth villagers' grumblings than for the actual building, he had returned to the poorhouse and bolted the door, hoping that by some miracle, if the farmers agreed to raise the men's wages and the parson agreed to a tithe abatement, then everyone would be contented. He had not counted on the mob from Salter and Cumvirley arriving with a different aim in mind, which they had hatched of their own volition, imparted to no one and had come armed to carry it out: for 'Tater' himself had been incarcerated temporarily over the winter in the poorhouse as a pauper along with his own family a year before and one of his children had died there and so he hated the place as much as any man.

When Mussett opened the door, the leader of the Salter contingent was polite and respectful, since it seemed to be less bothersome to those on the receiving end. 'I would be obliged, Mr. Mussett,' he began, touching the brim of his hat, 'if you and the mistress would get yourself and all of the inmates out of the poorhouse as soon as you can, for this house is coming down today by the will of the people. We are here to demolish it, every last brick of it!'

For a few seconds, Mussett stared back at him stupefied, then he recovered himself. 'You cannot do that,' he protested, incredulous.

'We can and we will,' the leader of the Salter contingent told him forcefully.

'But there are old men and women in here and sick children,' pleaded the poorhouse master, which was the truth. 'It would be an act of madness to do what you say. You would never get away with it. I beg of you, please, do not destroy the house. It is my livelihood.' Then, unexpectedly for someone with his reputation as 'a little Napoleon' he added: 'Think of the inmates, think of the old and the sick. Think of them. This is all the home they have.'

A lesser man than a part-time smuggler, which 'Tater' was, might have felt ashamed: he had not expected to have to discuss the matter of the destruction of the poorhouse with its master: he had assumed he would order Mussett to leave and he would just leave, taking his wife and whatever possessions they could gather up with them.

'T'is the future inmates we are thinking of,' declared 'Tater,' waving his hand airily in the general direction of the two hundred or more standing on the road staring at him through the railings. 'The people are determined it will be got rid of it. If it is not here, they won't have to come to it. It is their will against yours. They have decided.'

'But some children are ill with a fever,' the master protested again, still hoping to dissuade them and keep his livelihood.

'We will move the women and the children into the old men's ward at the end and mark the window of that room,' replied 'Tater' politely again. 'That will not be touched so they will be safe there. No one will be harmed if they are in there. The women will look after the children. This poorhouse has seen its last day. The rest of it, every brick and tile of it, comes down today, Mr. Mussett, and there are upwards of two hundred of us to see that it does.'

The master of the poorhouse, faced with so large a gathering, armed with hammers, iron bars and wooden clubs and seemingly all grimly resolved, was not going to argue the matter over long: he knew full well how despised the actual building was: the shame of having to go to the poorhouse had blighted the last years of many of the aged in Inworth and the other villages around and the authorities were cursed for having built it. Looking at the resolute faces all staring at him, in the end, Mussett simply shrugged his shoulders. 'So be it,' he said, 'if that is your will. All I ask is that you give my wife and myself time to take out our goods. We have things here we do not wish to lose.'

'You have a half-hour to get your things together,' the Salter leader informed the poorhouse master, tipping one finger to his temple the way some men do to finish a conversation and depart. What he did was to go back into the road and shout out his agreement with Mussett to his own column and state that he and his wife were not to be touched on any account, but were to be allowed free passage through them with whatever goods they were carrying.

While they waited, 'Tater' Sack posted guards at the gate so that no destruction was begun ahead of time and sent a short, red-haired, freckle-faced youth, aged about eighteen, who was his lieutenant, in search of something to make the promised mark on the single window and door of the men's sick ward, which was located at one end of the building: the youth returned with a tub of white distemper found at the back of the building and painted a large cross on the single window and door. At the same time, stern orders were issued to the waiting mob: no one was to enter the old men's ward, take from it or demolish any part of it, roof, door, window or walls, or they would answer to him and his fists: the old men were to be left where they lay and the rest of the place, in effect, pulled down around them as best they could, leaving all walls of that ward standing and the ceiling, doors, roof and windows intact.

Also while they waited, five men and some women went into the building to carry the four old women and the five sick children from their wards into the old men's ward: their beds, too, were manoeuvred along the passageway. It was hard to say which caused the old men greater distress, the arrival of four females and five sick children in their midst and the loss of privacy and space which it entailed or the news that the rest of the poorhouse was about to be demolished around their ears. Whatever it was, a great wail went up and those who were trembling with the palsy of old age began trembling even more.

Not that that bothered 'Tater' Sack in the slightest: the poorhouse was coming down that day no matter what and he had rounded up two hundred or more to do it: and, just as in Dick Dollery's approaching column, not all in the Salter contingent were there willingly. 'We are here only because we have been pressed to be here,' complained one Lesser Tottle man bitterly as he helped Mussett and his pale, thin wife load their clothes and personal goods on to a wheelbarrow.

'T'will do you no good whether you are pressed into this or not,' a peeved Mussett retorted. 'If you are here when this thing is done, you will be held to account for it the same as anyone else. If you have half a brain in your head rather than in your boots, you will get away from here and leave the damned tomfoolery of this to those who do not care about themselves.'

With that, he set off down the road, with his wife scurrying along behind, so fearful of everyone that she did not even stop to pick up some of their own silver-handled cutlery when it slipped out of the bundle she was carrying: it was immediately swooped upon and pocketed by the one of the two Inworth women, who, becoming bored with the waiting outside the Anchor, had wandered away from the green and, by chance, came to the poorhouse just as the destruction was about to begin and so were able follow the mob inside and steal the bed linen from the family apartments, which were empty at that time.

No sooner were Mussett and his wife clear of the place than the guards posted at the gate stepped aside and, with whoops of delight, fifty or so of the Salter crew, urged on by the more cautious remainder, rushed forward as one, all trying to get through the narrow door at the same time, for there were pickings to be had inside as well as destruction to be wrought. Such are the ways of the young, almost as if they had never had such sport before, a number of the boys in the Salter contingent immediately surrounded the building, back, front and side, and hurled a succession of stones through all the unmarked windows, sparing the one with the cross daubed upon it, even as the others milled about inside, so that several were struck by the missiles flying in and let out angry bellows.

It was at this point, just as the destruction was beginning, that Dick Dollery's tardy marchers came tramping wearily up and, on seeing the crowd gathered around the gate and hearing the shattering of glass and the sound of splintering wood, became suddenly revitalised. Several gave the same whoops of delight as the Salter men had given and, forgetting their promise to join Jem on the green before the Anchor Inn, they pushed their way through the throng surrounding the poorhouse and piled through the gate and into the hated building, eager to do some destruction of their own and not to leave it all to the Salter-ites, whom they despised as much as they despised the Inworth-ites.

The more agile, Dick Dollery and Enos Diddams amongst them, climbed on to the roof to join those already there and gleefully began striking at it with their hammers and iron bars till the dust which rose resembled smoke from a burning building. When they had broken through into the roof space, they began to strip off the tiles and hurl them down into the yard with shouts of 'Watch out below!' and 'Stand clear!' Such was rain of the tiles shattering on the ground that the onlookers upon the road marvelled at the fact that no one was hit, particularly the Inworth women who came scurrying out with sheets, pillow cases, blankets and utensils, flour, potatoes and oatmeal anything else they could carry.

In no time at all, a dozen of the men, Hamwick Dean-ites working alongside Salter-ites working alongside Tottle-ites and others, had prised the poorhouse's twenty-gallon copper from its brickwork casing in the washhouse and, having rolled it into the centre of the yard without crushing anyone in its path, were gleefully beating upon it with their iron bars and hammers as if it were some supine animal which they had captured and wanted to kill rather than the inanimate vessel in which the inmates' soiled clothing was boiled.

This was the scene which greeted an out-of-breath Jem when he finally reached the poorhouse after his run from the inn: the destruction had been under way for some time by then, with the wreckers of the Salter contingent vying with the wreckers of the Hamwick Dean contingent to see who could do the most damage in the shortest time, all being cheered on and, in some cases, joined by the very men and women who had rushed off ahead of him to see the fun. They now formed a huge phalanx on the road to block his path and Jem had to force his way through: indeed, one burly fellow in his mid-forties, standing in the gateway itself, was most unwilling to give way and took great exception to Jem attempting to get by him, angrily pushing back at Jem, thinking he was trying to steal his place to get a better view of the spectacle. They might well have come to blows if others had not jostled them apart: if the man had been one of those on the green earlier, he clearly had forgotten Jem's mission in the village that day.

In the end, Jem took hold of the man and flung him aside, ignoring his threats and the abuse which were flung after him and that way managed to push through the gate into the front yard, just as a youth came out of the poorhouse front door carrying a table, its legs already broken off, and pitched it unceremoniously atop a pile of other broken furniture.

'Stop, stop! This is not what we are here to do,' Jem shouted, seizing hold of the youth in the vain hope of preventing him from going back inside. 'The farmers do not want this. It will undo all the good we have done.' The youth simply looked at him as if he were the mad one, pulled himself free and plunged back inside.

High up on the roof ridge, Dick Dollery and Enos Diddams looked down at Jem in astonishment when he shouted up at them, urging them to stop: they simply shrugged, as if they could not hear his words above the banging and clattering all round, and blithely carried on. In the building's entrance hall, Jem attempted to interpose himself between two Salter-ites who were smashing a cupboard, but they pushed him aside thinking he wanted to take over their sport and carried on. All around him, two score or three score or so of gleeful men and youths were sacking the building, chopping at the banisters and even the wooden steps of the staircase itself, uncaring of those on the floor above: others were breaking up doors, prising out windows, pulling down ceilings and hacking at wall plaster and wood panelling till the bare brick showed.

Great clouds of dust and dirt billowed everywhere in a choking fog: still Jem tried, but each time he found himself ignored: even John Romble greeted him with a smile as he shattered a door panel on the landing with his hammer. 'Sorry, Jem,' the perspiring wheelwright shouted back gleefully, swinging his hammer again, 'but we are going to smash this place to smithereens today and I mean to do my part in it.'

In one of the upper family apartments, he found Nathaniel Newman amongst a group of Salter men prising up the floorboards. 'Nat, Nat, no, no! This is madness!' Jem shouted from the doorway as there was no way to walk across to him. But so great was the noise of banging and crashing in the room that he doubted Nathaniel Newman, who was farthest from the door and had his back to it, even heard him: for he did not turn round, but continued to jump upon an inch-thick floorboard propped against a wall in an attempt to snap it with his weight. Before Jem could shout a second time, two men carrying the sharp, splintered pieces of the master's bedroom wardrobe along the narrow corridor forced him to retreat to the rapidly vanishing stairs which were so near to being dismantled by others that he decided it would be more prudent to quit the building altogether before it became necessary to jump out of it.

On the lower floor, he found Thomas Judd and William Stubbs swinging their hammers at a wall, both almost entirely covered in white dust from the billowing plaster and whitewash. 'We're doing what should have been done a long time ago,' was the ghost-like Thomas Judd's gruff retort before resuming his work.

In effect, all that Dick Dollery and the others were destroying was a system and their blood was up as much as any regiment of soldiers sacking a town and nothing was going to stop them. Several times in the yard, Jem begged men who came out carrying shattered furniture and broken floorboards and panelling from the master's rooms not to go back inside – standing in front of some, trying to reason with them: but all his pleas were in vain. The Hamwick Dean men sheepishly ducked past him, knowing who he was, of course, but determined to continue, while the Salter and Cumvirley men, not knowing him, pushed him angrily aside or sidestepped his outstretched arm with curses. The Inworth men also ignored him and cursed him also and told him to go back to Hamwick Dean, his assistance to their cause earlier in the day already forgotten: he could not keep them back, there were just too many crowding the corridors and the hallway and milling about the yard: they had a lust for destruction which he could not divert. In the end, all Jem could do was to stand clear by the railings and watch as the destruction continued.

The only thing which diverted a few of the wreckers was a cask of the master's favourite port, which had been found in a storeroom: from then on, some did nothing but drink, leaving the destruction to their comrades and pouring the cherished port into inmates' tin mugs and any other vessels lying about the place to wash the dust from their mouths. Unfortunately, so drunk did one become that, unable to stand, he sat astride the cask of wine so that he could lean forward every now and again and turn the tap to refill his tin cup without having to move at all till he fell off, that is, and lay sprawled on the ground, oblivious to the world and oblivious, too, to the fire set under the pile of furniture nearby which was soon blazing fiercely, sending flames crackling and exploding skywards and thickening the fog of dust which surrounded the place with clouds of black smoke.

By the time the mob had finished, the whole of the roof had been stripped of its tiles and timbers, every piece of crockery, matting and mattress had been thrown out into the yard, every floorboard had been prised up, every door, window frame, cupboard, bed, chair, tub and table had been shattered by axes, every wall had been tumbled by sledgehammers and iron bars – excepting those where the petrified paupers and children lay with their heads under their bedcovers, listening to the crashes and the commotion and the shouts and yelling all around them. The damage done that day, when assessed later, would run into several hundreds of pounds.

'Well, Jem, what does thee think of our work?' a grinning Dick Dollery asked, eventually, coming to stand beside his friend and watch the flames of the bonfire: he said it as if he were expecting Jem's approval of what had been done.

'I am sorry to see it, Dick, very sorry indeed,' Jem replied, unable to conceal the bitterness he felt. 'This could well hang a few of us.' It was as if he felt responsible for what they had done: the authorities, he knew, would not allow the destruction of their poorhouse to go unpunished: they would seek out those responsible no matter how long it took.

In answer, Dick Dollery simply clapped his friend upon the back. 'They will not dare to challenge us!' he declared, taking a swig of port from the tin cup he was carrying. 'This is a revolution, brother, a revolution! Our numbers are growing all the time. We are only just beginning.'

At that moment, Enos Diddams, John Romble, William Stubbs, Thomas Judd and Nathaniel Newman joined them, brushing the dust from their clothes, flushed and smiling after their exertions. 'I wish this was a revolution,' declared Thomas Judd, overhearing his friend, 'because the next thing I'd demolish would be all they damned churches, the whole danged lot on'em, with the parsons in'em.'

'You may get your chance,' William Stubbs told him, sarcastically, 'for there is to be a great meeting in the old fort at Hamwyte tomorrow for all the labourers in the Hundred. They say there will be hundreds there, thousands even.'

'See, I told'ee, Jem, I told'ee,' cried Dick Dollery, exuberantly, 'this is only the beginning, my friend, this is only the beginning. The revolution is coming...'

THIRTY-NINE

WORD of the great meeting to be held within the dual rings of the Iron Age fort on Cannium hill, a half-mile north of the Hamwyte high road, had been spread from village to village and inn to inn for several days beforehand: thus, early on the Saturday morning, long columns of men and women were to be seen tramping along the lanes to the small market town – men with stooped shoulders and weary, plodding steps, women in shawls and patched dresses with haggard cheeks, sullen-faced youths eager for the 'great lark' and adolescent girls, more interested in the strange boys they might meet from other villages than comprehending what was the actual reason for it all.

They came from every village and hamlet: six-hundred-and-fifty marching together from the estuaryside villages of Salter, Gledlang, Cobwycke, Copthall and Cumvirley: eighty or more from tiny Merchant Staplers alone, almost the whole population: a further sixty from Lower Rackstead, comprising two-thirds of the hamlet: and from Hamwick Dean itself, well over three-hundred-and-fifty, men and youths, women and girls, the greater number of the former still carrying the hammers, iron bars, staves, pitchforks and other implements which they had used so destructively over the past days, all heading for the old fort to swell a gathering of labourers from the lower part of the town itself, many of whom were also agricultural workers – when they could get work, that is – plus others from a dozen villages to the north, east and west so that by ten o'clock they already numbered above four thousand.

Curiously, there was no one from Inworth: the reason for their absence was at that very moment stumbling bleary-eyed out of the Anchor into the chill light of day: fifteen dragoons, led by a young ensign, who late the previous evening had ridden into the village from Wivencaster with cutlasses in scabbards at their sides. They had put themselves up at the Anchor and the villagers, realising for the first time the enormity of the destruction of the poorhouse, had shut their doors and watched and waited to see what they would do: all the dragoons did do, however, was to sit around in the old inn talking and drinking well into the night and anger the landlord, Samuel Chaplin, by breaking into his taproom after he had gone to bed and drinking dry one of his barrels of ale. Come the morning, they grazed their horses on the green and made no move to do anything: unsurprisingly, therefore, the villagers decided it was wiser to remain in their cottages rather than draw attention to the advertised 'rebellion.' Word of their arrival was sent out to the marchers approaching from the estuary villages and they simply by-passed Inworth's broad green altogether by the backways of that region, unknown to the troopers, and so arrived at the great meeting on Cannium hill that way.

During the night, a freezing mist had come filtering along the shallow valley of the Langwater and such was the gloom of the day as the contingent from Hamwick Dean set out that the oil lamps and candles were still aglow in many of the cottages. At the forefront of the procession, as was to be expected, was Dick Dollery, to the chagrin of his wife walking beside him, tootling on his trumpet and skipping along like a five-year-old at times as if to make light of the freezing darkness: for that day, the wives were determined to be there with their men. Emma Diddams was hurrying along beside her long-striding husband, who was playing on the pipes: John Romble, walking with his wife, was banging on a drum, while William Stubbs and his wife had hoisted a banner between them proclaiming 'Liberty For All': and Thomas Judd, one fist raised and pumping the air, was leading the whole column in a chant of 'Bread or blood! Bread or blood!' The only disappointment was that Nathaniel Newman's wife had resolutely refused to let her fifty-year-old husband go with them, saying he had work in his forge which he had neglected during his 'gallivanting' and, besides, he had made a big enough fool of himself already! Similarly, that day, too, Jed and Thirza were left with Dick Dollery's three younger daughters, as were the youngest children of the others.

Bouyed by their successes of the previous week, the villagers all seemed to be oblivious or uncaring of the seriousness of the destruction of the Inworth poorhouse or the arrival of the dragoons, which they heard from the Lower Rackstead contingent: however, it was with a certain sense of foreboding that Jem set out.

'We don't know how this day will end,' he told Jed and Thirza before he left. 'There may be special constables about so you must stay behind in case things go bad for us.'

'We'll meet any who come agin us,' declared Dick Dollery, taking a firmer grip on a five-foot cudgel with a heavy metal end which he had made especially so that he could stick it in his belt like a sword and also blow his trumpet: his almost boyish enthusiasm for what might lay ahead was enough to make Jem smile and temporarily to forget his concerns.

As it was, when he, Dick Dollery and the others of the long, straggling procession emerged on to Hamwyte High Street, midway along it by the Black Bear Inn, they found a line of men drawn up across it, barring their way to the top of the town, all armed with a weapon of some kind, a pistol, a blunderbuss, a cutlass and even an old halberd,. The well-to-do of Hamwyte, hearing of the destruction of the Inworth poorhouse and remembering the riot of thirteen years before, intended this time to protect their own, their money and their property from 'the labouring rabble,' though no attempt was made to impede Jem and the others as they crossed the broad high road and headed up the hill by the George towards the old fort, which lay within a stone's throw of the little-used ancient church, overlooking a small triangle of green, still surrounded by the old wool merchants' houses, which had formed the earlier hamlet.

The great meeting was already under way when Jem and the others began pushing in amongst the crowd, but so tightly packed within the concentric rings were the people that it was impossible to reach the front: most of the Hamwick Dean contingent were content to take up what space there was around the perimeter and to return the suspicious stares of those in front of them with equally suspicious stares of their own. Most within the fort were oblivious to their arrival: for all were straining to hear the words of a lean man in a tall black hat, with the red, white and blue ribbons of a revolutionary tied around it, who was standing atop a grassy knoll in the centre of the fort addressing them through a funnel-shaped, brass speaking trumpet such as a boat's captain might use to hail another passing craft across a broad stretch of water.

Speaking in a great bellowing voice, his free arm pumping the air, his face flushed and his eyes distended and protruding with the effort of it all, Joly Cobbold had returned to Hamwyte on a mission 'for the people on behalf of the people,' his people, his labouring brothers and sisters, his comrades! For that is what they were: his comrades, even though he had not set foot in the town since the day thirteen years before when he had watched from the window of the Black Bear as the troopers had fired at the rioters inside the George. He had seen, too, the fleeing youth cut down by one of the troopers, himself no older than the one he shot, and he had watched as the others were marched off with their hands in the air.

On the following day, Joly Cobbold had spoken to the brushmakers' society's secretary, William Mann, of his wish to resume his tramp and, with his blessing, had left the brushmakers' yard a week later, with a letter of introduction to 'whomever it may concern' from the secretary in his knapsack. Thus, on the actual day of the executions, he was seventy miles to the north, working in a brushmakers' yard in Norwich and it was a full year later before he returned to London by the brushmakers' western 'tramp,' Exeter, Poole, Salisbury, Southampton and Reading.

In the years since, he had married and had fathered three children, all under the ages of ten still, and had continued his desire to improve the lot of the downtrodden poor by becoming active in the radical reform movement in the capital, attending meetings in inns and workers' houses, speaking himself on occasions, and had even been imprisoned for six months in Milbank for addressing what the Bow Street magistrates had deemed an 'unlawful and seditious assembly' on a street corner while handing out pamphlets in Cheapside. In time, too, he had risen to become the secretary of his local branch of the Society of Journeymen Brushmakers, earning himself something of a favourable reputation amongst other radicals for his willingness to act in defence of his fellow working man and his firebrand oratory, which he had modelled on the great Henry Hunt himself, to whom he had listened on many occasions.

A coachman arriving in London two days previously had told him of the planned great meeting at Hamwyte: here now was an opportunity he could not miss. He knew the town, he knew the people, he knew the desperate poverty, too, of the town and rural labouring classes there: and, best of all, he knew that they needed a leader, a leader such as himself. That had been their downfall the last time: they had not acted together as they should have done, they had not been properly led and disciplined, which was why one foolish party had gone off to steal and rob while the remainder had tramped back into the town and gone straight into the George, got drunk and allowed the militia to creep up on them. Now there was hope of another rising, like the ones in Kent, Sussex and Hampshire, Gloucestershire, Wiltshire and Berkshire. It was almost with a sense of predestination that he had taken the first available coach back to Hamwyte, leaving his work at the Shoreditch brushmaking yard, as well as his wife and three children.

The town had changed little in the years since he had last been there, though, as a precaution, he had not booked a room at either the Black Bear or the George, but into the less popular and somewhat seedier Old Sun Inn at the bottom end of the town. He felt some sadness for those who had suffered death at the hands of the land-owning and property-owning magistrates all those years before when all they had been doing was protesting at their own slow starvation: there was, however, a certain satisfaction that they had been martyred in the holy struggle for the equality of all men.

In the week following the fateful riot, when it had been the whispered talk of the whole town, Joly Cobbold had fully expected that the town's two parish constables might start making enquiries about him and most particularly the pamphlet he had read out at the meeting: but no one had approached him: indeed, his small part in it all seemed to have been entirely forgotten or to have passed unnoticed. If it were ever commented upon at all by any of the rioters afterwards, no one seemed now to remember him: that had been his only worry, that someone might remember him and recall his words spoken at the meeting in Black Bear which had stirred them into action: but it appeared none had since no one had expected him to reappear after so long a time. Further, the old brushmaker's yard had closed five years previously with the death of the proprietor: the old secretary, William Mann, had also died: and, of those who had taken his urgings to heart, five had been hanged and seven others were most probably still in New South Wales or Van Diemen's Land, or dead.

As a precaution, however, he had sat in the parlour of the Old Sun in full view of all its customers for two successive nights and had walked the High Street from top to bottom the previous day to test for himself: no one had recognised him, though, of course, he had been a much younger man before

Now in his mid-thirties, with a lean, pinched face and dark, straggly hair falling to his shoulders, wearing a tall black hat and a black topcoat and a white neckerchief such as an impoverished schoolmaster or an equally impoverished lawyer or university student might possess – now he stood before a sea of faces, expanding on what was dear to his radical heart. Never in his wildest dreams had he expected to find himself addressing such a vast crowd, the same as he had seen his two great radical idols, 'Orator' Hunt and William Cobbett, do many a time. Why, there must be upwards of four thousand or even five thousand of them and more still arriving! Given the upheavals south of the river, west of the capital and now in the counties north of the capital, this must truly be the beginning of the great uprising of the people, the uprising of the common man which would sweep away once and for all the power of the landowning gentry and herald finally the reforms of Parliament for which he and others had clamoured for so long. It would be an end of the 'rotten boroughs,' the end, too, of corruption at elections where a limited number of well-to-do gentry chose the Member and were not above resorting to bribery and coercion to have their candidate elected. It would herald also the adoption at last of universal suffrage, when all men would vote as equals for annual Parliaments: governance of the country by the people for the people, a revolution throughout Britain to match that of the Americans and the French. Utopia! A rising against the King, a land freed of the influence of money and the landowning classes and freed, too, of the despised 'German monarchy.'

Like his two great idols, he, saw, the monarchy as little more than 'a great deceit,' an artful contrivance, an expedient to extract money from the pockets of the people: the Houses of Parliament were merely places of bribery and corruption: the Government, rather than being some wonderful mysterious thing, which it was to most of those who stood before him, was to him simply a corrupt and oppressive body, made up of mercenaries from the most idle and profligate of the community – prostitute lawyers and unprincipled adventurers and the more avaricious and idle of the nobility and the gentry, who, through the impunity of corrupt elections made their way into it and hired out their tongues and their votes to the highest bidder. Members of Parliament, he railed, were chosen by a privileged number of borough electors to serve for seven years when they ought to be chosen every year by the people and for the people, for they represented no one but their own kind: and in office were composed for the most part of self-serving factions under the guidance of certain powerful members of the nobility, themselves little better than murdering nabobs, in his view.

'Brothers and sisters,' he shouted through his speaking trumpet, thinking now to conclude his speech, 'brothers and sisters, my brethren, I am here to help you in your great cause, for no one is a greater enemy than I of the Corn Laws and the Game Laws and all laws that benefit the idle rich and oppress the industrious poor such as yourselves. I say to you that, if in His infinite wisdom, the Good Lord has decided that there must be high-born and low-born, rich and poor in this country, then so be it – so be it – but let the honest working man like yourselves have some of the comforts of life. Let him be paid a living wage as you demand, let him be employed six days a week year-long in order that he might earn that wage which you also demand and let him not be laid off at the whim of some landowner looking only to his own self-interest, and let him also have always the means to keep a roof over his head, the means always to feed his family, the means to live his life with dignity and without want, and let him, while he lives upon this earth, no longer be subject to the neglect of a Parliament which continues to be appointed by the few to lord it over the many. Parliament should be chosen by the whole nation, by us, too, by the working man as well as the idle rich, since the election of a Parliament is our only security against the exercise of arbitrary powers by the Crown. If the present inequality of representation and length of Parliament be the cause of parliamentary corruption, as they undoubtedly are, then, I say, we must remove the cause before the effect will cease!'

A great cheer went up at this and, pausing till it had subsided, he recalled a passage he had heard somewhere being spoken by one of the orators which he had memorised in its entirety: 'Darkness has long cast her veil over this land – persecution and tyranny have long carried universal sway – magisterial powers have long been a scourge to the liberties and rights of our people. It does not matter by what name those usurped powers are known, whether by king, parliament, potentate or stadholder, they are in all senses still usurped. Across the Channel, the yoke of bondage which once burdened our neighbours, the French, was broken forever by their revolution. That same blessing is awaiting us if only we have the will to seize it. The more tame you have grown, the more you have been oppressed and despised, the more you have been trampled upon. The day is at hand, brothers and sisters, when persecution and tyranny shall be no more in this land of ours, when enjoying the liberties of a free people we shall boast of having introduced amongst ourselves that same equality which the French have already acquired. To possess such an acquisition, we must, as the Bible says, "Cast off the works of darkness and put on the armour of light." Revolution, brothers and sisters, revolution!'

FORTY

AS JOLY COBBOLD stepped down from the knoll amid cheers and clapping, a stooped and white-bearded veteran of the soil, dressed in a worn and faded smock and a wide-brimmed straw hat, was helped up by several hands to take his place: so feeble were his words at first that, had he not had the speaking trumpet, they would scarce have carried beyond the first twenty feet: as it was, they barely reached Jem's ears thirty yards back.

'People round here is worse fed and worse housed than a prisoner in gaol,' the white-bearded old man declared in a voice quavering with emotion. 'We're no better off to my way of thinking, than the negro slaves they take out o' Africa. The only difference between the two on us that I can see is that they feeds the negro on his plantation so as to git the work out o' him, us they starves and 'on't let work when we wants to. And them people is supposed to be God-fearing, Jesus Christ Christians! We, land workers, we common labourers, we know why there is no work to be had all winter for any of us excepting them that has been kept on by favouritism or need by some farmer with a bit of sun in his heart instead of ice in his veins and there are very few of they. T'is all down to the new machinery they have brought on to the farms in the name of profit and greed, the infernal threshing machine. 'is because of that and that alone that our numbers are cut in the winter where once there was winnowing to keep us in work and put money in our purses and our families were housed and fed and kept warm through the coldest part of the year.'

The crowd, which had done him the courtesy of falling silent to listen, now applauded, which cheered him, suppressed his nervousness and helped to increase the range of his voice.

'Not n'more, not n'more,' he went on, raising a gnarled and shaky fist in imitation of his predecessor. 'Now we are laid off, told there is nothing for us and that we must go on parish relief. But the overseers will only pay a pittance to a man out of work and, if he has, say, seven or more little ones, as does my eldest son, they tell him he has too big a family for them to keep and that the poor rates collected are not enough to sustain so many men out of work for so long, from Michaelmas to Lady Day – '

There was a swelling murmur of agreement amongst the crowd, punctuated by shouts of support: 'That's the truth!' and 'Listen to him, listen to him!' from some when others started conversations amongst themselves and those close by could not hear what was being said.

'Families are evicted from their cottages because the men have no work to pay their rent,' the white-bearded labourer continued, even more loudly. 'They are told to go to the poorhouse and they will be found work there. Well, I tell you, brothers and sisters, I have done their work – stonebreaking, which is what they give you – I know what kind of work it is: hard, cruel, dreary, drudging work and paid a pittance for it. T'is not work, t'is more like slavery. Slavery of the common man – !'

Overcome by his own emotions, the white-bearded labourer hesitated, unable to continue: so Joly Cobbold climbed up on to the mound again and took the speaking trumpet from him and he was helped down and tearfully led away to a muted, yet sympathetic, round of cheers.

Joly Cobbold now held out the speaking trumpet to any who might take it. 'Now is the time to have your say, brothers and sisters,' he cried. 'Come, who is next? Who else would like to speak? Who else among you is brave enough to let the rich landowners know how ill used you are. Let them hear your voice, brothers! Let them know you are Englishmen, free-born and country-bred. This is your land, brothers and sisters, your land. No man has a right to take it from you and leave you to starve. Come, who will tell all the fine lords and ladies and gentlemen of leisure and idleness what is really in the hearts and minds of the agricultural labourers of England?'

Eventually, a shout of 'I will' came from a heavy-set man in his late thirties, with a round rubicund face and dark sidewhiskers. Irritated by the cajoling of one who was not only a stranger to him but who spoke with a London accent harsh to his ears, he allowed himself to be pushed up good naturedly on to the mound by several of his fellows. Having instructed the new speaker on the use of the trumpet, Joly Cobbold stood back with a gesture and a smile, conceding the mound and the multitude to him.

'The poor of my parish have been ground into the dust by these Poor Laws of the rich farmers and gentry,' the new speaker declared forcefully, clenching one fist above his head as if making some form of military salute, like a legionnaire in Roman times. 'We know why our masters say they cannot pay us a living wage. We only has to look up from our work when we are in the fields to see why, those of us who can git work, that is – and what do we see? Our masters and our mistresses riding by in their fine carriages and a pair of pampered horses up front, that's what! They has enough money to spend on them and on the lad sitting up front dressed in a fine livery. They has money for that. So why has they not money to pay us?'

Raucous cheers from his companions greeted his words: the heavy set man smiled back down at them.

'Around our village,' he went on, 'one or two on'em has money, too, to keep a pack of hounds – dogs – and well-fed dogs at that! Yet they pay us barely enough to keep body and soul together. I have had no work since harvesting ended. I have tried to get work, for I have a pregnant wife, with one infant at her knee and another still feeding off her, like. I have offered myself in all directions, but without success. Even the best workmen cannot find employment where I live. I make no bones about it, to my mind, we are approaching starvation, all on us, all on us working men and women. And who is to blame for all this? Why the damned farmers who buy these threshing machines that do the work in a week or two that kept fifteen of us comfortably employed all winter once. If we must smash all the threshing machines in this area to keep our winter work, then so be it, brothers and sisters, so be it, we must do it. T'is the one way open to us. To me, it is a question of starvation or fighting for food – fighting for our very lives and the lives of our womenfolk and our children. That is the way, I see it, brothers. Smash the machines, I say, smash'em and be done with it.'

When he jumped down, he rejoined a group of youths and was heartily slapped upon the back by them all, and by others.

Another speaker, a pinch-faced, round-backed man with dark hair and a sharp nose, wearing a smock almost bleached of all its colour by repeated washings, now climbed on to the mound and took the trumpet, fired up by the heavy-set man's speech.

'The upper classes tell us what we the poor ought to think, what we the poor ought to do and how we the poor ought to spend our lives,' he began in such a fierce tone that the hub-bub of the crowd, still discussing the previous speaker's words, was immediately quietened. 'In subservience to them, that is how they want us!' he went on. 'Well, I say we have suffered our pain long enough. You may say you are loyal to your King and Country, but I say, "Damn the King!" What business has a man to possess two or three millions a year to keep himself and his palaces as our Kings does? What business, too, has a great lord to possess half-a-million as do some? What right have they to have all that money while those they have robbed are starving for want of a crust of bread? Eleven children have I and we have been near to starving as any one can be without their toes curling up! Three year agoo, I received for my wife and children eleven shillings and sixpence a week from the poor rate, ten shillings and sixpence for my family and a shilling extra for an ill child. Now I gets only three shillings and sixpence a week and that is soon to be cut again by the vestry. That is how they treat us, those who call themselves our betters. They want a good blowing up and I would not mind laying a trail of gunpowder and doing for them, the whole damned lot of 'em!'

When he jumped down, he was immediately replaced by a thin-faced, red-haired youth from amid a group of a half-dozen other youths, none above the age of eighteen or nineteen, who had been standing right at the front of the gathering under the black banner of the anarchist. As their comrade took the brass trumpet and began to speak, they looked fiercely about them as if willing to challenge any who might dissent from what their comrade was about to say, which none dared to do: most of the onlookers were content to remain silent, but attentive and interested.

'I have brought my hammer and I mean to set to work with it, just as the men of Kent and Sussex and Hampshire and other places south of the river have done already,' the red-haired labourer roared into the trumpet: and as he spoke he pulled a short-handled lump hammer from his clothing and raised it above his head. 'I will follow any man to smash as many machines as I can, but I cannot do it by myself. If you have brought your weapons, then let us get on with the rebellion, brothers and sisters! My friends have brought their weapons. We are all one. Bread or blood, I say! Bread or blood! What say you?'

'Bread or blood! Bread or blood!' was the cry returned from hundreds of voices in various quarters of the crowd, while the black flag was waved even more vigorously by the group of youths at the front.

'Is there one here who will lead us?' the red-haired youth demanded from the mound, casting his eyes over the throng. 'Is there a Captain out there to lead us? If there be one amongst you, let him make himself known to us and I will follow him!'

FORTY-ONE

FIREBRAND though he might be, Joly Cobbold was also a man of some guile. When he had set out for Hamwyte, he had envisaged himself as perhaps a new Wat Tyler of the provinces, the leader of a new Peasants' Revolt: but, as he sat in the parlour of the Old Sun, disturbing news from south of the river, brought by passing coachmen, had caused him to hesitate. The militias and the yeomanry had been turned out in force to quell the riots in those counties and the justices were holding special meetings to swear in local landowners and their sons as mounted yeomanry and special constables: the magistrates in Kent, Sussex and Hampshire and other counties to the west, previously lenient in their dealings with the rioters, had performed an about-face: their earlier leniency was forgotten: wholesale arrests were now being made: the anger of Parliament was finally revealing itself: caution was now advisable. Further, he had heard that very day that dragoons had been seen on the road riding to a village not five miles away where a poorhouse had ben sacked.

Experience had taught Joly Cobbold that sometimes it was better to direct events along the path which one wished them to take, ushering others along from behind rather than to be at the front leading. So, in view of the latest events, he had decided he would help to guide these rural labourers, to counsel them, to set them on the right path – indeed, he would even join them on whatever endeavours they undertook: but it was not yet time to announce himself as their leader. That honour must fall to someone else till the way ahead was known, till the revolution was clearly set on its course, unstoppable: then he would step forward and claim his place at its head. Till then...

'So who will be our Captain then? Who will lead us?' the thin-faced youth holding the hammer aloft demanded. 'You all talk a good speech, but who is for doing something? Who is for marching and smashing the damned thrashing machines like they are doing down in Kent and Sussex and Hampshire? I say we start here. I say we start now! We need a Captain! Who will lead us. Who will be our Captain?'

It was time for Joly Cobbold to make his move: quickly, he came forward to the front of the mound and, taking the trumpet from the youth, raised it to his lips. 'Aye,' he shouted. 'Who is willing to lead us? Whoever leads us as our Captain must, by rights, be one of you, one who can speak for you, one who knows you and who you know you can trust, a labouring man like yourselves. Come, is there a Captain amongst you – one who dares?'

Everyone began looking at their neighbour in the hope that someone alongside or nearby would shout out or push forward to volunteer: but, amongst a crowd of four thousand or more, none did.

'If another will lead us, I will be his lieutentant, if you wish me to be, and do it gladly,' Joly Cobbold tried as an inducement, looking out over the multitude. 'I am not an agricultural worker, but I am a working man like yourselves and I am here to support your cause. The Captain, though, should come from amongst you. He should be one of your own.' Wry cheers greeted this: they had noted that he had commanded the meeting well enough, though none knew his name or from where he had come: if he were willing to do that, then why was he not willing to lead rather than being just a 'lieutenant,' as he called it? What was he doing, raising an army?

Joly Cobbold sensed their suspicions. 'Come, brothers and sisters,' he shouted into the trumpet, 'if the day should ever come when we are forced to take on the forces of the rich men's laws, then I assure you I will not be found wanting. You will not find me hiding behind a hedgerow or lagging at the rear. I shall be at the front, as a lieutenant – your lieutenant – helping your cause. That I vow.'

They were almost the same words spoken by 'Orator' Hunt at Spa Fields thirteen years before: he had remembered them well: then Hunt had been cheered and the crowd had thrown their hats in the air: but from the throng before him there was no response, just the same blank, sheepish faces, all waiting for someone else to offer themselves up. 'This is your cause, brothers and sisters, your cause,' Joly Cobbold cajoled. 'Is there not one amongst you who will lead us? One who is brave enough, one who has good cause himself?'

It was at that point that Dick Dollery let out a shout and began forcing his way through the crowd to the front, where he leapt agilely up on to the mound and took the speaking trumpet from a smiling Joly Cobbold 'Brothers and sisters,' he shouted, waving one arm to gain their attention, 'brothers and sisters, there is a man here who will be your Captain – he is right here amongst us, standing right there – ' He pointed a finger straight at Jem. ' – If you want a Captain, he will be your Captain. He was our Captain in our village and he can be yours, too. He is a veteran of the war, who rose to be a sergeant in the service of the old Iron Duke himself and has had as rough a time of it as any man here since he came home. Thanks be to him, we have persuaded most of the farmers in our village to agree to pay us all a proper wage and thanks be to him we have got the tithe reduced and thanks be to him again we have got the parson to agree to contribute more to the poor rate than he ever did before and thanks be to him we have rid ourselves of the infernal threshing machines. And the man who led us and did all the speaking for us was my friend there.' Again his arm was outstretched, pointing directly at a reddening Jem, who was wishing the ground would open up and swallow him.

'Aye, aye, he is the man to speak for you,' Enos Diddams shouted, slapping a surprised Jem upon the shoulder.

Curious faces now turned to look at one who had been volunteered: suddenly, Jem found himself gripped by the strong arms of John Romble and Thomas Judd and led towards the mound, with Enos Diddams pushing from behind and calling out: 'Make way there, make way, make way for your Captain.' Even the men's wives were applauding, particularly Lizzie Dollery since she had feared that, when her husband had gone up on the mound, he was about to volunteer himself: she had at least been spared that.

With one last shove from a half-dozen pairs of hands, Jem was propelled up on to the mound by his grinning companions. 'Up you goo, Jem. For the brotherhood,' shouted Enos Diddams.

'Welcome, brother, welcome,' Joly Cobbold said, seizing Jem's hand and smiling broadly, though it seemed to Jem to be as much one of relief that he was not having to undertake the role himself as it was of actual welcome: then, turning to the assembly, Joly Cobbold shouted through the speaking trumpet which had been returned to him: 'Brothers and sisters, your Captain! I give you, your Captain!'

A great wave of cheering broke out: those who previously had been content to stand at the back of the throng now began pressing forward, eager to get a closer look at the man who had been presented to them, indeed who, by allowing himself to be forced up on to the mound, had 'agreed' to lead them: some even pulled their own hidden weapons from under their smocks and waved them in the air. While they had agreed with the sentiments of all the speakers, it had not escaped their notice that each had disappeared back into the throng and so they had been guarded in their own exuberance: now they had a 'Captain,' a man whom they could follow, who was going to lead them on their great crusade, whatever that was to encompass and wherever it would take them: it was as if the people had suddenly found a voice.

As he looked out over the thousands around him, as he accepted their acclamation, Jem realised that he could hardly refuse to lead them: it was almost a matter of honour, a revenge for Mary-Ann and all the indignities he had suffered, the loss of his land, the loss of his wife, the loss of his liberty, his pauperisation: reluctantly, he lifted the speaking trumpet to his mouth.

'If you wish me to be your Captain, brothers and sisters, then I will,' he declared and another great cheer rose up.

'Let him speak, let him speak,' shouted Dick Dollery, waving his arms for silence.

Jem realised, too, that, if he were expected to lead them, then they would want to know what were his opinions before they would even consent to heed him, let alone to think of following him: they had come from thirty different parishes to the great meeting in the simple and somewhat naive hope that the Justices and the large landowning farmers and the parsons of that Hundred and those either side would take note of the fact that they were there, that so many were there and why they were there: now they had a leader – a Captain – but he was a man whom the greater number did not know.

'Tell us what to do, Captain,' one of the black flag youths cried and gave a mock salute, which was immediately taken up by the other grinning youths.

Jem raised his free arm and, as if on command, the crowd fell silent, eager to hear what he would say.

'My friend has told you what we have achieved and it is all true,' he began, desperately trying to recall the words he had used in the letter he had read out to the farmers in the Wayfarers' Inn. 'For too long, the working man has suffered the privations inflicted upon him by the rich and the powerful of this land and we have done so without complaint in the hope that time and circumstances would bring about a change. Well, our hope is worn out with the waiting. Again and again our expectations have been dashed. We have no Member of Parliament of our own to speak for us in the Commons or the Lords, no newspaper to fight our cause. Our voices do not reach the ears of the high and the mighty who make the laws of this land. They do not hear us. Therefore, we must be our own champions, we must fight our own cause, we must win our own battle – ' Jem paused: the whole crowd was hushed now.

'It is for that reason we have come here today,' he went on, 'to make our grievances known – to ask redress for all our sufferings – and to demand an end to all the debasing treatment we have had to endure. We, the common people of this Hundred, are here to appeal to the good sense of the magistracy of Hamwyte, of Melchborough, of Steadleigh, of Shallford, Maydun and Wivencaster, to ask those gentlemen whether they think sevenpence a day is sufficient for a working man, hale and hearty, to keep up the strength necessary to the execution of the labour he has to do? We ask also whether five or six shillings a week is sufficient for a married man with a family to provide the common necessities of life? Have we not reason to complain when we are obliged for so long to go to our daily toil with only potatoes in our satchels and only plain spring water to quench our thirsts? And, on returning to our cottages, do we not find ourselves welcomed by our families half-famished? All we ask for is a wage sufficient to support us and our families, without being driven to the overseer to suffer his petty tyranny and dictation. If I am to lead you, then I shall lead you and we will go from farm to farm, from here to the county boundary if needs be, and we shall ask every farmer we come across to promise to us in writing to pay every married man he employs two-shillings and threepence a day up to the first of March and, from that date to the first of October, two shillings and sixpence a day. And for single men a shilling and ninepence a day to the first of March, and two shillings from that time after to the first of October. We must fix on that, all to ask the same and no difference between this place or the next or the farmers who are paying the most in one place will use the example of a lower rate in another place to trim their own wages and save themselves money. We all know how mean and grasping a farmer can be – ' There was laughter here from some, wry smiles from others who knew certain farmers well enough to know the truth of what was said. ' – This is what we ask, this is what we expect and we sincerely trust this is what we shall not be under the painful necessity of demanding by other means!'

Again Jem paused, allowing the meaning of his last words to sink in, before he continued: 'We want the parsons of every place to agree that all tithes and rents be reduced and for him to sign a paper to say so. Our intention must be not to hurt the farmer, but to help him by having the parson reduce the tithes so we shall have more wages. And, alongside of that, we want an end to the use of all threshing machines, as the others have said, for it is the machines which do the work of ten men which are to blame for us all being laid off winter-long and forced on to parish. I, too, have been on the parish and I, too, like many of you, am expected to be grateful for the fact that I and my children are allowed to starve slowly while the rich landlords and all the clergymen and the fat magistrates feast on the fruits of the land!'

A great roar of approval greeted this: people laughed and slapped each other on the back to hear it and fists punched the air. Here was a speaker! Here was a speaker indeed! They had never heard anything so audacious: this man was truly a 'Captain' and Dick Dollery, Enos Diddams, John Romble, William Stubbs and Thomas Judd were the loudest amongst those cheering: even they were mildly surprised by the unexpected eloquence of their friend: he was a deeper man in heart and mind than even they had suspected. Dick Dollery, in fact, was almost chortling with glee: in his friend, Jem, he had picked a winner, an orator. Even Joly Cobbold was murmuring his surprise and smiling: he did not mind being a lieutenant to this man since he would draw all the attention if he acted as he spoke.

Jem now changed tack with a warning. 'When we march out of here – all you who are going to follow – they will call this a riot and I have heard that the Act has been read in some places by the Justices – I hear, too, that they have got the militia out and have sworn in scores of farmers and their sons and townies as special constables to come and stop us. Well, do not let that scare you, brothers and sisters – riot and machine-breaking is all we have left before we all starve to death. I tell you, I, for one, would rather have work and not be here, but I am here and it is the use of the new machinery as does the work I used to do which has brought me here. I tell you, too, that there is only one road we can take – and that is to destroy all threshing machines. Do it for yourselves and for your wives and your starving children, but do it and do it this day and tomorrow and the day after tomorrow till every damned threshing machine in this Hundred – nay in this county – in this country – is in pieces. Then and only then will the powers-that-be take us seriously. We have done it in our village, which is a little enough place, and we can do the same elsewhere by acting together. Strength in numbers, brothers and sisters, strength in numbers!'

There was an immediate second swelling roar of approval: most of those there had set out that morning had done so expecting simply to listen and to do little else: to them, it was a day out, a gathering to air their grievances alongside others who were in the same fix as themselves, as if by being there with others some kind of reassurance might be obtained. Certainly, it was not generally the stoical countryman's way to show the excitement for which the rubicund man and others had called: that is, till Jem Stebbings spoke. Till then, save for a few braver souls, mostly the youths and girls, those amongst the older men and women who had given any sign of agreement with the speakers had mostly done so amid the security of the crowd and the hoped-for anonymity of it, knowing, indeed expecting, that there might well be spies and tell-tales amongst them. So they were forever turning their heads to look with suspicious, darting eyes at those alongside and behind, smiling embarrassedly should they be seen to shout or acclaim too loudly: that caution stemmed from the memory thirteen years before of seeing five of their kind hanged a mere two miles from where they stood and a not unnatural fear that the same furious retribution might well be exacted again if the authorities believed themselves provoked into action a second time: but Jem's words had roused even the cautious countrymen.

As he came down off the mound, Jem was cheered and greeted everywhere by smiling faces: some men had tears in their eyes: everywhere men and youths shouted and called out to each other: a great spirit of exuberance had overtaken them: a forest of arms rose up and clenched in their fists were hammers, scythes, iron bars, wooden staves, machetes and axes which previously had been hidden. 'Bread or blood!' they shouted again. 'Bread or blood!'

Jem himself felt a little giddy at the reception he had received: he had not expected the words to come so easily, but the memories of the past year, most particularly Mary-Ann's death and the reason for it, as well as his incarceration in Melchborough Gaol and the cause of that, had all come flooding back to him: it was the hate in his heart which had spurred him on: hate for Titus Broake, hate for the system which ground him and his kind down and, most of all, hate for the threshing machine which had killed his Mary-Ann.

'Well spoken, friend,' said Joly Cobbold, taking Jem's hand and shaking it vigorously. 'Well spoken indeed.'

'I do not know your name, friend – ' Jem began, but Joly Cobbold put a finger to his lips. 'No names, friend,' he said, 'no names. It is better for the both of us if we do not know each other's names. I do not know yours and I shall never ask and you do not know mine. It is better that way. Safer. There are always spies about, especially now. You shall be referred to solely as "the Captain" and we shall address you as such and, likewise, I shall be "the Lieutenant".'

Since Jem himself was known to all of the Hamwick Dean contingent amongst the crowd, he felt it was a peculiar decision for the stranger to make.

'It is better for a local man like you to lead them,' Joly Cobbold whispered in an aside as they walked through the crowd, acknowledging the smiles and back-slapping yet again. 'They will follow a local man, while they might not follow a stranger like me. Your cause is still my cause, friend, I assure you of that. My cause is for the working man whatever his labour.'

Supposing his companion had a reason for it, Jem did not dwell upon the matter of not exchanging names: he was more concerned with catching up with the head of the column: for so eager were some to be off that a mob more than six-hundred strong, comprising mainly the youths and younger men of the crowd, was already streaming away from the fort into open country, not even bothering to wait for their newly appointed 'Captain.' They were led by the thin-faced, red-haired youth, who had again raised the black flag and now waved it menacingly as if to display to everyone that he and his cohorts were the mob's honour guard.

As Jem, Joly Cobbold, Dick Dollery and the others of the Hamwick Dean 'People's Committee' hurried forward, the crowd opened a path for them, while those lining the roadside applauded and shouted encouragment, as if they were sending soldiers off to war.

FORTY-TWO

'WHERE do we go first, Captain?' the black-flag-carrier called out as Jem and the others reached the head of the straggling column: being unfamiliar with the country north of the town, Jem was at a loss to answer.

'I know where we can got,' declared one of the flag-carrier's companions. 'To Nester's farm, he has a thrashing machine. I have worked there. T'is only two miles from here – and from there we can go on to Cantrell's. He has a thrashing machine, too.'

'Lead the way then,' said Dick Dollery, with a laugh, 'We'll have thy Mr. Nester first and then the other one. We'll destroy their threshing machines and think it a good day's work. What we do today will serve as a warning to all others. They'll not hold us in contempt after this.'

'Aye, lead the way, Captain, and we will follow,' said Joly Cobbold and, at that, he ran forward a few paces and, turning to the column and walking backwards with one fist raised, shouted loudly through the speaking trumpet: 'Comrades, today it may be just the farmers whose cornstacks and threshing machines we destroy – but the time is coming when we will destroy their high and mighty lordships as well and every foul thing that makes them so grand and so lordly. Then the land will be returned to the people, as it was when the Bible was written, before it was taken from us. It shall be ours again. Yours and mine. And all the rivers will be for us to fish in, and all the woods will be ours to cut for fuel for our own hearths and, yes, even the cottages we live in will be ours, too, owned by us. Everything shall be returned to the people!'

Such was the passion with which he spoke, the almost manic look in his eyes, that it chilled Jem to see it: for he sensed that his new friend meant every word of it.

The black-flag-carrier, a ploughboy and shepherd by the name of Thomas Stuck, from a village north of the town, led them on to the Shallford road, heading northeastwards through a desolate countryside of skeletal trees and leafless, spikey hedgerows. All during the march,

Joly Cobbold repeatedly strode ahead of Jem and the others, as if he himself were their 'Captain' as he had originally intended rather than just a second-in-command lieutenant as he was: and every now and again, he would turn and wave his arms in the air, beckoning the throng to follow him, looking for all the world in his tall hat, with the red, white and blue ribbons tied around it and the brass trumpet in his hand, like some pied piper.

Not that Jem minded: for his part, he was content to leave the antics at the front to the others: his experience as a soldier told him it was better to march in the second or third rank and thus be sheltered from any winds that might blow or from sudden squalls of rain: it was also a precaution against anyone opening fire unexpectedly from an ambush such as might be laid by an ill-disciplined yeomanry. However, being in the third rank meant he did have to march alongside his friends and suffer Dick Dollery's continual trumpet-blowing and John Romble's senses-numbing drumming: only the more tuneful fluting of Enos Diddams on his pipes could truly have been called a pleasure.

Once they had turned into the high-hedged lane, at the end of which lay the first of the farms, the cohorts of the black-flag-carrier began their blood-chilling 'Bread or blood! Bread or blood!' chant yet again, while their prancing companion began to wave his flag all the more vigorously, encouraging them to shout even louder till the cry was taken up by the whole procession.

Six hundred voices of an approaching mob armed with iron bars, hammers, axes, even hedging adzes and cleavers and all chanting in unison was enough to put fear into any man: so it was a surprise when they arrived at the farm itself to find Farmer Nester, a portly fifty-year-old, with a rubicund face, had come out to meet them and was standing patiently at the gate, sucking at an empty churchwarden's pipe: since he had a threshing machine and knew the meeting was being held that day and he was one of the nearest to the town, he had anticipated that he would likely be a target.

As they drew nearer, the black-flag-carrier and his cohorts increased their display of menace: the farmer, however, remained composed and stared calmly back at the approaching multitude even as they surged up to him: so great was the number before the gate that it was only with difficulty that Jem and Joly Cobbold, as well as Dick Dollery and Enos Diddams, were able to push their way to the front again.

'I am the elected leader, their Captain,' Jem told him. 'We are told you have a threshing machine here.'

'And what concern is it o' yourn if I have?' demanded Farmer Nester, relaxing a little on seeing an older, more sensible man was actually the one at their head rather than the excitable companions of the flag-carrier. 'I don't know ye and I en't never seen'ee before. You're a stranger to me and I to thee. So why should I tell'ee what I have?'

'We are here to ask you to remove it or dismantle it or we will do it for you. That is how it concerns us,' Jem informed him, tersely, unfazed by the other's stubbornness. 'We are also here to get a promise from you to raise your wages back up to two-shillings and threepence a day for winter work, for a start, because no man can live on the shilling and threepence a day I am told you pay.'

'Aye, I know that,' answered the farmer, rather surprisingly, with a sniff, 'but two-shillings and threepence is too much for me. When I can, I employs eight men and two boys here for most of the year. T'would be too much for me to pay them that much money all year round. I pays'em what I can afford and tries to keep'em on as best I can, though I have had to lay some on'em off, I do admit that.'

It was certainly a different argument to the one Jem had heard at the start of the march from one of the cohorts of the black-flag-carrier. 'The farmer is an old skinflint, who pays his men worse wages than anyone,' the youth had said, '– a shilling and sixpence a day if he can get away with it. Farmers are a grasping, greedy bunch, who care nothing for their men, but lay us off every winter and tell us to go on the parish.' He omitted to state that he had been sacked by this particular farmer for stealing a half-sack of potatoes from the barn, not to feed his family of five brothers and sisters, but to sell to an aged widow for beer money.

'You laid off the young-uns a fortnight agoo, just like the rest, and you've only kept on the three married men, but you have cut their wages,' came an anonymous shout from a youthful voice somewhere amongst the throng behind, which Jem thought sounded like that of the same speaker who had informed him of the farmer earlier.

The farmer, however, was not fooled. 'If that be you, Daniel Barker,' he said with an angry sniff, glaring in the direction of the speaker, 'you knows full well why I laid 'em off, like I told'ee at the time, just as ye know what happened to thee.'

There was no response from the youth who had shouted, though somewhere amongst them a head was lowered and feet were shuffled.

'I can barely pay my own rent and my own tithes the way things are,' protested the farmer. 'There are people amongst you, I dare say, who know me. They know I am a fair man generally – ' To his credit, there were several murmurs of assent amongst the mob. ' – They know I am willing enough to raise my men's wages to two shillings a day, even two shillings and threepence, if I can manage it, but for me to do that the landowner will have to reduce the rent I pay him, which is too high by far, and the Church will have to reduce the tithes I give in money to the rector and I can't see either of they doing that. T'is the Church and the bigger landowners that ye ought to be having your argument with, not the likes of me. I am a tenant farmer with a hundred and fifty acres. My rents are pegged. It don't matter whether my harvest is good or bad – and I have had two poor ones in the last years – I still has to pay the same sum each year, if they don't they raise it, for I have never known them to lower it – ' He paused to allow the words to sink in. ' – I, too, has to make ends meet and laying off men when there en't so much work to be done is one way o' reducing my costs. I has to decide, either I have to cut my rates of pay or bring in machines to save on labour such as my thrasher and my chaff-cutter. And if I has to cut even more, then I has to lay men off. There en't no other anwer to it. Times is lean for me as well as thee.'

The labourers, being the ultimate losers in the hierarchy of which he spoke, paid him the courtesy of listening to his plea in silence: and when the same foolish youth at the back cried out, 'Bread or blood!' hoping to start a chant that would drown him out and halt him, others turned on hum and hissed for him to keep quiet.

'We used to have winter work around here, doing the winnowing,' another voice accused, again from the back of the gathering, 'but you and your kind have taken even that from us with your damned threshing machines.'

'Threshing machines is progress, I suppose,' said the farmer with a shrug, realising he could not deny it. 'You can't stand in the way of it. T'is inevitable.'

'We aim to,' Joly Cobbold declared, a fierce look in his eye. 'Are you with us or against us?'

'I'm neither with thee nor agin thee,' Farmer Nester declared calmly: and seeing he could not dissuade them, he stepped back. 'If thee is minded to smash up my thrashing machine, then thee had best get on and do it so's I can get back to my wife and children. They are in the house a-shivering with fright at the sight of so many of ye. Scared half out of their wits, they are – ' He nodded towards a low outbuilding which stood at the far end of the yard. ' –Thee'll find the thrashing machine in the wagon shed over yonder. Break it if ye must. I don't care what ye do. T'is leased from a contractor, anyway, so I 'on't stand in thy way, though why it do take all ye to come and smash it, I don't know. All I ask is that my buildings be left as they be and my ricks. If you destroy them, I can't rebuild them because they en't insured. I can't afford to pay the insurance on 'em.'

'There is a payment to be made,' Dick Dollery, who was carrying his heavy metal-ended cudgel, blandly informed him.

'Aye, we want five shillings off ye for doing the wrecking,' the black-flag-carrier, Thomas Stuck, declared, thrusting his face close up to that of the farmer, 'and you had better pay fast or else we will make use of our tinder box and matches despite what you ask.'

'I don't see why I should pay you to break my machinery,' protested the farmer with a sniff. 'Seems queer to me.' But he made no other protest than that and, fumbling in his pocket, took out the two guinea coins which he had brought for just such a charge.

'For the beer,' Jem informed him, taking the money and pocketing it: then he shouted loudly: 'No torches! Just the threshing machine!'

'Thank you for that,' said the farmer: and he swung the gate open for the mob to enter.

There was no doubt that many of those trudging past sympathised with his predicament: he had bravely faced a mob of six hundred-plus, armed with all manner of weapons: but by his calmness, his reasonableness and earnestness, he had quieted them and drawn a grudging admiration from them. Giving in to the inevitable, he had let them through without protest: and such was the shame of some that they turned their heads away as they passed, in acknowledgment of their shame.

FORTY-THREE

A HALF-HOUR after they had completed their business and were marching along another high-hedged lane, some of the more nervous amongst them sent word from the back of the column that they had 'definitely' heard the sound of horses' hooves on the road behind them. Jem, who was used to the sound of massed horses trotting or cantering across ground, went back and, calling for quiet, listened hard with his ear to the ground, but heard nothing out of the ordinary. As a precaution, however, he left Enos Diddams and John Romble and a dozen of the younger and bolder youths to trail the column as a rearguard, for he knew he could trust them, and similarly, he sent William Stubbs and Thomas Judd ahead with the same number to scout the way and guard against a surprise approach from that quarter: Dick Dollery he kept alongside, though, mercifully, he did not have to suffer his trumpet-blowing: that, like Enos Diddams's piping and John Romble's drumming, was stilled for the moment lest it give away their presence.

No horsemen appeared, however, though, it was known that the holding of the great meeting had been opposed by the town's gentry and magistrates, its two parish constables and the dean of the parish church, so it was not unreasonable to expect that the landowners and their sons and the yeomen farmers and their sons, perhaps all sworn in as special constables, might be roaming those self-same lanes at that very moment in the hope of coming across just such a column as theirs.

A mile farther on, almost as if someone had anticipated their route, they came upon a riot notice, issued by the County Sheriff, and nailed to the trunk of a large oak tree by the side of the lane.

'*Whereas,*' it read, '*notice has been given to me by ten of His Majesty's Justices of the Peace, acting in and for the said county, that information upon oath has been laid before them that divers serious riots and disturbances have lately taken place within this county and that there is just cause to believe that further riots are intended: and the said Justices having called upon me to take such measures as the law requires for the preservation of the peace of the said county, now I do hereby, by virtue of my office, call upon all knights, gentlemen, yeomen, husbandmen, labourers, tradesmen, servants and apprentices, and all other male persons above the age of fifteen years and able to travel, to be in readiness to aid and assist me in the preservation of the King's Peace within the said county upon pain of punishment. Hereof fail not at your peril.'*

It was torn down in anger by Joly Cobbold, but as word of what it said spread back down the column, some of the others, bizarrely, even let out a muted cheer, as if the posting of the notice were a recognition of their mission when it was obvious to Jem and others that it must have been put up several days beforehand. Rather than a reaction to the events at Hamwick Dean and Inworth, it was, in fact, a reaction to what had happened two weeks before in the distant west of the county where a barn had been burned down and ricks set ablaze as events had first spilled across the boundary from the neighbouring county.

However, there were one or two faint hearts, who, on seeing the torn pieces in the road and knowing its import, quietly detached themselves from the trudging company, feigning tiredness: and, halting by the laneside till the main body and the rearguard were out of sight, they then slipped away through a hedgerow or down a side lane to return to their home villages and, in time to come, would boast of how they were once 'part of the great march.'

The rest, however, trudged on, eager to strike a blow for all the impoverished and the downtrodden: though, to avert any confrontation with just such a body of horsemen as the notice warned, the black-flag-carrier, Thomas Stuck, who knew the country well, led them across a series of fields, some still-unploughed, with sheep grazing on the corn stubble, others meadows of clover and grass shrivelled by the overnight frost where silent cows watched them pass with baleful, suspicious eyes. In one field, a solitary plough stood forlornly on the headland like some curious medieval weapon of war abandoned on after some long-forgotten battle: in another, a long heap of turnips in the middle of a field looked for all the world in the enshrouding gloom like the ancient barrow of a long-dead Saxon nobleman.

Finally, they came out on to another lane, leading to the next farm, Cantrell's, which was reason enough for Dick Dollery to begin tootling on his trumpet again and for Enos Diddams and John Romble to join him on pipes and drum, while the younger, more boisterous element broke again into their cries of 'Captain Swing! Captain

Swing!' and 'Bread or blood! Bread or blood!' to add to the cacophony.

This time, however, their chanting brought no one to the gate to parley with them and Jem was able to lead them through straight to the barn, where the local men knew a threshing machine was housed. However, so keen that first day were so many to join in the breaking of a machine that those who had been denied their chance at the first farm by the small confines of Farmer Nester's wagon shed now rushed forward to get into the barn ahead of others, some two-hundred in all: but even in the more spacious barn, there were still too many wanting to swing their hammers, iron bars and axes and Jem, Joly Cobbold and Dick Dollery and the others had to step in to stop some of the men from fighting each other when one wanting to strike got in the way of another also wanting to strike. The destruction of the threshing machine was but a few minutes of vigorous work and those who were unable to get into the barn had to content themselves with setting about the already-broken pieces as they were heaved out into the yard, smashing them into even smaller pieces with as much venom as they could muster.

It was no surprise to Jem that, when the shout of 'Fire! Fire!' went up, Thomas Stuck and his cohorts should be nearest to the two blazing ricks: they had found some tar used for weathering the boards of the barn and it was a simple task to wrap rags around a stick, dip it into the tar, set it alight and toss it on to the thatch of the rick-tops. However, not content with firing two of the farmer's ricks, the black-flag-carrier now shouted to his comrades: 'Come on, boys, we'll get some beer or beer money out of the farmer here or we'll burn his house down as well and him in it!'

At the time, Jem was standing with Dick Dollery and Enos Diddams by the barn door, all three recovering their breath, having themselves wielded a hammer, an iron bar and Dick Dollery his special cudgel in smashing a chaff-cutter. There was little he could do to prevent the ricks from going up: the men and the youths were determined to wreak revenge on any machine, rick, barn or outbuilding or other asset of a farm which they came across. To them, each was a legitimate target for the years of misery and degradation they had suffered: just as breaking every threshing machine he came across was vengeance for Jem for the death of his beloved Mary-Ann.

In response to Thomas Stuck's shout, fifty or more of the men and youths broke away from the main assembly by the barn and began running towards the farmhouse, all whooping and calling out as they went: and running with them, to Jem's astonishment, was his secretive lieutenant, Joly Cobbold. The first two youths who reached the house began to bang loudly on the door, one on the knocker, the other on the panelling with his fist, all the time demanding Farmer Cantrell show himself, while others peered in at the windows and yet more began to hurl stones at one of the bedroom windows, shouting out gleefully that they had seen faces peeping out.

'Jem, we needs to stop them before they sets the house afire,' declared an alarmed Enos Diddams. 'I don't want the death of no farmer and his family on my conscience and nor do thee. Arson's a hanging offence and I have no wish to have my neck broke at the end of a rope.'

Jem was well aware of that fact and immediately set off after them: but so great was the number crowding around the door, eager to see the fun again, that he, Dick Dollery and Enos Diddams had difficulty in forcing their way through yet again: fortunately, they managed to reach the porch in time to push Stuck and several of his cohorts aside just as the farmer's wife bravely opened the door.

'Have no worries, mistress,' said the heavily-breathing Jem, as politely as he could above the noise of shouting behind him, touching his hat as a show of good manners which he hoped would put her at her ease. 'T'is your husband we wish to speak to since he has not put in an appearance, to tell him why we have done what we have done.' He indicated the burning ricks behind him as the reason he would have expected the farmer to show his face, if only to observe without protest from a distance.

'He is not here. There is only myself and the children,' the farmer's wife said firmly, with a slight movement of her head to indicate the three small faces staring down at them from the bedroom windows above. Her eyes betrayed her, however, for as she spoke she glanced towards the open countryside behind the mob as if looking for someone: and Jem, standing on the step, was just able to see over the heads of the men in the yard and gardens the figure of the farmer, astride his mount, disappearing through a far off gateway, gone no doubt in the hope of summoning the yeomanry or the special constables or most likely both.

'If you please, mistress,' Jem said, maintaining his politeness, 'the men would like some of your homemade beer, for it is thirsty work doing what we have done and we have all walked a long way today.' He realised himself that he had not had a drink since that morning and his run to the house, coupled with his effort in breaking the chaff-cutter, had induced a strong thirst in him as well.

'You'll not get one drop from me, not one of you,' snorted the farmer's wife, bristling up at the mere suggestion of it. 'I have not enough to give to you all and I would not give you beer if I had enough of it. That would be to encourage you to riot.'

'You don't call this rioting do you, mistress?' interrupted Enos Diddams sharply, irritated by her defiance, and as much in need of a drink as everyone else.

'I call it a riot when a number of men assemble together in so large a band to smash machinery, set fire to ricks and alarm others, whatever other name you might give to it,' declared the farmer's wife, contemptuously. 'And don't think I'm afraid or daunted by it because I am not. You are all silly men and no good will come of any of what you do.'

Till that time Dick Dollery had remained reasonably quiet, content to blow his trumpet and to vent his anger on the threshing machines rather than upon their owners: however, her remarks, as well as her refusal to give them beer, roused his ire. 'Riot and machine-breaking are all we have left before we all starve to death!' he interjected, angrily. 'I, for one, would rather not be here, mistress. I would rather have work, but I am here and t'is the use of the new machinery as does the work I used to do which has brought me here. There is only one road for us to take and that is to destroy the threshing machines the farmers use to take away our work and our bread. Then and only then will the farmers take us seriously. Would you take us more seriously, mistress, if we set fire to your house?'

'I certainly should be alarmed, but I don't suppose you intend doing that,' the farmer's wife answered, staring defiantly back at him.

'No, mistress, we do not intend any such thing,' Jem assured her, feeling Dick Dollery's harsh interruption unnecessary. 'Do not be alarmed, we have done all that we wanted to do and now will take our leave. Good day, mistress.'

With that, he tipped his finger to his temple and turned away: he could not help but admire the woman's courage: like the previous farmer, she had calmly stood her ground, refusing them what they had asked, alone in the house with just her children, while her husband galloped away on his hunter, trusting that no harm would come to her, though what they might do to him was a different matter and he did not fancy being tossed into his own yard pond.

'Are you not asking for a price?' Dick Dollery wanted to know as they turned away, somewhat upset that, having received no beer, Jem had not asked for any money either.

'Not here,' Jem told him and offered no further explanation, but simply signalled for the men to exit the garden in front of the house, which they did, even closing the gate behind them, and then retraced their steps down the farm track without even looking back and without their beer or any money to buy any. In a final act of defiance, the farmer's wife, standing atop the steps with her arms folded, watched them off her property and, the second the last of them reached the lane, slammed the door shut.

FORTY-FOUR

THEY SLEPT that night in two huge timber-framed barns, so ancient they were said to have been built by an order of soldier monks returned from the First Crusade six-hundred years before and so vast there was room for more than three-hundred men to lie comfortably in each without touching, with great beams to hold up their high, vaulted roofs and each with a double doorway high enough to take a full wagonload of sheaves from a cornfield with a man standing upright atop.

They also found themselves the recipients of all kinds of food, bread and butter and a barley broth, brought by the women of a nearby village, as they might have done for liberators who had chased off a foreign enemy: also, the three publicans of the local hostelries, as if wishing the marchers to know they were in sympathy with them, sent word that they would stand the cost a barrel of ale apiece if the marchers would leave them unmolested, which was as good an invitation for a night of carousing as any.

In consequence, the village's three taverns were immediately besieged by several hundred thirsty men and their oil lamps burned long into the night before the last of them returned to the barns and slumped down to sleep. Not that all the men got drunk, just the younger ones mostly, who, thinking what they did was the start of a new order and they were its champions, drank too much of the free ale and reeled about the place well into the small hours breaking the Sunday quiet with a false bravado of shouts and challenges. Consequently, they all arose late and the church bells were ringing, calling the faithful to prayer, when they formed up and set off again in the face of a chill north wind blowing across the open fields and along the muddy lanes. There had been some desertions in the night, but not over many, and there were still well above five hundred strung out on the road as they marched, led inevitably by the black-flag-carrier, Thomas Stuck, and Joly Cobbold, who, to Jem's thinking, seemed to be forming a mutual association.

It was mid-afternoon when they were met by a small group of men, who had come out to meet them from the next village to ask for their help in settling matters with a particular farmer, who had a threshing machine. They had parlayed satisfactiorily with the other farmers in the village, who had agreed to set their machines aside, but there was still one who stubbornly refused: the labourers had already sent him a letter and had held a meeting several days previously to demand he also pay the better wages which the others had agreed to do, though even at their highest they stood at only nine shillings and threepence a week: the same farmer, however, had refused to raise them.

'He is not a bad farmer,' said the village men's leader, a sturdy young fellow in his mid-twenties by the name of Jarrold. 'His wife, I know, is in sympathy with our cause and has spoken to him, but he has a family of five young children of his own and he says he pays too much in rents and tithes to be able to help us out as he would like and the threshing machine do cut his spending in half, which is why he sticks to it. I fear he'll never do anything unless we acts.'

'If he has a threshing machine in his barn, then that is good enough for us,' said Jem determindly. 'If he will not break it himself, there are plenty here willing to break it for him,' The remark was greeted with cheers and the waving of hammers and iron bars by those grouped around them.

'I'd be obliged if you and your men would wait until dark before you approach the farmhouse as there are some on us that lives here who do not want to be recognised,' the village men's leader requested.

'We have no objection to that,' Jem assured him, 'if, in the meantime, you will give us what food you can spare.'

While they waited for the dark to close in, which at that time of the year was by late afternoon, some of the marchers went off with the other village men to press other labourers of the place to join them in their cause that evening. They managed to round up fifty or more from their Sunday leisure: some came willingly, or at least smiling as if pleased to be a part of such a revolt: others, however, came unwillingly, even fearfully, worrying about the consequences to their own livelihoods if damage were done to farm property in their area by a great mass of strangers, amongst whom they were seen.

Eventually, with darkness come and the church bell tolling, calling the faithful to prayer, their number totalled well over eight hundred when Jem stood on a chair brought from one of the houses and, by the light of a lantern, held up his hand to address them. 'You all have heard that the yeomanry are about and that the magistrates are riding out and calling us all rioters and Luddites,' he shouted through Joly Cobbold's trumpet over the clanging of the bell. 'Well, we will let them see that it is not riot and disturbance that we want, it is bread that we want! Whatever you do, I ask you tonight to behave orderly as the leader of the village's men has asked us to do. If the whole hosts of Hell come against us, we will not stir an inch from that. So a warning to you all – if any one of you breaks the peace by acts of arson against a building, house or barn, tonight, we ourselves will deliver you up to the first magistrate we come to.'

The latter was meant especially for the black-flag-carrier and his cohorts, who, notwithstanding the fact that they were breaking machines, were ill disciplined: they seemed keener than most to set ricks ablaze for the mere sport of it and, if not watched, Jem feared they would likely resort to worse later.

It was pitch dark and torches had to be held aloft at the front to light their way when eventually they set off to walk the mile or more to the farm behind Thomas Stuck's black flag: in the distance, the solitary church bell was still tolling and the village men laughed on hearing it, as if to say, 'There will be no one in your congregation this night, vicar. We have more important business to tend to.'

As they neared the farmhouse, a whole sea of arms rose in the torchlight, fists were clenched in the air and pitchforks, hammers, axes, scythes and clubs all were waved, as if in defiance of anyone watching or who might think to try and deter them: so it was a noisy, shouting, trumpet-blowing, drum-banging mob which approached the farm. The instant they sighted the gates, the noise rather than the music increased in loudness: the younger men and youths ran ahead to open the gates, ready to break them if they were padlocked, but they were not and the whole column streamed through and up the track to the farmyard without hindrance.

In the house, a solitary lamp burned with a dull glow in one window, as if the occupiers had turned down the wick and did not want to reveal their presence: but the chants of 'Bread or blood! Bread or blood!' by eight-hundred men and youths standing in the yard, mixed with shouts of 'Captain Swing! Captain Swing!' could not be ignored. Eventually, the kitchen door was pulled open and the farmer and his wife came out, she dabbing nervously at her eyes with her apron, he carrying a pitchfork as a weapon for his and her defence, glaring determinedly at the crowd of men facing him, afraid not for himself but for the five children hiding under the beds upstairs.

As Jem presented the demands on behalf of the village labourers, the farmer listened quietly and then, to everyone's surprise, readily agreed to them: that is, he would raise the wages of all able-bodied men in his employ from seven shillings and sixpence to nine shillings and threepence a week, whether married or single, and, further, for all married men with more than two children, he would add the price of a gallon loaf, that is, a shilling and tuppence, for each child above that number. In the dark, none could see that the farmer's wife was weeping quietly with relief that her husband's stubbornness had given way to common sense: she knew full well the men of the village were desperate and that they feared starvation and she had been able to convince her husband to help them only after a fierce argument even as they marched up his track.

Consequently, the farmer made no protest when presented with the letter to sign by the village men's leader or when Jem, Joly Cobbold and Dick Dollery led almost the whole of the marchers off to the barn, which stood a good hundred yards from the house on the far side of a muddy field. Unfortunately, while Jem and the others were dragging the threshing machine out of the barn, as well as two cutting machines they also found there, so that others could set about them with their hammers and iron bars, Thomas Stuck and some of his companions, unseen in the darkness, had remained in the farmyard and now took the opportunity to surround the farmer and his wife, who had not had the heart to follow the men and watch their machines being smashed to smithereens before their eyes

'You have both been living on the good things of life for the past ten years while me and my kind have suffered dreadful,' snarled Thomas Stuck, thrusting his face menacingly into that of the farmer. 'Now it is our time. We will have five pounds off you or we will break your windows and your furniture.'

The cringing farmer and his weeping wife were both pushed on to their knees and the hammers of the black-flag-carrier's companions were raised ready to strike: she, poor woman, as if believing her last seconds had come, closed her eyes, put her hands together and began to mutter a prayer, the tears streaming down her face even more.

'I can only give six half-crowns to share among yourselves,' the cowering farmer pleaded. 'Take that, it is all I have.'

'You farmers keep more than that in your houses,' Thomas Stuck shouted. 'I dare say you have hidden it all somewhere. If you don't give us what we ask, we'll put a match to you house with you in it!'

'We want beer as well,' one of his companions shouted. 'They must have beer in the house.'

'We want something better than beer,' scoffed Thomas Stuck. 'We want gin!'

As it happened, Enos Diddams had noticed that there was no black flag waving amid the throng who were happily cheering every clang of iron upon iron and every sound of splintering wood by the barn and, wondering why, pushed his way back towards the farmhouse: he quickly realised what was afoot and went rushing back to warn Jem.

'Quick, Jem, Dick,' he shouted, 'those fools with the flag are about to do murder up at the house if someone does not stop them!'

Jem, Dick Dollery, Enos Diddams and the other Hamwick Dean men set off immediately for the house, barging their way through a crowd of two hundred or more who, unable to join in the demolition, were standing idly about the field: when they reached the yard, the half-dozen cohorts of the black-flag-carrier were still standing over the couple with their hammers raised.

Curiously, Joly Cobbold, who had been with them in the barn and had heard Enos Diddams's warning, did not bother to follow Jem and the others: it was as if he did not care what was done to the farmer and his wife, as if, to him, they were the same as gentry and it was no matter to him if they were abused like the aristocrats in France during the Revolution there.

'Lower your hammers,' Jem ordered, thrusting himself between the farmer and the hammer-wielding youths: at first, it seemed for a few seconds that they would not obey.

'Lower'em or I'll give thee a smack with this,' snarled Dick Dollery, lifting his cudgel with its heavy metal end to within a half-inch of the black-flag-carrier's nose: the determination in his voice and the presence behind him of Enos Diddams, John Romble, William Stubbs and Thomas Judd, all similarly armed, changed the youth's mind and that of his fellows. With an ill grace, muttering to themselves that they were only 'having a bit of fun' and they had 'a right' to demand money, since it was being done elsewhere, the youths lowered their hammers and iron bars and stepped back.

'I want no threats being made for money. It is not how I want things done,' declared Jem, sharply. 'We impose a charge for what we do and that is set at two pounds. That is beer money for our work. Nothing else. We do not do this to profit from others.'

'Two pounds is not enough to buy beer for eight-hundred of us,' protested the black-flag-carrier.

'It is what we *ask* the farmer to give,' Jem snapped back, careful to choose his words. 'I am the Captain, and what I say goes.'

The black-flag-carrier and the other youths might have protested further had not the farmer, scrambling to his feet, hoping to calm the situation and to avoid any confrontation that might lead to further damage to his property or to himself and his wife, said quickly: 'They have asked for gin. I have a flagon in my pantry. I will get it for them willingly.'

Jem was reluctant for him to do it, but did not say so: gin, he knew, if drunk too liberally, could inflame the situation all the more, but he did not want to continue with the confrontation: they had done their work, they had obtained the farmer's promise: that was enough for one night.

While the farmer went into the house to fetch some money and the flagon of gin, careful to leave the door ajar so as not to cause the youths to rush in after him, thinking he was about to barricade them out, Jem and the others returned to the barn to call away the rest of the men who were still swinging their hammers and iron bars, as if determined to reduced everything till not a piece of any machine remained that could be recognised or reused.

That, too, proved a mistake: for, when the flagon was brought, the youths began to fight each other as to who would be first to drink from it: and when that argument was settled by the tallest and burliest amongst them, they took to wrenching the flagon from each other's hands before one had even had time to take his full swallow in their suspicion that he might drink more than them. The outcome was perhaps inevitable: one youth punched another, hitting him so hard that he knocked the half-empty flagon from his hands and it shattered on the stone flags of the path, the spirit splattering everywhere. Both then began fighting, rolling over and over on the ground, punching and kicking at each other while the others stood around laughing and calling upon them to do better. Eventually, the men returning from the barn dragged the two brawlers apart, thinking they made them look an ill-disciplined bunch of vagrants.

As the men filed past the farmer back on to the lane, Jem turned to him and asked: 'You'll not know any of us after this, I hope?'

The farmer looked at Jem for a second or so and then said, with a shrug: 'T'is too dark. I can't see your faces so I doubt if I should know ye.'

Back in the village the local labourers all gave three cheers for Jem and his company: the sole public house was opened, even though the village's vicar frowned upon drinking on the Sabbath, and two large barrels of ale were rolled out into the street and, despite the cold, the whole assembly spent the rest of the evening drinking, bar a few who slunk away in the darkness, some back to their homes in the village, others to villages elsewhere, deserting, having done their part for the cause.

Again, it was early morning before the last of the local men said their goodbyes, pleased and smiling at the change in their fortunes, while the marchers slept where they could: upon the floor of the inn, in its outbuildings and also in a barn across from it.

FORTY-FIVE

THE NEXT DAY, in the early-afternoon, as Jem and the other marchers approached a village which lay in the fold of the hills where the countryside was more undulating, they came upon two small boys of no more than eight or nine years of age, dressed in ragged and patched hand-me-downs, standing by a great pile of turnips on a headland, attempting with great difficulty to turn the handle of a cutter. So small and undernourished were they that they looked for all the world like scarecrow dolls shivering and whimpering with cold in the freezing air, their cheeks white and bloodless, bare frozen toes peeping from the ends of their worn boots, each with a single knitted woollen glove on one hand which they used to work the handle, while the chilblained fingers of the other clutched at their buttonless coats in a futile attempt to retain some warmth about their bodies. On the ground alongside were two-and-half sacks of cut turnips, their sole production for the day when there should have been at least a dozen.

The mere sight of the two pathetic children alone in the vastness of the field on such a bitter, freezing day, labouring so poorly dressed for a rich farmer, was enough to stir the anger in the men who gathered around them.

'We have been trying all morning, but we can't turn the handle of the turnip-cutter properly by ourselves,' said the one who looked to be the elder. 'There is water in it and it has frozen solid. It is hard for us to turn it. If we don't do the work the guv'nor has set us, he'll say we have been idling and he 'on't pay us anything.'

Jem asked them how many days they had been doing the same work in the bitter cold: the answer was the whole of the previous week, six days for a shilling and sixpence, or threepence a day, which was enough in itself to set the greater number of the men growling for retribution. The two boys, it also transpired, had even had to work on the Sunday: on the Lord's Day, they were put to minding the same landowner's sheep so that he and his family could ride to church in their fine carriage and kneel in prayer with the rest of His more acceptable flock to thank Providence for their good life and His bountiful ways while in the chill, damp fields nearby two cold and miserable children of no consequence stood in the winds and rains to watch over a more commercial flock.

An hour's halt was called: it was a bizarre sight, two small boys surrounded by five-hundred and more sympathetic, feet-stamping, hand-rubbing, breath-blowing men and youths, amongst whom there were more than enough willing hands to help them with their task, expert hands who had done the same work scores of times themselves, though in better conditions. While some fed the machine, others worked the handle in turn, using hard, grown men's muscle to force it round against the drag of the ice inside: other willing hands, meanwhile, sacked the cut turnips and tied them and, in a little over the hour, the work of three or four days for two children was done.

Having helped the boys, the marchers continued on their way in a better mood, more cheerful at having done a good deed, but also more belligerent, more angry and more intolerant of those better off than themselves who treated their poorer fellows in such a callous way, which was to reveal itself when they finally reached the village where the despised landowner lived.

The afternoon gloom was deepening into the blue-grey dusk of early evening as they entered the main street: a party of men came forward to meet them: they had heard of the marchers' approach and had waited for them, knowing they had to come that way, though not knowing of the help they had given the boys. They wanted to tell where the church-going landowner lived and where he had hidden his threshing machine.

'He's a cuss of a man,' said a lanky, straw-haired youth, who seemed to be the villagers' leader. 'He is the biggest landowner by far round here, the holder of the great tithe, with nine hundred and more acres, a real hog-grunter, who treats his men like they are all nobodies and pays'em the same way, with bare enough to feed themselves let alone their families, yet he is always in church of a Sunday psalming and hosannahing. He is a right braggarty fellow. If ever a nasty piece of work needs taking down a peg or two, t'is he, though you'll have a real task on your hands as he 'on't take kindly to being bossed, even if there's ten hundred of ye.'

'Show us where he lives and leave the rest to us,' was Dick Dollery's growling reply.

'First we need to get out of this cold,' Jem declared. 'It's freezing too hard to stand out here.' And spying the church through the trees, he added: 'The church looks big enough to hold us all. We'll call a meeting of all the villagers and get everyone in there and the people can then have their say on wages and tithes, though somebody will have to go and get the vicar as we can't hold as meeting without him being there, can we?'

There was a cynical smile on Dick Dollery's face. 'Leave that to me, Jem, I'll find the bugger wherever he is!' he grinned, almost rubbing his hands with glee: even Jem smiled at his enthusiasm.

It took no more than a half-hour to round up the rest of the villagers, including several farmers, a surgeon and a lawyer: groups of men, each accompanied by one or two of the locals, went from house to house around the village, knocking on each door and 'inviting' the inhabitants to attend 'a parish meeting with the vicar and the farmers at the church.' Only those who were too young, too old, women who were pregant or with babies or sickly children were to be excused: most, however, went willingly, gladly, sensing that some good might come of it. Soon a steady stream of villagers numbering three hundred or more were pushing through the lychgate into the churchyard, their number swelled by the five hundred or so marchers.

The vicar, a portly, puffy-faced, effeminate, gesticulating type, did not take it kindly when a dozen strangers strode up his path, banged loudly on his door, respectfully tipped their hats when he opened it and declared, 'You are coming with us, Vicar, there's business at the church to be attended to!' And, before he could close the door, they had seized him by the arms and marched him down the path, along the street and up the church path to join the rest. When they released him in the porch, he scurried inside without more ado.

Having assembled the villagers, the farmers, the churchwardens and the vicar, it was then the turn of the despised landowner, who lived with his wife and family in an impressive grange at the farthest end of the village, circled by lawns and sheltered on its eastern side against chill winds by a line of mature horsechestnuts and other trees. However, when a group of villagers, led by the lanky, straw-haired youth, went to 'invite' him to the meeting, not unexpectedly, he refused point blank, shouting: 'Dam you all! I won't be called like this to any meeting and especially by a bunch of bumpkins to discuss what I pay my own men on my own farm. I pay them what they are worth and they are damned lucky to get that and that is an end to the matter.' With that, he slammed the door in their faces before they could seize him.

However, if any answer were guaranteed to arouse the ire of Dick Dollery and even the milder Enos Diddams, then it was that. Neither had particpated in the approach to the landowner, hoping that he would heed his own villagers rather than strangers: but, on hearing of his blunt refusal, they seized a farmcart from the front yard of the blacksmith's beside the church, planted Thomas Stuck's black flag in it and, with the help of others dragged it up the drive to the landowner's front door, intending he should be taken to the meeting in the same manner and with the same indignity which the French revolutionaries took their aristocrats to the great square and Madame La Guillotine in Paris.

However, even then the pompous landowner deceived them: as Dick Dollery and a dozen others went up the driveway with the cart, he slipped out the back door with his two sons, though, perhaps thinking better of it, he decided not to flee, but to make a stand and argue his own case and so made his way to the church by his own route, joining the other farmers and gentlemen of the village, the surgeon, the lawyer and the vicar in the chancel as if that were a place of safety from the mob of strangers and their own villagers and they would not dare to cross beyond the rood screen and enter a place so sacrosant.

Finally, when all the villagers were seated, the marchers shuffled into the nave after them, some so tired after their long day's tramp that they simply slumped down in the aisles or lounged in spare pews at the rear and, perhaps forgetting where they were, or not bothering where they were, lit their pipes, while others stretched themselves on the pews in the hope of sleep. By that time, there were upwards of eight-hundred cloistered in the church and so crowded was it, with every pew taken and every aisle blocked by seated or recumbent bodies, that, when a half-dozen of them, unable to find room elsewhere, stepped over the prone forms, intending to seek out a place on the chancel steps to sit, the vicar hurried forward to prevent them.

'It is better if your men remain in the nave and keep the rood screen between our two parties,' he said to Jem, having ascertained that he was their leader rather than Joly Cobbold, who, notwithstanding, had marched into the village ahead of Jem, still preferring to keep the company of the black-flag-carrier and his cohorts. Of course, as Jem's lieutenant, Joly Cobbold had not stinted on giving his own orders to anyone he thought was doing nothing.

'That way,' went on the vicar pompously, with a sniff, 'we shall both have our own territories. It would not be proper for your men to come any closer to the Lord's altar lest they do some damage which they may have cause to regret.'

It was almost as if he were unable to comprehend that these were men who did not care any more: they were determined to do something, anything, to draw attention to their plight. Jem, however, suspected the vicar was more interested in keeping them back from eyeing his gold candlesticks and silver plate, which mysteriously disappeared off the altar a few minutes later.

Thereafter, for a full hour, Jem and his band, including Joly Cobbold, Dick Dollery, Enos Diddams and the lanky local youth and several of his party, argued with the despised landowner, imploring him to pay his men the same two shillings and threepence for the winter and two shillings and sixpence for the summer as had been agreed elsewhere and to agree also to their other requests, as well as to have a reduction of the tithes. However, the burly landowner refused every argument.

'You can all go to Hell and damnation for all I care!' was his contemptuous reply to Jem, without a care as to the place in which he stood. 'You can talk and argue till you are blue in the face, whoever you are. My answer is, "No, no and no again." I decide what I pay, not a gang of vagrants come here to intimidate people. I hope the militia catches up with you and marches you all off to gaol. The men get what I think they deserve and, if it be a shilling and sixpence or even a shilling a day, then that is what I will pay them. I am not going to be told by a mob of vagrants what I should do and, if there are any out there who are not satisfied with the wages I pay, they can always go elsewhere to work and good luck to them. There are plenty more who will work for the money I pay and think themselves lucky to get it.'

At that, several of the village men, who could contain their tempers no longer, jumped up and cries of 'Judas!' and 'Skinflint!' and 'Devil!' and 'Miser!' as well as 'Bastard!' echoed around the vaulted darkness, for no candles or lamps had been lit and it was well after six o'clock by then.

'String the bugger up!' Joly Cobbold growled in Jem's ear:

'Give him a bloody good whipping!' Thomas Stuck suggested.

'Chuck him in the pond!' one of his cohorts added.

Frustrated by the man's intransigence, several of the village men, accompanied by several of the marchers, pushed forward towards the chancel: to Jem, their intention was quite clear. Sacrosanct or no, they would drag the stubborn man from it, bundle him outside and, once clear of holy ground and away from the sight of the others, decide what they would do with him: and, in the mood, they were in, Joly Cobbold's suggested lynching seemed a distinct possibility.

'Will you not change your mind?' Jem pleaded in desperation, for he truly feared blood might be shed if the pompous landowner persisted in his defiance.

'I will not! Damn you for your impudence!' the man shouted, contemptuously waving away the vicar, who was wringing his hands. 'Who do you think you men are? You are nothing but a bumch of hobs come to tell me how to run my own estate. I will see you all in Hell first!'

'It may well come to that,' Jem informed him with a weary sigh.

FORTY-SIX

FORTUNATELY for the landowner, it was at that moment that an idea came to Jem: if the man would not give way, then the whole 'congregation' would lay seige to those in the chancel and keep them there till he did change his mind: one way or another they would get the agreement they sought.

'Dick, Enos, John, lock the church doors and guard them!' Jem commanded and, as his friends hurried to do his bidding and banged the doors shut, he declared loudly and forcefully so all would hear: 'No one will be allowed to leave this place till the demands of these men here are granted in full and the whole thing is written down and signed. The whole damned lot of us, you included, Vicar, will stay here all night if needs be and all tomorrow, too, if we have to. We will not leave till that man signs an agreement the same as the others.'

The prospect of upwards of eight hundred and more, packed into pews, having to spend the night in the cold, dark and unheated church met with a mixed reception: some amongst the villagers, pleased that determined action was being taken, shouted their approval and even laughed to themselves. However, Jem's order was met with groans by some amongst the marchers, who had hoped to get the matter settled so that they could get some food, which the villagers had promised them, and, more to the point, get a drink of ale at one of the two hostelries in the village – free ale, they hoped, from a grateful populace.

The clear determination in Jem's decision that they would stay there till all was agreed was enough eventually to force the despised owner of the great tithes to retreat into the corner beside the altar with the other farmers, the gentlemen of the village and the vicar, where they could talk amongst themselves out of earshot of those in the nave. It soon became clear from the gesticulations and rising tempers of the others that they were actually arguing the cause of the labourers, pleading with the recalcitrant landowner to give in to the men's demands, urging him, too, to reduce his tithes for the sake of the public peace as much for their own benefit: but still he refused, waving them away, even shouting down one or two with volatile arm waving.

Meanwhile, while Dick Dollery, Enos Diddams and the other Hamwick Dean men guarded the doors, Jem and his lieutenant, Joly Cobbold, retreated to the pews to sit and await the outcome: even Thomas Stuck and his companions, it seemed, were prepared to wait, sprawling themselves in a pew of their own, where they seemed to occupy their time by spinning coins and playing penny-up.

An hour passed: by Jem's order, no lantern lights or candles were to be lit: the whole congregation would sit in darkness, all night if needs be: yet, even through the darkness, the fierceness of the debate in the chancel could be observed as well as heard.

For two further hours they sat in darkness, at times straining to hear what was being said amongst the farmers and the gentlemen: some dozed or fell to muttering amongst themselves: others lit pipes to stifle the boredom, ignoring the vicar's admonishment that they were 'in a holy place.' Children, complaining to their mothers, were allowed to scurry about the aisles, while youths slyly edged closer to girls in the darkness until a sudden squeal in the blackness sent them sliding hurriedly back along their seats.

As the calls of nature cannot be denied, a steady procession of men walked to the back of the church, where a door was opened to allow them outside one at a time, but a semi-circle guard of a half-dozen of the marchers themselves was put around the door outside so that all, particularly the village men who went out, were forced to return inside. There being two hundred or more women amongst the 'congregeation,' they, too, were allowed out into the churchyard through the porch door guarded by Dick Dollery and three other marchers to perform their relief and, as they went out, each was put on her honour to promise to return or no more would be allowed out.

Eventually, the inactivity and the dragging time was too much for three of the village youths: they leapt from their seats and, with howls of fury, rushed forward, taking Jem and the others by surprise. Before they could be stopped, they had crossed the sacred boundary into the chancel, which they had never have done before, determined the reach the stubborn landowner and ready, too, to punch the head of anyone who got in their way.

Thankfully, several of the farmers managed to hold them off and push them back, though not with any great roughness, perhaps understanding their loss of patience. 'If thee doesn't make a decision soon, we will damned well leave thee to them,' one of the farmers bluntly told the quivering great tithe owner, who had scampered into a corner.

The action of the youths and the threat from the other farmers was enough to make the rich farmer yield: a promise to reduce rents and tithes was extracted from him and, with handshakes and sighs of relief, the weary and stiff-limbed villagers filed out of the church into the cold, moonlit night, happy at last that their demands for a living wage had not only been met but promised in the House of God and in the presence of the vicar and other more receptive farmers and honourable gentlemen. Therefore, they hoped, the reluctant landowner would not be able to renege upon the agreement.

There was free food from the villagers and free ale at the village's inns that night after all as the whole population celebrated and the marchers were made welcome everywhere: indeed so welcome that at least one of the youths who had joined the march from a nearby village the previous day disappeared into a barn with one of the village's girls and the outcome of that was borne out nine months later. Others contented themselves with eating what food was brought them by the grateful populace and supping the free ale, though Jem did place some of the money he still possessed on to the counter for the innkeeper's wife to take.

Only the black-flag-carrier and his cohorts caused offence: much the worse for drink, they paraded up and down the village's main street well into the small hours, shouting and singing and waving their black flag and disturbing everyone's sleep till several villagers opened their windows and threatened to throw something over them if they did not stop their racket: and they did not mean water!

Even as they marched away from the village in the morning, the great tithe owner, still fiercely angered by his humiliation, went around the district in an attempt to swear in special constables to pursue them and, in particular, to apprehend Jem, Joly Cobbold and Dick Dollery as 'the ringleaders.' But, of the fifty or so 'respectable householders' whom he approached and from whom he hoped to elicit some sympathy, he found only four who would take the oath and abandoned his attempt. In addition, despite his promise, he demanded a special vestry meeting be called to reverse the promises he had given, though that was refused at that time by the vicar, who, having signed the promise himself, did not want the marchers returning and possibly exacting a greater retribution.

The great tithe-owner was still pursuing his vendetta when, two miles away, Dick Dollery, looking back at the line straggling behind them, suddenly shouted to Jem: 'Look! There's smoke.'

Rising from the great tithe owner's farm at one end of the village were several columns of dark smoke: unbeknown to Jem and the others, Thomas Stuck and his companions, finding all other places full, had spent the night in the great tithe-owner's barn and, on leaving, had set fire to it and three ricks in the yard. They had done so by a means tried and trusted by those who sometimes made it their business to fire hayricks and straw stacks. Pieces of smouldering material had been inserted into the hollowed ends of a several lengths of bamboo, taken from a dismantled rose trellis in the landowner's grounds, and these had then been thrust deep into the various corn stacks and roof thatch of the barn. The smouldering material had finally burst into flame after an hour or so, by which time the perpetrators were fully two miles distant along the road. That way, they hoped, no one would actually know who had done the deed and could only guess as to how since the blaze would destroy the means.

There was nothing that Jem or any of his friends could do but shrug their shoulders and continue their tramp: indeed, only Joly Cobbold rubbed his hands and chortled with glee as he looked back at the rising columns of smoke: thereafter, he skipped along in a lighter mood and even slapped the black-flag-carrier on the back as he caught up with him.

FORTY-SEVEN

THE NEXT VILLAGE to which they marched was said by some to be one where the labourers were more degraded even than the last and in greater misery than any parish in the kingdom: threequarters of them were on parish relief from the poor rates to supplement their paltry wages.

The villagers had sent word of four more threshing machines at three separate farms owned by three well-to-do landlords who were known for their oppressiveness and self-interest and the haughty manner they displayed towards their workers: but, due to their late start, the marchers did not arrive at the village till well after noon and, in order to complete their work, before the early darkness closed in, it was necessary for them to divide to get round the three large estates.

Joly Cobbold, who still would not reveal his name, and the black-flag-carrier led the first two hundred, plus seventy of the locals, to a farm to the west of the village: Dick Dollery, Enos Diddams and Thomas Judd took a second two hundred, with fifty locals, to a large, high-walled estate to the south, while Jem and John Romble went with a further hundred and fifty, plus forty of the village's men and youths, to an estate of six hundred acres to the east, all marching behind another peculiarly-coloured 'Tricolour' of blue, black and yellow borne by a simpleton ploughboy of nineteen, named Daniel Downey, who had joined their crusade the previous day.

When the two hundred and seventy led by Joly Cobbold and the black-flag-carrier reached their goal, a grand early Georgian farmhouse, set amid a ring of tall elms, the lady of the house put her head out of an upstairs window and tried to bargain with them.

'How much do I have to give you to go away and leave us in peace?' she asked in a haughty tone, as if that alone would serve to placate the armed men standing on her lawn.

'We are not here to bargain, mistress,' Joly Cobbold shouted back with a sneer. 'We are here to break any threshing machines and any other machines that you have in your barn which deprive men of their rightful work. That is what we have come for and that is what we will do.'

'I will give you five shillings if you will all go away,' the poor woman tried, more nervously now, sensing perhaps that they could not be bought off easily.

'The charge for our work is two sovereigns,' Joly Cobbold shouted back.

'That is far too much. I do not have two sovereigns in the house,' the woman protested.

Thomas Stuck, however, was in no mood for prevarication. 'Give us the money, you old hag, or else!' he shouted.

'I'll bloody persuade her!' one his cohorts declared: and, with that, he climbed agilely on to a high wall enclosing a small gravelled court, no wider than a path, which placed him at almost the same level as the white-faced householder and not six feet from her. With great ceremony and a flourish, the youth first bowed and tipped his hat to the worried woman and then, to the loud cheers of his fellows, slowly and deliberately pushed off the wall with his boot one of six Grecian urns ranged along the top to hold draping flowers and hanging ivy.

The poor woman at the window let out a shriek of alarm and was almost beside herself as she surveyed the shattered remains of the precious urn and its contents splattered all over the courtyard.

'Cough up the money or I'll knock the bloody lot off!' shouted the youth: and, standing on one leg, he began swinging his boot idly backwards and forwards as if preparing to take aim at the next urn: for he was ready to kick off each in turn if necessary.

'I have no money in the house,' the woman at the window wailed again.

At that, a second youth climbed up beside the first, this one carrying a sledgehammer. 'We don't want any shilly-shallying, lady,' he shouted, brandishing the sledgehammer in the poor woman's face. 'Rich people always have money in the house. T'is us poor who have no money for ourselves. If you don't give us what we ask, I'll climb up on your roof and knock your bloody chimney down! And when I have done that, I'll smash every damned window in the house with this hammer of mine.'

'Please! Please! Wait!' the woman cried and, realising that the youths meant what they said, added hastily: 'I have some money, a little. I will get it for you.'

Her head disappeared inside the window and, when she reappeared, some twenty seconds or so later, she was holding a small muslin bag which jingled faintly. 'Here are four sovereigns,' she cried, passing the money across the gap to the first youth. 'Now you have your money, please go.'

'Thank you, lady,' the first youth cried and jumped down: the second, perhaps disgruntled because he had been deprived of his chance to cause any damage, swung his hammer at the nearest of the urns, shattered it and then, because of the weight and momentum of the hammer's head, lost his balance and pitched forward after it, almost braining one of his companions below and falling to ground with a thud, which provoked roars of laughter from the men and youths streaming away towards the outbuildings in search of the threshing machine and whatever else they could smash and what ricks they could burn.

At the second mansion, some two miles away, to which Dick Dollery and Enos Diddams had led their band, the door was opened by a red-and-gold liveried servant, who held himself stiffly upright, looking down his nose at the mob of raggedly-dressed agricultural labourers gathered before him on the shingled driveway.

'Is thy master in?' Dick Dollery asked.

'No, he is out. He has business elsewhere today,' replied the servant, haughtily.

'Where does he house his damned threshing machine?' demanded Dick Dollery, irritated, by what he perceived as the man's feigned indifference to the fact that an armed mob ringed the door at which he stood.

'I should think such a thing is kept in the barn, wouldn't you?' the servant replied, with the same superciliousness. 'One would hardly expect to find it here in the house, would one? But it is no use you going there, it is already in pieces. The master has already had it dismantled so there is no point in you doing anything further to it. You are too late. Your journey here has been a waste of time so you may as well leave.'

'We'll be the judge of whether it has been a waste of our time or not,' Dick Dollery growled and, reaching out, he grabbed the servant by his veleveted arm and hauled him outside.

'We'll not be leaving till we have seen for ourselves,' the lanky labourer told him. 'Show us where the damned machine is or we'll toss thee in yonder pond.'

The bewildered servant was quickly hustled across the yard to the barn, followed by fifty of the men and youths with hammers, axes, cudgels and iron bars, while the remainder waited by the house, some sitting on the fence around the yard, others perched on a pigsty wall and yet more seated on the lowered shafts of a wagon, for the yard was too mired to stand for too long on one spot or to sit anywhere.

In the barn, just as the man had said, they found the threshing machine had already been smashed, for its wooden parts were much splintered and pieces of its metal parts were laid out on the ground along one wall.

'Who smashed it?' an exasperated Dick Dollery wanted to know.

'I do not know,' replied the servant, much put out at the indignity of being force-marched across a muddy yard. 'It is only rented by my master. I do not know who broke it. I do not work in the yard or the barn. I am not a farm worker. I remain in the house. I am a house servant.' Again the condescending tone of his voice angered Dick Dollery.

'The farmer must have done it himself,' Thomas Judd suggested. 'The crafty beggar has done it too avoid paying rental on it. Either that or he is aiming to claim insurance for it, if it is insured.'

'Smash the pieces anyway!' Dick Dollery ordered. He felt cheated: they had walked so far and he was determined that they would not leave without some reward: so the fifty who had followed him across the yard dragged the pieces outside and set about reducing them even further till the threshing machine lay fragmented in a hundred pieces in the mud.

'I hope you are satisfied with your day's work,' the servant sniffed, before asking in an arrogant tone: 'If you are done, may I go now?'

'No you cannot!' cried Dick Dollery and, taking the man roughly by the arm again, he propelled him back to the house. 'We are not yet satisfied. There is the matter of a fee to be paid – two sovereigns – then we might be satisfied. We have had it elsewhere and we will have it here.'

'I have no money to pay you,' protested the servant. 'I do not know where the money is kept.'

'Yes, you do,' Dick Dollery told him, 'I have never known a servant yet who did not know where his master hides his cash box. You had better find it quick or we'll put you in the pond like I said and mess up your fine livery for you.'

Foolishly, when they reached the back door of the farmhouse, the manservant, feeling that he had done all he should to accommodate them, tried to dash inside and would have bolted the door on them had he been able.

'Oh, no you don't,' cried Dick Dollery, seizing his arm. 'We will have that money we ask and then we shall think what to do with you.'

With that, he and three others marched the protesting manservant into the house and were taken to the drawing room where the cash box was produced from a compartment of a portmanteau. 'There's plenty here,' said Dick Dollery, running his fingers over a cache of dulled silver sovereigns, 'we'll help ourselves to five. I should think that would be enough.'

The poor servant's face went white. 'But this is robbery! You said two – ' he began.

'Aye, but it has been a long walk here and it is a long walk back,' said Dick Dollery, pocketing the coins, 'and the men will be thirsty. This'll do for their ale money. There is, though, one other thing we has to do afore we leave – like I promised'ee.'

The poor man must have seen the look in Dick Dollery's eyes, for he immediately let out a howl of fear, but three still had hold of him and, despite his struggles and protestations, he was hauled outside again and frog-marched across the yard. On the bank of the farm pond, four lifted him up by his arms and legs, swung him to and fro and, on the count of three, launched him well out into the muddy water amid loud cheers and laughter. Several times the poor servant attempted to crawl out, but so angry was Dick Dollery at his attitude, and at being called a 'robber' when it was only a fee he was 'charging,' that he pushed him back in again: it was several minutes before the poor man was at last allowed to stagger out, spluttering with rage at the final indignity and brushing the weed from his sodden uniform.

'He and his kind will not be so keen to laugh at us again,' growled Dick Dollery as they walked away.

FORTY-EIGHT

THE ESTATE to which Jem and John Romble and their hundred and ninety went contained a large, three-storey Georgian mansion of some twenty or so rooms, with extensive lawns at the front, side and back: a wide paved veranda, with steps leading up to it and an ornamental balustrade, ran along its length at the rear, the whole overlooking a half-acre of scythed grass patrolled by stately peacocks. The estate, as it turned out, was the seat of the Member of Parliament for the nearby small town of Levendon, Sir Dinkley De'Ath, who happened also to be the chief landowner of the parish and was hated for his pomposity and his meanness and his vindictiveness towards the men whom he employed.

A measure of his sympathy for the poor labourers who lived in his tied cottages could be gauged from the fact that, after he had taken part in enclosing the common land some fifteen years before, saying that it was a waste of agricultural land to give small parcels to the poor, he had, during the debate in Parliament on an amendment to the Settlement Act, risen to declare coldly that he would pull down all the labourers' cottages on his land if Parliament voted to make length of residence a legal method of gaining settlement in a village. When it was quietly pointed out to him that, if there were no cottages on his land, there would be no labourers to work his farm, he had declared it no matter: the labourers he employed at that time already walked three miles to his farm every morning as it was, setting off from their homes before five o'clock in the morning and not returning till after seven o'clock in the evening, for they worked from six to six, and he expected them to be punctual and waiting at the gate when the farm bailiff arrived to allot them their tasks and not to leave even so much as a minute before their time.

The Member also sat on the magistrates' bench at Levendon and there were some amongst the forty villagers who stood before his house that day who had appeared before him and who had been sentenced by him and had spent two or three months picking oakum or working the tread-wheel in the Steadleigh House of Correction for such 'felonies' as being drunk and disorderly and causing an affray on market days. Third, and worse in their eyes, however, was that, as an influential member of the select vestry, in league with the parson of that parish, he was responsible for administering the parish rate and there were those amongst those same villagers who not only had appeared before him but had also suffered from his parsimony when handing out relief. Several had been forced to take up stone-breaking on the roads all during the cold and wet and snow of the previous winter just to earn their family's bread and now they wanted their revenge for that and other slights: they had a special reckoning.

Though the peacocks set up a din at the sight of so many men spilling across the lawns, they were quickly chased away by three dogs which had accompanied the throng: it was at the barking of the dogs rather than the general murmur of those assembled on the lawns which induced her ladyship to come sweeping out of the main doorway, where she stood regarding the throng over the veranda's balustrade.

'Why are you here?' she demanded in the imperious tone of her kind. 'Do you not know you are trespassing?'

Her question was immediately met with scorn from John Romble: 'Aye, we know we are trespassing, lady. What are you going to do about it, have the parish constable arrest us?'

Her ladyship reddened under the men's laughter: she had not been spoken to in that way in her life before: to her way of thinking, it was insulting and blatant defiance.

'We have come to parlay with your husband,' Jem informed her, politely. 'We are here to break your two threshing machines and to ask you to pay the men whom you employ a higher wage, a wage which they and their families can live on. And we want a letter signed to that effect by your husband before we leave, if you please.'

'Sir Dinkley is in London,' her ladyship declared, sharply. 'The House is sitting, as you well know. I am an unprotected woman, but, seeing many of you are my neighbours, and though armed, I am sure you will do me no harm.'

Several of the village men bowed their heads at that and protested that, indeed, they meant her no harm. 'We have come to ask for our wages to be raised in general keeping with the rest of the wages in the county, your ladyship,' one of them said.

'I know nothing of wages,' her ladyship retorted, somewhat imperiously. 'Such matters are dealt with by Sir Dinkley. Why have you risen up? There is no apparent distress in the village of which I am aware and the wages are the same as they had been for several years. I have been in several of your cottages and I have never seen an appearance of distress.'

'Then you are blind, woman,' one of the younger village men, less inclined to be polite, shouted back fiercely from amongst his colleagues.

'I receive five and sixpence a week in wages and a shilling and sixpence from the parish,' another younger villager also shouted, hidden from view behind him. 'I have heard that the shilling and sixpence is to be discontinued. How am I to manage then? Tell me that, your ladyship.'

'You will not improve your position by idling as you are here,' her ladyship retorted, more concerned that they had trampled across her lawns and that there was no sign of her peacocks. They were so careless where they walked these country people that, had it not been winter, they would almost certainly have destroyed all the flowers in the beds, for their footprints were everywhere and they had already trodden the turned earth into a hard crust in places.

Her remark was too much for Jem, 'They say they have been oppressed for too long, your ladyship, and will bear it no longer,' he told her firmly.

'You must see my husband on that matter,' was all she could think to reply: she was genuinely at a loss to understand why the men should rise up and march in a mob on to her husband's estate in such numbers. In her befuddled brain, it did not occur to her that the men rioted because they were near to starving, most as a result of the laws passed under a parliamentary system which her husband supported and which he so readily abused for his own benefit.

As the mob's attention was fixed on her ladyship, Jem saw several figures disappearing through a small wicker gate at the far end of the lawn at the side of the house: he smiled: they were the servants: they were not foolish enough to stay if there was going to be trouble: they wanted no part of their mistress's problems.

In the end, all they could do was to go into the barn alongside the house, drag out Sir Dinkley's two threshing machines and smash them and everything else they found there: and, because her ladyship's remarks had so angered him, Jem made no attempt to stop the younger village men when they set fire to five of his ricks in a field alongside as well.

They did not bother to return to the house to request any money for their day's 'work' as her ladyship had flounced back inside and had locked the doors on them, still wondering about her peacocks.

FORTY-NINE

THEY WERE into December now and the countryside was strange to Jem: he knew by the names of the villages that he had not been that way before.

Word of their successes over the previous days had flown ahead of them, for the next day, as they marched along the narrow lanes, cottagers en route came rushing to their gates to watch them pass. One group of men, digging drainage channels in the middle of a large flooded field, even downed their spades and splashed their way through a small lake to the headland at the sight of the black banner and the curious blue, black and yellow 'Tricolour' bobbing along the hedgerow, waving their hats in the air and cheering with all their might as the long straggling column passed.

At one place, they were met by a local Justice, mounted on a horse, who read them the Riot Act in the hope that the mere reading of it would frighten them into turning back: but since he was alone and unarmed, the men and youths simply jeered him and tramped on past into the village, where they did their usual work at two farms, extracting the usual fee, and so impressed forty or so of the younger men of the place that they immediately fell into step alongside their fellows, resulting in rousing cheers all along the half-mile length of the column.

Much to Dick Dollery's chagrin, amongst the newcomers was a former cavalry trumpeter who repeatedly blew loud military blasts on the instrument he had brought with him, which Jem recognised and which put his friend's unskilled tootling to shame. However, it did induce Enos Diddams to return to playing his pipes, at which he was more accomplished, and which, after an initial burst of enthusiasm, he had mostly neglected: it also inspired John Romble to beat his drum again and revitalised the flag-wavers.

Others, too, thinking it all a great lark of no real account or the beginning of an actual revolution also fell in step: and as quickly as their number fell below five hundred from overnight desertions, so it would rise again towards six hundred, the same almost as had set out from Hamwyte four days before. That the newcomers were also prepared to do their share of machine-breaking was evidenced by the fact that all who joined shouldered either an iron bar or an axe or a hammer or a club of some kind and several who joined from one village also carried peculiar long flail-poles which had heavy chainshot attached to them rather than the normal flail chains: they would do a deal of damage to anything they struck, head or wood.

However, not all who joined were welcomed by Jem and the others from Hamwick Dean: for amongst the newcomers were several rough elements, woodland dwellers and travellers from an encampment, who had joined on the fourth day and slunk along mostly at the rear: they did not seem to care at all about the causes which had launched the men's crusade – to break threshing machines so as to secure winter employment and have all men's wages raised so that they and their families might live without fear of starvation or eviction. They saw the march solely as an excuse to commit blatant robbery at any house they came across or any traveller they happened to meet upon the road.

Once the head of the column was out of sight, especially as they traversed the steeply undulating county in the north of the county, a half-dozen or so would detach themselves and run gleefully up the path of some respectable house by the roadside, bang loudly on the door till it was answered and then demand money from the householders, counting upon the fact that a long column of men passing by with banners and flags held aloft and hammers, iron bars, pitchforks, axes, poleaxes and other implements at the ready would be enough to convince them of the folly of refusing. None did.

In one village, they unceremoniously upended a black-suited vestry clerk to empty his pockets of coin when he stood in their path, not to protest at the column's arrival or the intention of going on to three of the local farms, but simply at the 'obscene noise' the woodlanders and travellers were making and the language they were using: the poor man was several sovereigns lighter when they left him sitting muddied and dishevilled upon the ground.

When a smart carriage, emblazoned with the coat-of-arms of a local lord, drove out unexpectedly from a sunken sidelane, they quickly seized the horses' bridles to bring the carriage to a halt: and, before the coachman could turn the vehicle round in the narrow confines of the road, a half-dozen grinning faces were peering through the window at the lord himself riding in it.

'We'll have a sovereign from you, if you please, your lordship,' said their leader, a burly, red-bearded ruffian, with yellowed teeth, holding out his hand and smiling broadly: and, though it did not please his lordship at all, he paid them anyway before he was allowed to drive on.

The black-flag-carrier and his cohorts were quick to follow the woodlanders' example and for a while they disappeared from the front of the march, leaving just the Tricolour-carrier to lead it: they, too, realised there were good pickings to be had from a fearful and cowed populace. That same day on the road, as they approached the next village, they met an old woman selling rabbits coming from it: led by Thomas Stuck, several surrounded her and began to snatch at the rabbits which dangled from a pole she carried over one shoulder.

'Get away! Get away from me, you thieves!' she cried, swinging round and round with the pole, hoping to catch one of the youths around the ears.

Fortunately, Jem, Dick Dollery and Enos Diddams were nearby at the time, having gone back down the column to speak to a small group from one village who had intimated that, while they would stay one more day, they wished to depart for home the following morning: Jem was hoping to dissuade them. Suddenly, they were alerted by the shouts and laughter of others: and when they made their way through the crowd to the rear, they found the old crone backed into a hedge, surrounded by the youths. 'Let her be and give her back the rabbits!' shouted Jem as the black-flag-carrier and his cohorts were about to scurry away with them. 'Give them back! I order you as your Captain.'

For a moment, it looked as if Thomas Stuck and his companions would defy him, for several took a tighter grip on their own cudgels and hammers and turned to face him: but then Dick Dollery stepped forward, with his iron-tipped club raised, followed by Enos Diddams with his weapon, and they obeyed, gave back the rabbits and let the old woman pass, though they did it with great reluctance.

Once again Joly Cobbold remained at the head of the column, plodding onward, seemingly unperturbed by the incidents of rick-burning or the robberies and petty larcenies occurring behind. What worried Jem, in particular, was that his Lieutenant was encouraging it, so he discovered when he attempted to prevent one of the black-flag-carrier's cohorts from firing a rick at one particular farm. 'The Lieutenant told us it was all right to burn any ricks we come across,' the youth retorted, struggling to pull himself free from Jem's grip. 'He gave us our orders. We are only doing what he told us to do.'

'It helps our cause, comrade,' Joly Cobbold had said by way of explanation when Jem had reproached him later. 'The more rick fires the authorities see burning all around them at night, the more they will heed our demands. It is a pity we cannot fire the churches and the big houses, too. Then we should have the landowners' rents and the parson's tithes brought down overnight. There is nothing like a threat to a man's property to make him change his mind.'

'And there is nothing more likely to put a rope around all our necks,' an angry Jem had retorted.

They had continued to argue the matter for a further hour, but such was the number of woodlanders and travellers in their midst that Jem knew he was really powerless to prevent further acts.

'We has to accept it, friend,' Dick Dollery had said, laying a hand on his arm another time to draw him away from a group who were about to fire ricks at one farm after they had smashed the machinery and had pocketed their normal two pounds charge. 'There is nothing we can do to stop them if they has a mind to do it, so let them have their fun. It does no real harm save to a farmer who has not had them insured and that is his fault, not ours.'

In the end, Jem accepted that he could do nothing to stop them: his mission had been to break the threshing machines which had taken the life of Mary-Ann: and that he had more than accomplished, with by that time upwards of twenty-five rendered as little more than kindling for a farm parlour's grate. At one place, when the farmer had asked if they would please leave the pieces a little bigger so that he might find a use for them elsewhere on his farm, out of anger they smashed them into even smaller pieces, none longer than eight inches and useless for anything except kindling.

FIFTY

GENERALLY, on entering a village, the men and youths would go round all the houses in small groups, knocking on the doors and asking for a drink of ale or a slice of bread and butter to sustain them on their tramp. As best he could, Jem insisted upon politeness as the likeliest way to get a favourable response from a householder. Sometimes, if no food were forthcoming, the men would accept whatever coins the householder could spare, even if offered only a few coppers: but woe betide any householder who did not answer their banging or did not do so quickly enough or who foolishly refused to give them food or money: they became 'enemies of the people's march' and were liable to have their windows shattered by stones out of pure pique.

It so happened that, on the seventh day, just before noon, they arrived at a small village of only sixty or so houses and made their round as usual, but because of their great number, the cottagers, who were half-starved themselves, were reluctant to offer overmuch, though they still gave what little they could spare. As a result, many of the marchers were still hungry when they came into the centre of the village, which was a large green. As they did so, a great shout went up, first from a few at the front, then from fifty and then from almost the whole host of them: for on the far side of the green, tucked away behind a spreading horse-chestnut tree, was a baker's shop, from which came the enticing smell of freshly baked bread. It was too much for some of the men: instantly, there was a running scramble towards it, men pushing over men and pulling at others to hold them back. The cry now was simply 'Bread! Bread!' The 'blood' part was momentarily forgotten.

Fortunately, Jem, Dick Dollery and the other Hamwick Dean men, being at the head of the assembly, were nearest to the bakery and managed reach the door first and to block it or five hundred or so hungry men and youths would have forced their way inside: as it was, the clamour for freshly baked bread and the great throng outside so petrified the baker that he readily acceded to their demands and gave them all his loaves. However, he had baked only two dozen or so that morning for his villagers and, though he also provided some circles of cheese, it was not nearly enough to feed all those who were still hungry.

All Jem and the others guarding the shop could do was quickly to gulp down a portion of bread for themselves as they took it from the baker, for they, too, were hungry, then slice each of the other loaves into a dozen or more pieces with a knife: but, as they attempted to distribute them, each pushing out from the door in a different direction into the throng with the cut bread in their arms, too many grasping hands reached out from either side, grabbing at it and even snatching at pieces as others pushed them into their mouths. At the same time, Jem and the other providers found themselves driven backwards against the shop window itself and were in grave danger of being forced through the panes of glass. Their only recourse was to strike out with their fists at the arms, shoulders and even faces of those nearest to them simply to force them back, for some, having seen others wheel away chewing on their piece of bread, refused to believe that the baker had no more.

'Get back! Get back!' shouted Jem. 'The baker has given you all the bread he has. You must share it with each other. There is no more. Get back or you will break the window!'

Reluctantly, those pressing forward obeyed and the pressure eased, though those who had nothing did it with ill grace: not surprisingly, some of the bread was knocked to the ground as one man jostled another which resulted in two dozen or more scrabbling on the road for the last half-dozen pieces. Further fights might have broken out had not a shout gone up at that moment on the far edge of the common: for, while all this had been going on, a small band of men who had left the main party had been taken by one of the villagers to the biggest of the houses there, the rectory, set well apart from the rest on the outskirts of the village: their hope was that, in so large a house, they could not fail to find fare of a kind the half-starved cottagers could never provide. They returned with two basins of cold pork and mutton, a half of game pie, two-and-a-half loaves of home-baked bread, some butter, a half circle of cheese, a jar of pickled eggs and a half sack of potatoes, which went some way towards appeasing the hunger of those men and youths who had missed out. But what they also found were the rector and his wife hiding under their beds: the men already knew they were as despised as was any self-serving clergyman anywhere, so the two were summarily dragged out and marched to the village green, where by that time the marchers had been joined by most of villagers themselves: thus, an assembly of eight hundred or more now formed a ring around the quivering pair.

'Please, do not harm us,' croaked the white-haired rector on his knees, his hands clasped together as if praying, while his wife, also on her knees beside him, clutched at his shoulder for protection. 'Do not harm my wife, I beg of you.'

'We are not here to harm either of you,' Jem told him, taking his place before the man. 'I am as much a stranger to you as you are to me. Why should I harm you? The people here of your village just wish to have a word with you, that is all.'

At that, several of the village women came forward and helped the white-faced pair to their feet. 'We hope you are both all right and not injured at all,' one of the labourers' wives said with obvious false politeness, a sly smile on her lips as the other women were patting them both on the back as if to brush off any dirt, but actually making sure they did not escape.

Equally politely, the labourer's wife, a large, buxom woman, with red freckled arms, a red face and no teeth and, with fifteen children to feed, the most impoverished villager there, added, still with a smile: 'And of course, you'll agree to come down three hundred pounds on the tithe, for sure, won't you, Rector, like we asked you to?'

The poor man, surrounded by so many and clearly fearing for his life amidst such a mob, readily agreed. 'Yes, yes,' he gulped, 'three hundred, as you say, three hundred. Yes, yes. That will be all right.'

'Good then,' said the smiling labourer's wife: and she and several others patted the rector on the back again to thank him for his generosity. 'Fetch a quill pen and an ink holder and get him to sign it,' she ordered one of the other women.

The quill and the ink holder were quickly brought from a nearby house along with a sheet of paper: and, when the words of the agreement had been scrawled on it in a reasonably legible hand by one of the women, the quivering rector readily signed it.

'Thank you, Rector,' said the buxom labourer's wife, holding the paper aloft for all to see. 'You may go to your home now.'

The white-faced clergyman and his equally white-faced wife hurried away with their heads lowered as if in shame: a short while later, their gig came rattling out of the rectory gateway and went bowling along the road the way the marchers had come, eager to escape to the sanctuary of someone else's parsonage.

It was at that moment, not thirty yards away, that the baker appeared in his doorway with a blunderbuss in his hands, pointing it at a half-dozen of the same rough woodlanders and travellers who had joined the march two days before: while others had been concerned with the rector and his wife, they had gathered around the shop, whispering amongst themselves, as if contemplating rushing in on some nefarious purpose.

'What do you want?' the baker demanded. 'I have given you all the bread I have. I have no more.'

'An ounce of baccy,' said one of the men weakly, taken aback by the baker's unexpected belligerence.

'Very well,' replied the baker, who was also the purveyor of general goods in a separate part of his shop: so, with his eyes still on the men before him, he called over his shoulder to his wife at the back of the shop to make up an ounce: but when she appeared with the small cloth bag, the baker took it from her and declared: 'Here is your baccy, but I want to see the colour of your money first.'

Reluctantly, with the gun pointed at him and his companions, the man who had spoken before went nervously forward, holding his palm upwards to show the coins in his hand so that there would be no mistake: and, having paid for the tobacco, he sheepishly retired into the crowd and his friends followed him.

Jem had no illusions that the woodlanders and travellers had intended to rob the baker by sheer force of numbers. The previous day they had threatened violence to a young curate of a nearby hamlet when he attempted to intervene physically as fifty men entered a tithe barn beside his church and rectory to smash the threshing machine there. Hardly had they began than the young curate, who could not have been long out of college, came hurrying up, drawn by the noise of the horns and the cheers of the men standing on the road: the foolish youth not only called upon them to stop but even began citing passages from the Bible, listing Book, chapter and verse, as some form of deterrent, which irriated the irreligious woodland dwellers and travellers no end. In consequence, several seized hold of him and were about to throw him over a five-foot wall on to the farm's dung heap when Jem stepped in and physically forced him away, saying: 'This is not the place for you to be. Now is not the time to talk of the Bible. These men are in no mood to listen to your sermons today. Go, for your own good.'

The young curate went protesting, but he went all the same.

FIFTY-ONE

EVEN BEFORE the Great Meeting at Hamwyte, the Government, alarmed by the rapid spread of machine-breaking and incendiarism in the counties south and west of the capital, had offered fifty pounds' reward for anyone providing evidence which led to the conviction of a machine-breaker and five hundred pounds for the conviction of an incendiary: as a further inducement, a free pardon was also offered to any informer who had not themselves committed an act of incendiarism and was willing to testify again one who had.

Jem knew about the rewards being offered and the possibility of betrayal of him and the others had crossed his mind on several occasions, but mostly he had dismissed it: there was no sense in worrying about whether anyone might inform on him: it was too late for such a thing. If the Justices caught up with him, then so be it: he had committed himself wholeheartedly to the cause, to destroy the hated threshing machines and avenge Mary-Ann's death and there was no going back: as Dick Dollery had said at the start of the march, 'We have burned our bridges now, brother.'

This was brought home to Jem on the Saturday, their eighth day on the road, when they smashed five threshing machines in an afternoon at one village: at the second farm, the grey-haired farmer sat on horseback, watching them, as if making a note of their faces, though how he would remember the five hundred or more who surrounded his farm or the sixty who did the actual breaking was a mystery to Jem. All the while, he taunted the breakers with remarks such as, 'Is that the best ye can do?' and 'Give it a good whack, it matters not to me. T'is all insured so you do me no disservice!' and 'You'll be boated like as not for this, the lot on ye!' and 'The yeomanry'll be out looking for thee. What'll thee do when they catches thee – run? T'won't do thee no good, they'll hunt thee down, as sure as my name is Silas Huckle!'

He continued his sneering remarks even when Jem thanked him for the two pounds they took off him and even when, with the help of Dick Dollery and some of the local men, he managed to usher some of the more rebellious element of the mob away from the farmhouse, where they seemed to be contemplating doing other mischief as a reprisal for the farmer's taunts.

Still the farmer would not relent: even as Jem was passing through the gate back on to the lane, he nudged his dappled mare forward and rode alongside and, in a casual, almost disinterested way, said: 'How long does thee think thee'll last afore one of thy men informs on thee and claims the fifty pound reward that is being offered for information on the likes o' thee. Sooner or later one of thy men will inform on thee, for the money offered is more than any o' they can make in a year?'

As it happened, one of the labourers of that particular village was walking alongside Jem. 'We've had enough of thee and thy tongue, you old bugger!' he cried: and, raising his stave, he struck the farmer's horse hard across its rump so that it reared and almost threw off its rider: then it bolted across the field, with the farmer pulling hard, but unsuccessfully, at the reins to turn it back. In the labourer's village, they had a different standard of honour from that imagined by the farmer.

'You have nothing to fear from us, Captain,' the local man declared. 'We are all loyal men here. There's not a man or boy who would think to betray ye or any of the others after what ye have done for us.'

When the farmer did eventually manage to rein in his horse, the same local man led twenty of his comrades into the field, where they pelted the farmer with clods of earth to deter him from returning and taunting them again: the farmer was last seen trotting off across another field, driven from his own farm, his day's humiliation complete.

Even then, several of the woodlanders and travellers were not finished: they broke the windows of his house, fired three ricks in the field alongside, then chased the hens around the yard and wrung their necks before taking them away to cook. After that, they went on to three more farms, where much the same scenes were enacted, and that night there was more drunken revelry at the village's three inns, paid for by the money they had collected: and when a fight started in one between a villager and a traveller, it spilled out into the street despite the cold until thirty or forty men were brawling.

That evening, for once, Jem and Dick Dollery did not remain long with the drinkers: they were seated in a barn where they were to spend the night, arguing with Joly Cobbold over the direction of the march.

For that day, a handbill had been given to them, stating that another great meeting of labourers was to be held on the Monday afternoon, December the sixth, on Rushmere heath, near Witchley, some twenty miles away. *'We will not starve!'* the handbill declared. *'Remember Brussels! Remember Paris! Imitate them on December sixth. Remember! Remember!'*

Jem and Dick Dollery were both in agreement that the mass meeting at Witchley should be their goal, for it would give the men an incentive to march on for a further two days, especially as they had been eight days on the road by then. Not unexpectedly, Joly Cobbold was not at all keen: he was all for continuing on their present route, demolishing threshing machines and firing ricks and robbing the better off householders as they went, anything that would affect the pockets of the hated landowning classes, whether they were actual owners of the land or merely tenants farmers who rented it: being a town-dweller, he neither considered nor cared about the distinction.

That day they had trudged through driving lines of sleet: the weather clearly was worsening daily: the great gathering at Witchley would be a good place to disperse the march before the yeomanry and the special constables, now roaming the countryside in troops of two-hundred or more, caught up with them.

It was something which Jem and Dick Dollery had reluctantly agreed between themselves after Enos Diddams, John Romble, William Stubbs and Thomas Judd had announced the previous evening their intention to leave the march at daybreak on the Sunday: for no one was forced to continue upon it: men made their own choices. They had become disillusioned with the conduct of the woodlanders and the rough travellers and wanted to leave before someone was killed, they said.

'We have been talking among ourselves,' John Romble had said as they had sat on the hard dirt floor of another barn, unable even to light a fire for fear of setting light to the straw all around them and burning the place down. 'I think it is time we went home. We have done all that is in our power to do. I have been away from my family long enough. Eight days of this is enough for any man.'

'Aye, the weather is getting far too cold,' agreed a shivering Enos Diddams. 'I have had enough of this marching everywhere. I don't even know what day it is. I would like to get back to my family, too.'

Jem and Dick Dollery looked at each other: they had hoped that they would all continue on together to Witchley. Disappointed though he was, Jem would not prevent his friends from leaving: he knew full well that the spirit of rebellion was slowly fading They had already lost a further fifty the previous night, all from the one village, who had slipped away in the early morning darkness while Jem and the others slept: not that Jem would have stopped them: he understood how they had become weary of the privations of the march, the bitter cold, the continual hunger and most particularly the aches and pains they suffered from the hard floors upon which they slept. He could not blame a man who, having participated in the breaking of more than two-dozen threshing machines, considered his allegience to the cause done.

Jem, however, would remain. 'The men have elected me as their Captain so I must remain with them,' he told his friends. 'I will take them on to Witchley for the gathering there. We will go via Burstead Market as the shortest route. I cannot prevent you from leaving and I will not. I will go on by myself if I have to – '

'I am not leaving, Jem,' Dick Dollery broke in, indignant that anyone should even think he, too, was ready to quit. 'I am staying with you. I am as much a lieutenant as Mr. No-Name over yonder.' He indicated the sleeping Joly Cobbold, lying where the black-flag carrier, Thomas Stuck, and his cohorts had earlier set out their bivouac before departing for the inns. 'I am sticking with thee, Jem, come hell or high water, special constables or yeomanry. I am with thee, friend, all the way to the end. Tell my missus, Enos, when thee gets back, I will be home when I am good and ready and not before.'

'I never thought I would miss my own bed so much,' sighed William Stubbs later as they settled down to sleep on the bare earth, for there was not even enough straw for them all to lie on.

'T'is not his bed he misses,' laughed John Romble, 'it is being in it with his wife. Once he gets back, she'll be dropping another sprog come next August or September, you mark my words.' The conversation continued in the same jesting vein till they had all fallen asleep.

In the morning, which was heavily frosted yet again, Jem rose cold and stiff and as hungry as ever: and such had been the drinking and merriment of the previous evening, that it was some time before all the sleepers could be roused and the march resumed: by then Enos Diddams, John Romble, William Stubbs and Thomas Judd were well on the road home.

Unhappily, as the surviving three hundred marched off to the sound of the Sunday church bells ringing across the countryside, the old habits remained: passers-by on their way to church were persuaded by the woodland dwellers and travellers to hand over a sovereign apiece and house-dwellers were again bearded on their doorsteps, though even that was not without its lighter moments. One aged, bespectacled member of the gentry, whose large Georgian house was surrounded by fifty or more men, was relieved of five pounds which he protested was intended for the parson's Advent plate: he was left fuming and gesticulating under his portico as the long column marched past, jeering and throwing small stones at him, not to hurt him, just to irriate him further.

'Vile blackguards! Country scum! Farmyard clod-hoppers!' were the milder insults the supposed gentleman and scholar hurled at them. When some of the woodland dwellers heard his cruder epithets, they turned back, intending to assault him somehow and would have done so had not Jem and Dick Dollery also turned them back yet again and ordered them to continue on their march. Not that they received any thanks for it from the old man: infuriated by their laughter, he picked up a stone and inexpertly, with the pathetic arm action of a woman, hurled it at Jem. However, it struck Dick Dollery on the cheek instead and, so surprised was the old man that he had actually hit someone, he scuttled back inside and bolted the door, fearing he might be held to account for it.

Jem was still laughing at poor Dick Dollery's misfortune when they rejoined the head of the march and turned towards the small market town of Burestead Market, unaware that elsewhere events were gaining momentum.

FIFTY-TWO

ON THE DAY following the destruction of his threshing machines, Titus Broake, Member of Parliament for Hamwyte, Justice of the Peace, lord of the manor of Hamwick Dean, was seated with two of his fellow magistrates at Hamwyte, swearing to a deposition giving his account of the events at the Hall, which, of course, his brother magistrates had no cause to disbelieve. The testimony and word of one of their own was to be trusted implicitly, in that he had been confronted by a mob four hundred-strong, some of whom he knew and some who must have come from other places, and he had been threatened with injury when he had attempted to remonstrate with them and deter them from their action. He then described to his brother magistrates what had happened and, cross-examined by them, identified one Jem Stebbings, of Hamwick Dean, whom he had 'seen many times about the village,' as having been at the front of the mob and to have heard him cry 'Break the machinery!'

'The man Stebbings,' Titus Broake told the Hamwyte magistrates as the clerk scratched down his depostion, 'was undoubtedly their leader. He led them towards the barn and I saw him inside when the fire started. Stebbings was definitely leading them. I saw that with my own eyes. It was only through good fortune and the quick action of others that it did not burn down.'

Titus Broake also took with him his bailiff, Heginbotham, who swore to his own deposition: the whole proceedings took no more than thirty minutes and the warrant was sworn out and delivered to the parish constable, Ephraim Simms, that afternoon, who then went with Titus Broake and Heginbotham to Jem's 'cottage' on the back lane to Lower Rackstead, but neither he nor his children were there. That day, Jed and Thirza were with Dick Dollery's wife and Jem was making his way to Inworth, for it was the day of the poorhouse's destruction: and, though he returned to the village late that evening, Ephraim Simms was still abed when Jem and the others set off the next day for the great meeting at Hamwyte and so he missed him again, which did not endear the grocer-cum-parish constable to the lord of the manor.

In the days which followed, further depositions were sworn to by Amos Peakman, Marcus Howie and Joshua Godwin: and, as a result of the information given, warrants were issued for the arrest of six other Hamwick Dean men – Richard Dollery, Enos Diddams, Nathaniel Newman, John Romble, William Stubbs and Thomas Judd: they, along with Jem Stebbings, were the prime ones: warrants for the arrest of others might well be issued in due course, but these would do for a start.

More than anything, however, Titus Broake sought the apprehension of the leader of the mob who had humiliated him so, the felon Jem Stebbings, recently released from Melchborough Gaol: nothing would satisfy him till he was held in chains again, him and that drunken layabout, Richard Dollery, who was always in his company and was equally as guilty. He had been told they always sat together in the Wayfarers' Inn: the whole revolt had most probably been planned there. For some reason, though, they had both vanished: but he would bide his time: sooner or later thay would return to the village and he would have them both, them and the others from the village who had also mysteriously disappeared: he would have them all: he promised himself that.

In Wivencaster, when the first reports filtered back that a great body of farm labourers – six-hundred strong, it was said by some, a thousand-strong, by others – were roaming the lanes and byways in the north and northeast of the county, armed with all manner of weapons and causing all manner of disturbances, the first action of the alarmed Justices of the old Roman town had been to send an urgent letter to London on the *Flyer*, calling for help from the new Metropolitan Police Force, offering them free cottage bed and board. However, the London police, being used to better things than draughty country cottages for their lodgings, wrote back demanding that their experienced constables be accommodated in the town's best inn and, further, that they be given expenses for their food and drink and also, while there, paid their normal wage. It was too much for the local Justices and, after due consideration, they withdrew their request, while they considered what to do next.

The events determined their course of action: night after night, the fierce red glow of burning hayricks and now barns was lighting up the sky as other men and youths, hearing of the success of the marchers success and seeking to emulate their brazenness, scampered across fields in the dark to set ricks and barns ablaze with impunity, from the marshy coastline in the east to the rolling heights in the west. No one, it seemed, was afraid any more: in village after village, labourers were meeting openly in what the Justices deemed 'riotous assemblies,' but which the men themselves called simply 'meetings' or 'gatherings.' If the Justices were to put a stop to it all, they would have to act themselves.

Finally, on the third day, following the great meeting at Hamwyte, the Justices of Hamwyte, Wivencaster, Shallford and Levendon convened their own great meeting in the Moot Hall of the garrison town: four-hundred and more of the largest landed proprietors of the district, gentlemen of the various towns and large farmers of the region were invited to attend, the same landowners, gentlemen and farmers who had for so long looked with utter indifference and without pity at the destitution of the labouring poor. That day, the town's High Street was so choked with their gigs, traps, four-wheeled post-chaises and other carriages that the *Flyer* returning from London was unable to reach the yard of the Red Lion opposite to change the horses and, consequently, its passengers had to trudge through the mud when they dismounted and the horses had to be trotted out and changed in the road by the yard boys, all of which delayed the mail coach by a half-hour.

As was to be expected, the chairman of the Moot Hall meeting, himself a magistrate, was scathing in his opening remarks of the new-found power and unity of the labouring classes. 'Goodness gracious, what is the world coming to?' he cried. 'This must be stopped and stopped immediately or the country will go to the dogs!'

Not unnaturally either, the first thought of the landowners, gentlemen and large farmers was to re-activate the yeomanry, of which several of the older men present had been members in earlier times: they would be sent out into the countryside to apprehend any and all of these blackguard machine-breakers, especially the barn-firers and rick-burners and most particularly their damned ringleaders! Get those and the whole rotten busines would come to an end! The ringleaders were the ones who were leading on the others. Damned radicals! Damned rascals!

The yeomanry would, of course, be drawn solely from the ranks of the wealthy landowners and the gentlemen of the towns and their sons, since they were the ones more likely to own a hunter or two and also to be able to ride properly: it was no use having men who could not ride properly, especially if they had to chase those blackguard rioters across several fields and jump the odd hedge in order to bag them.

Amongst the first to offer to serve, as was to be expected, was the lord of manor of Hamwick Dean, owner of a thousand and more acres and one of the very first victims of a mob made up of the same ungrateful villagers whom he often employed, who had broken both of his threshing machines and had even attempted to burn down his barn. All during the debate, Titus Broake was amongst the fiercest of the speakers, haranguing the others for being so laggardly in dealing with 'these damned machine-breakers and rioters,' particularly some of the middling farmers, who seemed to find every reason not to act. He himself had already taken action and had had warrants sworn out for the arrest of seven of the blackguards who had broken his threshing machines and those of three other farmers and he was determined not to rest until they were all locked up in gaol: he would be damned if he would! He fully supported the reactivation of the yeomanry and warmly welcomed the appointment of a retired colonel of horse as their leader: he hoped a man who had seen action at Waterloo would get after those damned machine-breakers and rick burners at the earliest opportunity and run them down the same as he had run down the damned Frenchies! He sat down to ecstatic applause.

Several of the farmers, however, knowing how angered the men of the villages were by the severity of their wage reductions, blithely informed the landowners and town gentry that sending a hundred or so of them out into the countryside as a body of yeomanry would not deter the spirit of rebellion running through the parishes: indeed, it would more likely inflame it even more. For a start, a mob of farm labourers, variously reported at one time or another to be between six hundred to a thousand, all armed, were unlikely to be afraid of a mere hundred yeomanry and were more likely to stand their ground and stone them for their presumptuousness. Besides, now that the tithe-paying and rent-paying farmers had the ear of the richer landed proprietors all in one place, they were more interested in formulating resolutions calling for reductions in their tithes and rents than chasing all over the countryside after a mob of machine-breakers. Most leased their machines, anyway, and so were not so bothered if they were smashed: only the rick-burning bothered them, for that could cost them good money, though since the start of the troubles there had been a steady stream of farmers going into the County Fire Asssurance office farther down the High Street, just in case. The clerk there had never done such business!

In consequence, the magistrates found it equally difficult to enlist 'special constables' from amongst the farmers, even though the chairman of the magistrates, who was himself a large landed proprietor with nine hundred acres to the north of the old Roman town, announced that he would reduce his rents in the hope that the farmers would serve. However, few went forward to take the oath: only fifteen, in fact, of all the farmers at the meeting. The traders of the town were also unwilling to serve when they were asked later and those who did were coerced somehow into swearing the oath, mostly through debt owed, not by them, but to them, for several of the gentlemen and their sons declared they would not feel obliged to pay off what they owed if men 'shirked their duty to England.'

As it turned out, three of the more affluent farmers from Shallford, who had grown fat off the land and considerd themselves almost as equals with the other landed gentry, did put themselves forward as 'special constables': though, mysteriously, within a day of taking the oath, their barns and ricks were set alight while the sole well-to-do farmer to join from Higher Rackstead had a death threat pushed under his door. Yet another of the 'special constables' raised by the Justices, a pompous fool of a farmer from Salter, who also thought himself grander than the rest of the farmers in that parish, was set upon by a mob when he unwisely rode up to a gathering of labourers standing in the road by the maypole, opposite the Queen's Head, discussing the happenings to the north, and ordered them to disperse. Instead, as his contemporaries had warned, they threw stones at him, dragged him off his horse, debagged him there and then and would have given him over to be dealt with by the women – and Salter women were known to be a crude bunch – had he not punched and kicked his way clear and outrun them till he was a couple of miles distant, halfway to Inworth, in fact, which was all uphill. Eventually he fetched up at Hamwyte, breechless still, complaining to the Justices of his 'barbaric treatment,' though there was little that they could do or wanted to do, except give him a pair of breeches to wear.

None of this bothered Jem and Dick Dollery in the least: on that very day they were more than twenty-eight miles from Hamwick Dean: and, in crossing over a river, which formed the northern boundary of their county, they had already entered the next county, on their way to Burestead Market, through which they had to pass en route to the great meeting at Witchley.

314

FIFTY-THREE

THE SMALL TOWN of Burestead Market, lying just over the boundary of the next county and more than thirty-five miles from Hamwick Dean, as the crow flies, had been in a state of great alarm for some days, ever since tales had reached them of a mob of upwards of a thousand men and youths tramping the back lanes only a few miles away and heading in their direction. The result was that every traveller and coach driver who arrived in the small town was besieged for news and most replied with lurid tales of fires glowing in the night as ricks and barns burned, of a column of fierce-looking men seen trudging along a distant back lane with flags and banners flying, all the while giving out a dreaded chant calling for the 'blood' of any gentry they came across, stopping travellers and robbing them and even robbing roadside houses as they passed. Why they had even heard a rumour that they had burned down one house and murdered its occupants! And it was a known fact, too, that all the farmers to the west of the town for thirty miles or more had had their machinery destroyed by a band of malcontents led by a lanky black-flag-carrier and a youth waving a peculiar blue-black-and-yellow 'Tricolour.' It was like the French Revolution all over again!

What was fact was that a four-storey silk mill in the small town of Longstreet, a few miles to the north in the same county, had been burned down by a mob three days before. The rioters had surrounded the building in the mid-morning and had stated their determination to knock it down because of the brutality of the foul-tempered senior overlooker and the indifference to it of the manager and the owner. Children as young as nine worked there, twelve and fourteen hours a day, wearing nothing but rags, without stockings or shoes, dirty from head to toe, their hair thickly matted since they had no means to cleanse themselves: often they were beaten with a strap by the brutal overlooker if they did not do their work correctly or if they fell asleep towards the end of the evening shift: it was the very place to which three of Dick Dollery's daughters and both Enos Diddams's girls had been sent by Joshua Jaikes.

Yet, it was not the mill workers who had attacked the mill: the place was their livelihood and they considered it better that a child found sleeping in work hours be beaten rather than fined, for none could afford to lose even a little money. They themselves were poorly paid and frequently laid off or had their hours reduced unexpectedly and were as near to starving because of it as any agricultural labourer: and like them, too, those who fell ill received no wages at all, but had to resort to pawning all they had if forced to remain abed for any length of time.

The sixty-strong mob which attacked it had comprised mostly agricultural labourers from a nearby village, roused to anger by an overly zealous radical amongst them: to them, the mill was simply another place full of machines and machines were the Devil's invention, whether power looms to weave silk or threshing machines to thresh corn, for they enslaved everyone, even the small children. Their solution was to smash them all, smash the mill's steam engine, smash the hundred or so power looms and that way the misery of all would be ended for ever, or so they reasoned.

They hated, too, the owner, who was a large local landowner and the Member of Parliament for the nearby town, yet was American-born and had come to settle in England only to make a profit from the toil of the English labouring classes and who was known for the meanness of his ways and his indifference to their suffering. Even so, the manager of the mill, who was on three per cent of the profit from its production, the five overseers, the clerks and even some of the workers themselves, were ready to defend it when the mob marched up to the mill's gates, as much for the retention of their own livelihoods as for it being the property of their master. They barricaded the doors and kept a cauldron of water boiling ready to throw over any who attempted entry.

Initially, the manager went out under a truce and offered fifteen pounds to the leader if he would march his mob off somewhere else, an offer which was refused with scorn: and so the battle began. Two agile youths were hoisted on the shoulders of others to break a window high up and to climb through and that way they were able to open the main doors for the rest to pour inside. The manager, the overseers, the clerks and the small band of loyal workers were soon forced to retreat from the building: and, once they had been driven off, the hated machinery was smashed with hammers and iron bars: a hundred power looms, a great steam engine, indeed the whole mill itself, all were demolished.

The concern of the inhabitants of Burestead Market at the news of the approach of a mob bearing every hallmark of being the very one which had wrecked the silk mill at Longstreet was understandable since the market town's principal industry was its own silk mill, which lay at the lower or western end of the cobbled market place, along the banks of a river which ran through a shallow valley, right next to the town's brewery.

They had heard, too, that the same mob, on their progress towards them through one of the villages the previous day, had taken a clergyman from his parsonage and dragged him along the road with a halter round his neck: they had heard, too, first hand from a gentleman who had been attacked on the road, that he had shot and killed two of that same mob and had driven off the remainder: true or not, he was lauded by all as a fine hero.

Another landowner, a retired colonel, whose house five miles away had been approached by a mob, was said to have wheeled out six small cannons which he had kept in his own small armoury: with his three footmen and gardeners standing by the other five ready to put the fuse to the powder, he had fired off one of them with all manner of nails and bolts packed into it and this had at least intimidated the mob into retreat as they came up his drive, though they went away shaking their fists and vowing vengeance.

As things happened, it was the mob of sixty or so mill wreckers which the townsfolk of Burestead Market thought approached them: they were not to know that Jem and his companions had never been near the silk mill or had a cannon fired at them or had two of their number shot at by a gentleman on the road, though they had bearded several clergymen: Jem's object was simply to pass through the town, perhaps to extract some donations towards their victuals as they did so, and to march on to Witchley, but nothing other than that.

That Sunday of December the fifth, the people were in a state of panic when late in the afternoon a mob, led by a man in a tall black hat with the red, white and blue ribbons of a revolutionary tied around it, with a second at their head carrying a black flag, a third hoisting a peculiarly-coloured blue-black-and-yellow 'Tricolour' and two others playing trumpets, came over the brow of the hill to the southwest of the town, all chanting 'Bread or blood! Bread or blood!' in their loudest voices.

The good people of Burestead Market were not to know either that, except for the sound of tramping feet and occasional calling between them, all had been silent for two hours or more beforehand and that their chanting and flag-waving had begun only when they had sighted the steeple of the parish church rising between tall elms: it was all simply a show of bravado by a weary, flagging column, intended to make others believe they were all of one mind and invincible, like advancing armies did when cheering and yelling as they moved to the attack.

The Burestead Yeomanry, some fifteen in all, under the command of a young lieutenant and armed with pistols, muskets and an assortment of other weapons, had been waiting on the cobbled market place: immediately, the marchers' approach was reported to them, they mounted and trotted out with the town's senior magistrate at their head and drew up in four lines across a narrow part of the high-hedged lane so as to bar their approach. To the consternation of the young lieutenant, a farmer's son, dressed in his father's old militia uniform and seated on a large hunting horse, who had expected only the sixty, he found himself facing four-hundred or more. Even though their number had been reduced yet again that very day by more desertions on the road, it was still sufficient to put fear into the heart of any magistrate, landowner or unsympathetic farmer whom they came across.

'I fear there are too many of them for us, sir,' the young lieutenant quietly counselled the magistrate as the yeomanry and the marchers came to a halt some thirty yards apart.

'Nonsense!' replied the magistrate, a bulky, bewhiskered, heavy-set fellow, who owned the town's brewery, lying no more than a half-mile behind them and, therefore, directly in the path of the advancing horde: its defence was the true reason he had ridden out. 'I am sure they will listen to reason. There is nothing for them here.'

With that, he kneed his horse, one of the brewery's delivery mares, forward a few yards ahead of the standing troop. 'Which of you there is the Captain?' he demanded.

Jem was about to answer when he felt a tug on his sleeve from a hand behind: it was Dick Dollery. 'Say nothing,' his friend hissed, then, for the benefit of all behind, he added: 'No one is to say who is our Captain. We'll hear him out first.'

When no one answered him, the bewhiskered magistrate declared in somewhat of a bluster: 'We know who the ringleaders are. We have their descriptions. We have their names. We are here to arrest them in the King's name and any of you who get in our way will be treated likewise. If any of you men resist, it will be all the worse for you. We are armed and we have the King's authority to do what we do.'

'You may have the King's right,' Joly Cobbold, standing with the black-flag-carrier Thomas Stuck and his cohorts to Jem's left, shouted back, 'but we have the right of all humanity on ours.'

'Will your Captain make himself known to us?' demanded the magistrate again, his voice showing impatience. 'We will only parley with him.'

'We're all bloody Captains,' shouted Daniel Downey, the Tricolour-carrier, to laughter again. 'We captain ourselves. That way we do not have to do as you tell us. We do what we like.'

The bewhiskered magistrate, confused by their lack of a sensible response, could only take certain action: so he pointed his pistol straight at the grinning Daniel Downey as the last speaker and shouted to the lieutenant and two troopers who came up alongside him: 'Arrest him!'

As the three troopers eyed the smirking Downey, flattered to be singled out amongst so large a number, the magistrate called to him: 'You, young man, you must consider yourself under arrest.' It was said, however, more in hope of forestalling the inevitable clash, which lay but moments away, than in any likelihood that he would be heeded.

'You may threaten us all you like,' Joly Cobbold shouted, stepping forward to stand ahead of the throng as if he were their leader, 'but we aim to go this way and no other and we shall not be turned from it by the likes of you.' Behind him there was a chorus of agreement.

'You will go no farther this way,' declared the magistrate firmly. 'We are here to prevent that. You men have done all the mischief you will do this day or any other day.'

Thomas Stuck then stepped forward to stand even beyond Joly Cobbold and Daniel Downey: he had handed his black flag to a companion and now held a sledgehammer in his hands: 'You will not stop us,' the thin-faced ploughboy declared. 'We're going to Witchley, whether you like it or not, and we are going to break every damned machine that we comes across on the way, so you had best get out of our way. There's hundreds of us and only twenty of you.'

In making that statement, Thomas Stuck, not knowing Burestead Market had a silk mill, exactly the same as the one which had been destroyed at Longstreet, determined the senior magistrate's next course of action. If at all possible, the magistrate had wished to avoid a clash between the labourers and his small troop of volunteer yeomanry: there were other ways to Witchley, a turn-off not a mile back, for instance, which, though roundabout, would still get them there. If the mob progressed any farther, he was under no illusion as to what would be the outcome: the town could not afford to lose its silk mill and he could not afford to lose the contents of his brewery. If they came across that, from all the stories he had heard of their revelry at various inns while on the road, they would likely drink him dry. There would be nothing to stop them either: for, though he had locked the gates, the yard was surrounded only by a low wall, no more than three feet high, which a man could easily jump over.

If they were so determined to get to Witchley, then it was his duty to convince them to go another way: and the way to do that, he reasoned, was to arrest one of them to show that he and the yeomanry meant business. The mouthy youth with the hammer was as good as any, since he was nearest and had been the most threatening: and, after all, the King's law was on his side no matter what was denied by the mob.

Urging his horse forward to within a couple of yards of Thomas Stuck, the magistrate demanded in a haughty tone, almost as if in a court and the other were an accused before him: 'What do you say you will do, boy?'

The foolish Stuck, emboldened by the laughter behind him, called out the same answer: 'I said we're going to Witchley whether you like it or not and we're going to smash every damned machine we comes across on the way, every damned machine, no matter what!' He did not say 'every damned threshing machine': the magistrate simply noted that he said 'every damned machine' and that meant the machines in the town's silk mill.

'Are you boy?' retorted the magistrate: and suddenly, half-wheeling his horse, he leaned forward in his saddle and, reaching down, made a grab at Thomas Stuck's arm, intending to haul him back towards the yeomanry before anyone else could react. But Stuck was too quick for him: he sidestepped, lifted his hammer and swung it viciously at the magistrate's head. Fortunately, the blow only struck the magistrate's hat and sent it flying into the mud: off balance and trying to control his skittish mount, the magistrate was still within range when Stuck raised the hammer a second time.

He would have brained the struggling rider there and then had not Jem jumped forward and seized the haft of the hammer in mid-swing: with one mighty shove, he sent the lanky ploughboy stumbling against the bank. Red-faced with anger, Stuck recovered in an instant and, raising the hammer, which he had retained, this time made to strike at

Jem rather than the magistrate. Dick Dollery and two others saved him, stepping between the two with their own weapons at the ready.

As he trotted back to rejoin the yeomanry, there was a curious look of disbelief on the bewhiskered magistrate's face that anyone should have acted so on his behalf, particularly a rioter: however, he still had his duty to do.

'Cock your weapons and fire over their heads,' he ordered the yeomanry as he wheeled his horse round again. 'See if that will deter them.'

It was not the wisest of orders: the lane was overhung with trees and wide enough for only four mounts to stand side by side between its high-hedged banks: in consequence, those behind the front four had to discharge their weapons straight up into the air rather than down the length of the lane: the result was that, when they squeezed the triggers, they succeeded only in showering themselves with the twigs from the overhanging branches.

At that, the marchers all began to laugh, which infuriated the magistrate all the more: then from behind Jem, a stone sailed over his head and struck the bridle of the magistrate's horse. The animal reared and barged against the young lieutenant's ride, almost knocking him from his saddle: and, in attempting to steady his mount, the lieutenant blundered against the next man. For a half-minute or so there was disorder and confusion in the ranks of the yeomanry: horses were backing off, trying to turn, in some cases wheeling right round, while some at the rear even trotted back a score or so yards to escape the general mayhem.

Suddenly, from somewhere amid the mob came the shout which the magistrate had dreaded to hear all along: 'Come on, lads, we can't stand here all day. There's a good brewery in this town, I am told, and my throat is as dry as a bone. Let's charge this lot and make for the brewery. We can drink our fill there.'

'Aye, let's drink the damned place dry,' shouted the Tricolour-carrier. 'And this sorry-looking militia are not going to stop us. To the brewery, everyone, to the brewery and free ale for all!'

A great cheer went up: more stones landed amongst the milling horses and riders, striking animal and man alike and causing more confusion. Then, with a roar, they surged forward, all four-hundred of them, with Joly Cobbold and Thomas Stuck and the Tricolour-carrier Daniel Downey in the lead, running straight at the horses, swinging their iron bars, hammers and bludgeons and hurling sharp-edged flints so fiercely that the troopers were forced to pull their mounts round and canter away. The poor flustered magistrate was almost engulfed, but managed to extricate himself and, having ridden his horse up the bank and through a gap in the hedge, was last seen galloping across a ploughed field back towards the safety of the town.

When they reached the market place where the yeomanry had been bivouacked, there was no one to be seen: troopers and townsfolk alike had scurried off into their houses and the doors of all had been bolted shut.

The marchers, however, were interested only in the brewery: they ignored its locked gates and poured over its low wall: the building itself was quickly broken into and the two weekend watchmen and barrel cleaners still there chased out: sundry barrels of beer were rolled into the yard and tapped, to be drunk by all who would have their fill.

They were still there, sitting on the low wall, carousing, talking and arguing, when the moon rose: there was little option but for them to remain in the brewery for the whole night, which was as good a dormitory as any in which they had slept over the past few nights. Better, most said, since it provided free ale!

Witchley was only a few miles farther on: they would head there in the morning.

FIFTY-FOUR

THE SUDDEN TOLLING of church bells awoke Jem and Dick Dollery, as it did most of the others who had spent the night in the brewery, sleeping off their drinking: it was only when they came blinking into the bright sunshine that they saw the lines of horsemen drawn up at the far end of the long, wide market place.

During the night, a hundred yeomanry had been gathered from amongst the rich landowners in that part of the county, their sons and their servants, led by a half-pay captain and incorporating the small Burestead Market troop under the young lieutenant which had wisely retreated the previous day. With them, all duly sworn in by three magistrates, who now rode at their head, were a further seventy-five special constables recruited from the larger farmers, their sons and their servants, willing or unwilling, as well as the more well-to-do householders and tradesmen from two nearby towns.

What troubled Jem was that the front rank of the horsemen was formed not by yeomanry but by twenty-five blue-jacketed Royal Dragoons, who had ridden out from Witchley at the summons of the magistrates and now, under a colonel, sat calmly astride their mounts with sabres unsheathed and glinting in the morning sunlight. Positioned behind them were four lines of the yeomanry astride their hunters, again twenty-five to a line, all brandishing pistols, sabres, axes and shotguns, with the special constables in the next three lines, astride donkeys, trap ponies, dray horses and plough horses, all with their batons drawn and all waiting patiently for the order to ride Jem and the others down, which they were confident they would do since they were on the higher part of the market place and the impetus of any charge would be in their favour.

At dawn, as the sun began to climb above the dark cloudbank along the horizon, they had ridden quietly into the town and positioned themselves at the eastern end of the wide, sloping market place, which there stretched for well over a hundred yards and was fifty yards in breadth at its widest point: that way, the bright winter sun would be shining along the whole of its length and, being at that hour just above the rooftops, would blind any who looked towards them from the lower end. The bells of the parish church had been tolled as a call to arms of any citizen who was brave enough to join the special constables in their fight against the mob, who, having invaded their town and near enough drunk their brewery dry, were now expected to attack their silk mill as well. However, only four shopkeepers and their sons had joined the special constables, forming up at their rear on foot, though they did so more because they were fearful of any looting which might occur should the mob prevail than as a duty on their part. They, too, were armed with axes, spades, even hammers, any implement, in fact, that came to hand and which would crack a head or break an elbow or an arm and so force an opponent into retreat so there would be less chance of themselves getting hurt.

'God Almighty!' was all Dick Dollery could say, cupping one hand to shield his eyes against the low sun.

'There must be two hundred or more of them and all properly mounted, too,' a man near Jem whistled in surprise.

'I don't care if there's two thousand of them on elephants,' another man said determinedly, 'we're fighting for our rights and the right of the poor people to live a proper life, without having to bow and scrape to the likes o' the gentry and the lords and ladies.'

'We'll crack a few heads before we're through here today, eh, Jem?' Dick Dollery said, almost gleefully, gripping his five-foot bludgeon with its heavy end more fiercely and flaying the air as if practising his striking power.

'It's about time the yeomanry gentlemen showed up with their fine horses,' declared the Tricolour-carrier boldly. 'We'll give 'em a taste o' what they French revolutionaries gave their aristocrats.'

'I've got my hammer and I aim to crack a few heads with it afore I'm through,' declared Thomas Stuck with a grim determination, his black flag cast aside, his face set almost in a snarl.

Jem knew it was simply empty bravado: he had stood on too many fields of battle watching enemy cavalry leisurely forming up, close packed, their harnessing jingling, the sun glistening on their swords or the forest of pennants fluttering from their lances. He had felt, too, the ground trembling under the drumming hooves of hundreds of horses, had heard the chilling yells of the riders and waited with musket in hand and bayonet fixed as the full-blooded charge came straight at him and his comrades – so of them all, perhaps, he knew best what was about to happen.

The slope of the ground, which from end to end of the market fell nearly a dozen feet, and the slipperiness of the cobbles for shod horses would prevent a full-blooded charge: but, in the open of the market place, even at a canter, they would be ridden down by the first line, the dragoons, knocked flying and scattered as they passed through: then, before they could recover, the second line of yeomanry, if it were directed correctly, would barge into them, clubbing and slashing, perhaps to be followed by a third and a fourth line till they were surrounded and overwhelmed and each man solely at the mercy of a ring of horsemen. Yet he felt duty bound to stand his ground: he had not run before the French cuirassiers or the Polish lancers of Napoleon and he was not about to run from a motley band of gentry, shopkeepers, farmers and their sons armed with pistols, swords and clubs: only the presence of the dragoons truly troubled him.

Nor was Dick Dollery about to turn tail, or the youths Thomas Stuck and Daniel Downey, or any of their cohorts: some, remembering their rout of the local yeomanry the previous day, foolishly began to laugh at the sight of the special constables: but then, as Jem knew, that had been fifteen against four hundred. Now, he estimated, it was two hundred or more, led by professional cavalry, mounted, armed and disciplined, ranged against the same four hundred – if all stayed – most of whom were much the worse for their evening of heavy drinking, suffering all its blearying effects, still dazed with sleep, cold and hungry, uncertain, undrilled and ill-disciplined, and unused to the mass charge of cavalry of any kind.

Patiently, the horsemen waited a good twenty minutes for the youths and men around the brewery to wander out, to stare at them and then to take up their own positions: some men boldly formed themselves into a ragged line no more than two or three deep and stood stiffly to attention with their weapons, like a revolutionary army, though, facing east, they found the low morning sun was shining directly into their eyes and they had to cup their hands to their foreheads just as Dick Dollery had done to see any distance at all.

Joly Cobbold came to stand alongside Jem to eye the horsemen, who occupied the whole top quarter of the market place. 'It's an excuse for serving soldiers led by jumped up gentry to spill the blood of half-starved men and no more than that.' he said calmly. 'If they attack us, you and your friend see to the right, comrade, I'll see to the left and may all three of us be standing afterwards.'

With that, he moved away from Jem and Dick Dollery, disappearing into the crowd standing at the left end of the line: it was the last time he was to be seen by Jem that day or ever afterwards: for while Jem and the others were squinting into the bright sunlight, he vanished as mysteriously as he had emerged from the crowd on the morning of the great meeting at Hamwyte, stepping up on to the hillock in the centre of the Iron Age fort as the people gathered and, without a by your leave, as though he had called the meeting, addressing the crowd through his speaking trumpet. None then had known who he was or from where he had come: all Jem and the others ever knew about him was that he spoke with a London accent, called everyone 'comrade' or 'brother' and his talk was always of revolution, of overthrowing the upper classes, even dethroning the King and establishing a Utopia in which the rights and aspirations of the working people were to be first and foremost the concern of the Government in which he hoped to serve.

What actually happened was, when Joly Cobbold reached the end of the line on the left, he gave a few loud commands to those around him, so that his voice was heard, such as 'Stand fast, lads. We can beat this lot. We beat them yesterday and we can beat them today.' His remarks were greeted by smiles and weak cheers and the sheer arrogance and optimism of it induced several who had been hanging about at the rear to push forward and take their places in the line. Having given his rallying call, Joly Cobbold then declared loudly: 'Where are the rest?' And, turning to the man nearest to him, he added: 'Stay there, I am going to round up the slackers. We need every man in the line.'

With that, he hurried through the brewery's gates into the building itself and, unobserved, kept going, exiting it through a door at the far end, then out through the rear gates, down a lane, through a wood, across the fields beyond and was never seen again.

He was not alone: a number of others who had come wandering out of the brewery at the sound of the tolling bells, bleary-eyed and dull-witted, had taken one look at the silent lines of, to them 'militia cavalry,' at the far end of the market place and, detecting an air of determination in their quiet, disciplined manner, had themselves found an excuse to go back inside. Once inside, they, too, kept going, till a steady stream of men and youths was fleeing through the rear gates and the lane was full of running figures, most reasoning that they had had a good time, they had smashed many of the hated threshing machines, they had drunk their fill of good ale over the five, six or seven days they had been on the march, so what was the use of getting their heads broken over it? The consequence was that, instead of the four hundred who should have made their stand, there were only two hundred or so at the lower end of the market place facing an equal number of dragoons, yeomanry and special constables, as well as the shopkeepers and their sons.

Meanwhile, from the far end, one of the magistrates had trotted forward in the company of the colonel and a half-dozen of his dragoons to a midway point and had shouted out that he was going to read the Riot Act, which he proceeded to do: '*Our sovereign Lord the King chargeth and commandeth all persons, being assembled, immediately to disperse themselves, and peaceably to depart to their habitations, or to their lawful business, upon the pains contained in the said Act for preventing tumults and riotous assemblies. God save the King.*'

The words of it, however, were lost in a hoots of derision and shouts of defiance, to be followed by a shower of stones, which forced the magistrate, the colonel and his detachment of dragoons to retire to their lines, whereupon the colonel, the captain, the young lieutenant and the three magistrates conversed for a minute or so before wheeling their horses back into line.

'Right,' said the colonel, red-faced still from the abuse he had received, 'let's put an end to this damned nonsense. Bugler!'

So began the battle of Burestead Market, with a short bugle call. However, not all battles begin well and the sudden blast of the instrument so unsettled the hunter on which one of the magistrates was riding that it flinched and turned two full circles before he managed to bring it under control, much to the disgust of the colonel and the captain and the smiles of the dragoons themselves. But already the front line of dragoons, followed by the four lines of yeomanry, had jolted into motion with a jingling of harnesses and had begun their 'Walk march' towards the brewery and the mass of men and youths assembled at the far end.

'Trot,' came the next command, then, 'canter.'

FIFTY-FIVE

AT THE OTHER END of the market place, unused to the sight of so many horses trotting at them over cobbles and unused, too, to the sun glinting on so many unsheathed swords and sabres and gun barrels, some of those in the facing line broke to the side even as the horsemen began to move, flattening themselves against the walls of the houses, their courage deserting them. Others sought their escape down an entry between the buildings, while yet more turned and ran for the hoped-for sanctuary of the brewery building itself. Jem, Dick Dollery, the Tricolour-carrier Daniel Downey, the black-flag-carrier Thomas Stuck, and his cohorts, and a hundred and fifty or so others, mostly the younger men, stood their ground, however.

As the dragoons came up, a pistol was fired straight at the marchers' lines by an ill-disciplined rider in the yeomanry's first rank, unable to contain himself: the ball ploughed into the shoulder of the Tricolour-carrier Daniel Downey and sent him reeling back, clutching at the wound and screaming in pain, 'I am hit. They have killed me, they have killed me!'

Even as he sank to his knees, the cantering dragoons crashed into their line, striking indiscriminately with their sabres at any head, shoulder, arm or back they saw, to be followed almost immediately by the first, second and third ranks of the gentlemen's yeomanry. The marchers retaliated as best they could, with swinging hammers, whirling axes and flailing iron bars and whatever weapons they had brought with them, stabbing and slashing with pitchforks, billhooks, turnip knives, hooks and scythes at horse and horseman alike: neither man nor animal was spared.

Meanwhile, as had been planned, the fourth line of yeomanry and the special constables had held back from entering the actual fray: the colonel did not want too many bodies getting in each other's way in the confined space of the lower end of the market. Instead, as the battle was joined in front of the brewery, the two remaining lines separated, one went left and the other right, trotting down either side of the market place, keeping close to the walls of the houses and shops, intending to encircle the fighting and cut off the escape of any of the invaders, hacking as they went at any of the cringers who were still huddled there and forcing them back into the middle to be dealt with by the others.

As Jem had known it would be, the fight was lost before it had begun, as the wiser men and youths who had made off had already adjudged it: the sheer impetus of the dragoons' assault told as much as did the ineffective showing of many of the more drunken element amongst the marchers, who jumped over the low wall or streamed back through the gateway and, once in the brewery yard, if they found a means to get away, took it, leaving only the most forward of their comrades to fight a futile battle on the cobbles. The only fortunate thing for Jem and the others was that the impetus of the dragoons as they crashed through their line took a half-dozen of them leaping their mounts over the same low wall into the brewery yard itself, where they circled for a short while in an attempt to cut off the fleeing men and so temporarily took themselves out of the battle till a bugle blast recalled them. That still left nineteen disciplined men hacking at heads and arms and the four lines of yeomanry pushing forward in support to divide and surround them.

As a result, the marchers who had stood their ground quickly found themselves cut off into small groups, just pairs some, singly others. All over the cobbles at the lower end of the market place, desperate battles were being fought: indeed, the fury of the fighting was such that no quarter was being given and none was expected: fingers were cut off, heads opened up, arms near severed, all manner of bones broken, skulls concussed, noses and ears sliced, faces gashed and ribs driven in. Screams of pain rose up everywhere so that within a few minutes many desperately wounded men and youths upon both sides lay intermingled on the cobbles, moaning and groaning and being kicked and hit by any of the opposite force who saw them and trampled by neighing, blood-covered horses even as they lay there.

Injured horses, too, lay kicking on the cobbles, trying to rise but unable to do so because a leg was broken: for several of the marchers were striking directly with their hammers and iron bars at the animals' legs as they milled around them in the hope of bringing them down so that they could then deal with their fallen riders. They, in their turn, were charging at anyone on foot carrying an axe, hammer, bar, pitchfork, stave or knife of any kind in an attempt to bowl them over and skewer them on the ground.

Outnumbered and surrounded, for Jem and the others it was a matter of fighting where they stood, almost back to back: no thought of retreat entered his head or that of Dick Dollery: besides, the latter was too busy swishing viciously at as many heads and backs and arms and kneecaps of the yeomanry as he could reach with his long metal-ended bludgeon, determined to go down fighting.

Jem himself was also fully engaged: he had barely dealt with two of the dragoons as they rushed past him, poleaxing one from his galloping mount with a long stave of his own and expertly ducking under the swinging arm of another, than he had to strike out at three circling yeomanry from the line behind them. But such was the rapidity of his lunges with his stave as well as the discipline of his way of fighting and countering their strikes, that one was cracked upon the nose, a second bruised about the ear and a third received a fractured kneecap before they recognised the attributes of a soldier trained to fight at close quarters with braver foes than they. Wisely, they withdrew, preferring to continue circling him rather than launch an outright attack in which they would most probably sustain even worse damage to themselves.

After finally chasing off the three nervous yeomanry, who found their adversary could not be intimidated and so turned away to find easier prey, Jem found himself isolated from the main bunch of defenders, who had been forced back through the brewery gates into the yard. He had just beaten off a special constable, who attempted to slash his head open, when a young rider of no more than seventeen or eighteen years charged straight at him, intending to swipe with his own sabre from the other side. Jem again managed to duck under the swing of the blade before the flank of the onrushing horse rammed into his side and sent him sprawling on to the cobbles: fortunately, the momentum of his charge took the young rider a few yards past and, as he attempted to rein-in his horse and pull it round, its hooves slipped on the smooth sloping stones.

It was time enough for Jem to get to his feet and take up a position of defence: so when the young and inexperienced rider came trotting back at him, with his sabre pointed ready for a thrust at Jem's throat, he was able to step quickly forward and, before the youth could strike, give his mount a hard and vicious prod on the blaze with the end of his stave, which stopped the horse in its tracks and made it rear up, sending the rider reeling backwards in the saddle. It was a trick Jem and other troops had used with their long bayonets against milling French and Polish cavalry in Spain. As the horse's flailing hooves came crashing down and the young rider struggled to bring himself upright, Jem stepped forward again and this time cracked the youth hard across his shoulder, enough to break his collar bone, which he knew he had done from the fierce scream of pain which the rider gave out. Then, as he clutched at his broken shoulder, Jem whacked the rearing horse hard upon its rump, which sent it careering off through the melee, bumping into other mounts, disorientating them and being cursed by their riders.

'Behind you, Jem!' The shout came from where Dick Dollery and a group of ten or so others were fending off a half-dozen dragoons and twice that number of yeomanry, warily circling them, exchanging curses and boasts, but, it seemed, not inclined to attack and get their heads broken. Before Jem could turn to face the new threat, he was clubbed fiercely across the back of his head from behind: it was the father of the injured youth avenging his son. The blow sent Jem slumping to his knees amid the melee of trampling hooves and he knew little of what followed, for a second blow struck him as he attempted to rise and a dark curtain descended.

FIFTY-SIX

IT WAS sometime later – how long Jem did not know – that he sensed himself being lifted and carried over a man's shoulder with his throbbing head hanging down and blood dripping off his nose and forehead: the next thing he remembered was a dark grey curtain slowly dissolving before his face as he regained consciousness and the unmistakeable voice of Dick Dollery whispering a welcome return to the light. 'Glad to see thee are still with us, Jem. I thought thee were done for,' he said, but it was spoken in a low growl as if in warning not to react too violently.

'Thee must have a hard head and no mistake,' his friend went on. 'Some old fellow had a right goo at bashing thy head in. Gave thee two rare old cracks and no mistake.'

'How long have I been out?' Jem asked with a groan: and, without thinking, he raised his hand to feel the large swelling on the back of his skull: immediately pains shot up his bruised arm, ribs and shoulder, causing him to groan aloud. One side of his face felt stiff where blood had run down past his ear and had congealed and the back of his skull felt as if it had been split open: he realised, too, that someone had removed his topcoat and had torn off the whole of one sleeve of his shirt and had made it into a crude bandage to wrap around his head.

'Thee's been out three or four hours,' Dick Dollery infomed him, still in a low voice. 'T'is midday now. The bleeding has mostly stopped. I saw thee goo down, but I couldn't do anything to help ye. I was clubbed down myself, out cold, which turned out to be a blessing for the both of us.' He said it with a grin and a grimace of his own.

Looking about him, Jem saw that he was lying in a small hollow, some three feet deep, amid the roots of an ancient oak and Dick Dollery, similarly bloodied and for once not smiling, was lying upon his front and peering cautiously out over the rim through a screen of grass and dead brush which he had dragged across to cover them. Jem knew immediately where they were: they were in the large wood which lay behind the brewery and circled the western and north sides of the town. In the near distance, he could hear the sounds of men's voices, the the jingle of horses' harnesses as well as the shouted commands of various special constables and the more recognisable accents of the gentlemen yeomanry, who were hunting them down.

Suddenly, Dick Dollery placed a finger to his lips to signal for silence, at the same time lowering his head and sliding carefully back into the hollow: not thirty yards off, some horsemen trotted past along a track, but did not stop. After a half-minute or so, Dick Dollery slowly raised himself again to peep out: whatever danger there had been, it had passed.

Suddenly, a cry of 'Tally-ho' went up and there were loud and excited shouts and the sound of several horses drumming across earth: more shouts and then a great cheer: someone had broken cover, had been chased and had been caught: almost immediately the cheers were silenced by a man's stern rebuke as though he were reprimanding the gentlemen Yeomanry.

It was then that Jem noticed the open gash on Dick Dollery's face: it started at his scalp line and went right down across his left eye: the eye itself was covered by a neckerchief compress, which his friend held against it with a bloodied hand.

'Got caught in the eye,' Dick Dollery said, almost apologetically. 'Can't see a damned thing out of it. I reckon I've been blinded. It hurts something awful. Pain like a hot knife. Need to get me home to the little woman. Let her wash it and put something over it.' He smiled through his pain. 'We make a fine pair, don't we – me half-blind and thee with half thy scalp peeling off.' Had Jem's head not throbbed so much, he might have smiled with him.

As it was, they lay in the hollow at the foot of the old oak all afternoon, screened by the grasses and the brush, till the hunt moved off in a different direction: then, when darkness came early at about four o'clock, they slipped away in the opposite direction, circling the town first to the south, then away to the west, Dick Dollery having to help his old friend all the way, for he was still groggy and several times would have collapsed had he not been there.

They walked though the night, skulking along hedgerows and through woods, for there were still horsemen everywhere: the whole countryside, it seemed, was being scoured for those who had fought at Burestead Market and made their escape. Fortunately, the next day, a grey fog descended to cloak the fields and lanes and their progress was easier, though several times they had to go to ground as riders passed nearby: and once a group of special constables rode along one side of a hedgerow, chatting to themselves, while Jem and Dick Dollery lay unmoving on the other, scarcely daring to breathe.

As they made their way back towards Hamwick Dean, Dick Dollery took the opportunity to reveal how he had come to be injured: he had been attacked by one of the Yeomanry armed with a hunting whip loaded with iron at the end, who had flailed at him from a distance, catching him in his left eye and blinding him. In self-defence, Dick Dollery had seized a hammer dropped by its owner and had hurled it at the farmer, breaking his jaw and rendering him senseless on the cobbles. In retaliation, he had been set upon by three other yeomanry, comrades of the first man: fortunately, they were only carrying staves rather than sabres and once he had been rendered unconscious, he was left for dead: his face, arms and legs, ribs and back were a mass of bruises and his shirt and jacket were black with grime and blood.

'I managed to give a fair number some right good whacks till this chap caught me in the eye with his whip,' he boasted, but winced as he said it, for even speaking was an effort. 'I thought he had taken it right out at first. I managed to do him with a hammer I picked up, but I couldn't see properly and the next thing I knew I was being whacked by some others. They gave me some fearsome cracks for my trouble and must have thought they had done me in because they left me and went off after someone else. But I've got a harder head than that.'

While he and Jem lay unconscious, the fighting had continued for a further twenty minutes or so around the brewery yard before the last men broke and ran: though most did not get far and ran into the special constables and yeomanry who had cut off the lane at the back. It was enough time, however, for Dick Dollery to regain his senses and cross to his still unconscious friend, lift him on his back and carry him off down an alleyway between two of the shops, dodging the ineffectual grasp of two wounded yeomanry, who, though they each had been clouted hard with an iron bar, one with a broken thigh bone and one with a broken arm, still sought to make a captive of him. Three special constables also attempted to clatter after them, but were thwarted by washing lines and fencing and Dick Dollery was able to gain the safety of the woods where he went to ground.

It took them the whole of the next day to reach home, so slow was their progress: the late afternoon dusk was deepening into darkness when they crested an undulation in the farmland and, ahead of them, saw in the fold of the hills below the lights of a building which they both knew. 'That's the Green Man at Lower Rackstead,' cried Dick Dollery, pointing to a faint glimmer through the trees, 'We're home,

Jem, boy, we're home. I'm damned if I don't feel like stopping for a drink afore I go any further. The landlord'll put it on the slate, I'm sure. He knows me.'

Fortunately, the old inn was empty at that hour, though they made a strange pair as they sat in the snug warming themselves before the open fire, recovering, drinking as quietly and as unconcernedly as if they had just come out of the fields: not that they fooled the landlord, Abraham parrett, who put their drinks on his slate and brought them some bread and butter and pork to ease their hunger, almost as if he guessed what they had been about.

'Was thee at Mile End then, Dick?' he asked, setting two tankards down on the table.

'Mile End?' queried Dick Dollery, frowning and wincing at the same time.

'Aye,' said the landlord, thinking their puzzlement was a mere pretence, 'Mile End heath yesterday.'

'Noo, noo,' Dick Dollery replied, shaking his head and deliberately elongating the vowels for effect.

Clearly, the landlord did not believe them. 'Thee didn't get they cuts and bruises crawling through a hedge, I don't suppose, Dick Dollery,' he sniffed sarcastically.

On the same Monday morning as they had stood and fought at Burestead Market, another four hundred labourers from nearby villages had assembled on the heath to the east of Wivencaster, not thirteen miles from Hamwick Dean, for the purpose of getting farmers to sign a paper agreeing to raise their wages to two shillings a day, with beer, up to Lady Day. Five farmers had signed when, in the mid-afternoon, a troop of fifty special constables, led by a knight and a magistrate, had ridden up and had dispersed them with a charge: there had been fighting and a dozen of the labourers had been arrested.

The details of the event were still sketchy: so when two local men entered his hostelry in muddied clothing the day after, one with a bloodied shirtsleeve tied around his head, the other permanently holding a kerchief to a bloodied and swollen eye, both with several day's growth of beard and both walking exceedingly painfully because of bruising, Abraham Parrett, assumed they must have there, most probably since then hiding in a barn somewhere, even though they told him they had not: he hardly expected them to say anything else.

The outcome of the great meeting at Wivencaster, not the battle of Burestead Market or the great meeting at Witchley, was the talk of

Hamwyte, Hamwick Dean and the other villages around at that time: the other happenings were in another county and thus of no concern to the labourers of the lower county: they had their own melee to talk about.

'T'was a shame when all they wanted to do was to hold a meeting to help them raise their wages,' the landlord added with a sniff.

'Was there not a great meeting at Witchley, too?' Dick Dollery enquired, as innocently as possible.

The landlord had heard of that from one of the wagoners, who regularly stopped there and who had heard it, in turn, from a coachman. 'T'wasn't held,' he said glumly. 'The mayor and magistrates swore in all the town's tradesmen as special constables, whether they wanted to or not, as I heard it. Then a couple of hundred of the county yeomanry were mobilised along with a squadron of Royal Dragoons to occupy the heath. They wouldn't let anyone into the town, turned everyone back, they did, so that meeting was never held. There was some trouble over at Burestead Market, though, so I heard, a big fight with their yeomanry and some dragoons sent to stop some others marching there after they tore a silk weaving mill down, so I heard – '

He did not realise how interested his two listeners were.

'I heard, too, some was arrested and are all locked up in the county gaol at Edmundsbury along with a hundred others they took elsewhere for other things,' the innkeeper added. 'The gaol is full to burstng, they say. The county yeomanry and the special constables are said to be scouring the countryside right up to the county boundary looking for others. Just as well you weren't there.'

'Aye,' replied Dick Dollery, innocently, 'just as well we weren't.' Despite the pain from their cuts and bruises, both managed a smile.

FIFTY-SEVEN

HAD ANYONE been walking along the ridge-top road towards Hamwick Dean in the mid-afternoon of the next day, they would have seen a very disconsolate Ephraim Simms trudging towards the lane which led to Lower Rackstead with his official truncheon of office hanging from his belt. That same passer-by might well have noticed the parish constable's dismal countenance and deduced that something was definitely amiss – it was: that day Ephraim Simms was wishing he had not been elected constable for that particular year – any other year, yes, but just not that year.

At first, all had gone well for him following his election at the Easter vestry: during the summer, there had been little to concern him: a dispute over some cattle straying through a hedgerow on to the Merchant Staplers road, a suspicious snare found by Titus Broake's gamekeeper in one of the woods, an argument between two of the village girls over a boy which had ended with hair-pulling and face-scratching. After that, there had been the theft of a petticoat belonging to one of Marcus Howie's four daughters, supposedly from a washing line at Smallponds Farm, though he suspected what had happened there, judging from the faces of the two maids, was one of them had burned it with an iron and had hidden it somewhere to escape chastisement by her mistress. Those were all he had had to concern him, plus the usual friendly warning to the landlord of the Carpenters' Arms to observe Sunday properly and to close his premises while the divine service was being held or he would have to take him off to Hamwyte to face the magistrates again and he did not want to do that, especially as he occasionally liked to drink in the Carpenters' Arms himself of an evening.

Then had come the rumours of rick burnings and machine-breakings south of the Thames by angry farm labourers: it had been the talk of the Wayfarers' and the Carpenters' Arms' and throughout October had seemed to sweep along the southernmost counties like a contagion, before circling up into Wiltshire, Berkshire and the northern Home Counties, village by village and Hundred by Hundred, till eventually it had reached the Hamwyte Hundred itself in the mid-November and most particularly Hamwick Dean. Then the whole village seemed to have gone mad: first had come the threatening letters to the Titus Broake, the parson and the three farmers: then someone had put a pistol ball through the parson's window and, following that, a crowd of three hundred or more, so Parson Petchey had informed him, had surrounded his parsonage and forced him to reduce the tithe, which he was not at all happy in doing. After that, near enough the whole village, including half of Lower Rackstead and Merchant Staplers, had gone on the rampage, smashing five threshing machines, two at the Hall and one apiece at Amos Peakman's farm, at Marcus Howie's place and in Joshua Godwin's barn. There was, too, the business over what he had been told was an attempt to burn down Titus Broake's barn, but that was in dispute because he had been told by others that, though someone had set it, others of the men had put the blaze out themselves!

Things had got worse, it was true, with the wrecking of the Inworth poorhouse: the way he had heard it, it had been a mob from Salter which had started it and done most of it, led by 'Tater' Sack, who everyone knew was a part-time smuggler anyway, but he and four others from Salter had all gone missing: they had slipped across to Belgium on one of their smuggling boats, some said, and were most probably sitting in a port there with those with whom they did business in brandy and silks, waiting for all the troubles to die down. There were rumours that Dick Dollery, Nat Newman, Enos Diddams, John Romble, Will Stubbs, Tom Judd and, some were saying, Jem Stebbings, too, had been seen there, though Ephraim Simms had heard varying accounts of what Jem Stebbings had been doing in Inworth on that day, though he suspected that might not be the case with the six others.

Without a doubt, the Inworth poorhouse riot thirteen days earlier was the worst incident so far, but what could he do about that? He had not been there to see it for himself and no witnesses had come forward to identify anyone for sure from Hamwick Dean, Merchant Staplers or Lower Rackstead: even, Mussett, the poorhouse master, was saying he did not recognise anyone and, from what Ephraim Simms had heard also, other than 'Tater' Sack, there had been too many of them to be identified individually anyway and one could hardly arrest six hundred or more! That matter would have to be left to the Justices since Inworth was a separate parish and what happened there was not his business: they had their own parish constable, the haberdasher,

Benjamin Easter, and he had been 'sick abed' on that day, so he and his wife both said.

On the other matters, the farmers who had agreed voluntarily to pay the men what they should have been paying them anyway had not made a complaint to him about it: and, since most of the whole village had taken part in the destruction of the five threshing machines and he had been 'away from the village' at the time and so had not seen that either, he could hardly be expected to arrest everyone in Hamwick Dean: he had to drink with the men and serve their wives in his shop, which made everything even more awkward. He was not going to lose trade over a few new-fangled threshing machines, which were insured anyway, he had discovered, so there was no great loss to anyone.

Besides, this threshing machine business was happening all over and was not peculiar just to Hamwick Dean: and he had heard, too, that the magistrates in Kent had let off a lot of the men and youths who had come up before them for the very same thing: if they did not think it so great a crime, then neither did he!

He was glad Jaikes had gone: he would not be missed: and Parson Petchey had written his own letter saying that he was prepared to reduce the tithes so he could not see what action he could take there, even if he was claiming that he did it under extreme duress: besides, he knew that one or two of the farmers had secretly put the men up to it in the first place: so who was the more guilty?

As far as those 'Captain Swing' letters were concerned, he had given up trying to find out who had written them: he had his suspicions – he was not a fool – and supposed it to be any or all of those whose names were being mentioned the most, but he was, after all, a grocer first and he had no intention of asking everyone in the village if they could write and then demand they give a sample of their handwriting to find out for sure. Anyway, he did not think it so serious a crime: just the men protesting and copying the daft goings-on in other places and thinking themselves big because of it. The firing of the pistol ball through the parsonage window was far more serious than the actual letters, in his view, though he was convinced whoever fired did so to miss since the ball had hit the ceiling rather than the back wall.

As things went, he was no further along with that investigation than he was with anything else: he just wished he had not been elected, particularly as that day he was in possession of a warrant which could not be ignored, a warrant from the Hamwyte magistrates' bench to arrest one Jem Stebbings, someone whom he had always admired, a man who had fought for his King and Country and had actually helped to beat Boney on the battlefield at Waterloo. Jem Stebbings had had a hard enough time of things as it was after the shocking death of his wife not two months before while he was in Melchborough Gaol: and it had been reported to him that Jem Stebbings had, by his leadership, managed to curb the worst excesses of some of the youths and get the men of Hamwick Dean and Lower Rackstead and Merchant Staplers all what they had asked, including the guarantee of work threshing the corn in the barns till the March ploughing began, as they used to do.

If only they had left the threshing machines alone and not broken them up, damn them, the fools, he would not have to be doing what he was about to do: but the warrants had been sworn to by Titus Broake, Amos Peakman, Marcus Howie and Joshua Godwin and even Parson Petchey, in front of the Hamwyte magistrates and had been brought to him to serve with the instruction that it was his duty to carry them out as soon as he was able. At first, he had not been able, for when they reached him on the Saturday, Jem Stebbings along with Dick Dollery, Enos Diddams, John Romble, Will Stubbs and Tom Judd had all gone missing and had been for a week: unusual, but then they were unusual times.

Then that noon, word had reached him that Jem Stebbings was back: he had been seen the previous evening leaving the Green Man at Lower Rackstead with Dick Dollery: and, as it was reported to him, he had a shirtsleeve bandage wrapped around his head, it most probably meant he had a run-in with someone, more than likely the county yeomanry over at Mile End, if he were any judge.

Like everyone else, Ephraim Simms had heard of the trouble between labourers and yeomanry at Burestead Market up in the next county, but that was of no interest to him: Jem Stebbings's return was what interested him, though he had no intention of asking him where he had been for the past week, not unless someone laid a complaint against him over that. He had enough on his plate carrying out the warrants which had already been issued: it had made him the most unpopular man in the village – after Titus Broake and Parson Petchey, Amos Peakman, Marcus Howie, Joshua Godwin and the thankfully absent Joshua Jaikes: people were beginning to look at him in strange ways – ways he did not like.

But when all was said and done, he was the parish constable and was expected to do his duty: what galled him was having to carry out his instructions at the instigation of two men whom he himself heartily despised, Titus Broake, who, in his view, was the cause of most of the misery in the village, and Parson Petchey, who, also in his opinion, ran the lord of the manor a close second for causing upset and strife. The old goat of a parson was, also in his view and that of many others, a sanctimonious hypocrite, who preached that the meek would inherit the earth, but ensured that they did not do so while he was on it: from what Ephraim Simms had seen, he lived in a state of supreme luxury. The whole place, the parish constable had often thought, would be better off without either of them, Petchey and Broake!

It was true the complaints of Amos Peakman, Marcus Howie and Joshua Godwin had added to the warrants and he had taken Enos Diddams, John Romble, Will Stubbs and Tom Judd into custody when they had returned on the Monday from wherever they had been. On that day, however, he had had the three special constables from amongst the tradesmen in Hamwyte for company to help him escort them to the magistrate's house: this time he was having to act on his own because, so Heginbotham had told him at the Hall, Titus Broake was off riding somewhere with the reformed yeomanry, gallivanting all over the county after other lawbreakers, he supposed, while Amos Peakman, Marcus Howie and Joshua Godwin, having been sworn in as special constables at Wivencaster, had ridden over to the coast that very morning where several instances of arson and machine-breaking had occurred the day previously and they were out to round up the perpetrators.

It was just pure coincidence that, as Hamwick Dean's parish constable was walking towards Jem Stebbings's hovel of a 'cottage' on the lane to Lower Rackstead, so Jem, still with his head bandaged, was walking along the same ridge-top road on his way to Ephraim Simms's grocery shop, with Jed and Thirza beside him: so there was no way that Ephraim could avoid him or that he could avoid Ephraim.

'I was just on my way to see thee, Jem,' the parish constable said, rather sheepishly.

'I was just on my way to call at your shop, Ephraim,' replied Jem, knowing that the parish constable would not be visiting him for any other reason than the purposes of the law and trying to act as if he suspected nothing.

'Jem, I am sorry to have to tell thee,' returned Ephraim Simms, 'but I have a warrant for thee from the magistrates at Hamwyte.' He produced a roll of paper from inside his coat, but without any flourish.

Though not surprised that Ephraim Simms should eventually seek him out in the name of the Justices, Jem still affected surprise: a man was innocent till proved guilty. 'A warrant? What for, Ephraim?'

'Thy arrest, Jem, I am sorry to say. I have to do my duty.'

'On what charges?'

'Thee can read as well as I, Jem, read it for thyself,' said the parish constable, thrusting the scrolled paper at him.

Jem saw that the warrant had been sworn to by Titus Broake and signed by two of the magistrates at Hamwyte: it charged him with being the leader of a mob which had smashed his threshing machines and further charged that he had attempted to burn down his barn.

'Warrant: William the Fourth, by the Grace of God of the United Kingdom of Great Britain and Ireland, Defender of the Faith. To the Sheriff of the County – Greeting. We command you that you omit not for any liberty in your bailiwick, but that you enter therein and take Jem Stebbings, late of the parish of Hamwick Dean in your said county, labourer, if he shall be found in your bailiwick, and him safely keep so that you may have his body before our Justices of Oyer and Terminer ... to answer to us concerning certain felonies whereof he stands indicted...'

Ephraim Simms eyed Jem closely. 'I have to ask thee,' he said, stepping back a pace and resting one hand on the truncheon of office in his belt, 'are ye willing to come to the magistrate's house with me?'

'Aye, Ephraim,' Jem answered, with a sigh. 'I have no quarrel with you. I will not give you any bother.'

'I thank'ee for that, Jem,' said Ephraim. 'I have to escort thee to the magistrate's house at Hamwyte – thee and Dick Dollery. Thee are the last two. I am sorry to say that I took Enos, John Romble, Will Stubbs and Tom Judd a couple o' days agoo when they come back ahead of thee and they have already been afore the magistrates at Hamwyte and are in Melchborough Gaol this very day. Nat Newman I took a week agoo. I'm sorry to say, Jem, today I have to take thee as well.'

'Are all the warrants sworn to by Broake?' Jem wanted to know.

'Aye, but not only him,' replied the constable. 'Peakman, Howie and Godwin have all sworn to warrants as well and thee and Dick and are named in them all, as are the others, but thee and Dick are said to be the ringleaders.'

The constable gave an embarrassed cough. 'The parson has also sworn out an oath and has named thee over his tithes being reduced,' he added, reddening at the fact that he himself had said at the time, 'It is a damned good thing. It is about time they were reduced. Men can't afford to live paying that high an amount.'

'I am sorry for thy children,' said the parish constable, looking down at Jed and Thirza. 'I will give thee time before we set off to make arrangements with one of the women of the village to look after them while ye are gone.'

'Thank you for that, Ephraim,' said Jem.

'I'm sorry again, Jem, but I has to cuff thee,' said the parish constable, taking the cuffs from his coat. 'I wish thee good luck because I don't know what will happen to ye after this, but I wish thee good luck. I'd rather I wasn't doing it, but I has no choice.'

All Jem could do was to shrug his shoulders and hold out his hands: it was no less than he expected: there was no sense in running away from it, no point in trying to evade the law: it would only have made the whole situation worse. He consoled himself with the knowledge that he had expected sooner or later that Titus Broake and the parish constable, perhaps with Amos Peakman and a couple of special constables in tow, might pay him a call after his return: he consoled himself, too, with the knowledge – his belief, at least – that he had done what he had done in the name of humanity, to ensure that starving men, women and children would no longer starve slowly on the parish and that would stand him in good stead before any magistrate.

Jem was led first to the Wayfarers' where he found Dick Dollery seated in the bay-windowed parlour surrounded by his wife and all six daughters, three of whom had recently returned from the demolished silk mill at Longstreet, as well as the wives and families of the other four who had been taken on their return and who were there to give support to Lizzie Dollery. Though handcuffed as well, Dick Dollery was still managing to drink a pint of ale, while next to him his wife looked both angry and despondent, knowing what might well happen and fearing it, and his six daughters hugged each other, white-faced and tearful. 'You, too,' was all Dick Dollery said with a forced smile when Jem, a tearful Thirza and a blank-faced Jed, entered.

Indeed, the glumness only came upon Dick Dollery's face when, unexpectedly, thinking of something to say, he asked Jem: 'Have ye heard the news of poor Mr. Able? He was found dead last Wednesday in his summerhouse. Funeral was Monday. We missed that, I am sorry to say. T'is a sad day for thee and me to hear of his going, sad for all of us, Enos and the others, too, and no mistake. We could do with him now, I reckon.' He gave a sigh and a sad shake of the head. 'Well, life goos on, so here's to a good old friend remembered.' With that, he raised his tankard with his cuffed hands and drank its contents in one swallow, before rising to his feet.

For the first time since he had met Ephraim Simms on the road, Jem felt the weight of depression descend upon his shoulders: without Mr. Able's willingness to help them, their cause, though not lost, was made all the more difficult: with his death, they had lost a learned friend indeed.

'T'is time to goo, t'will be dark in an hour,' said the constable, consulting his pocket watch: and immediately the room was a bedlam of crying children and weeping women.

'Don't worry, Jem, my wife will look after your two,' Dick Dollery assured him.

'They can stay with me and mine. I will do my best for them,' said his friend's tearful wife.

'Look after yourselves,' Jem said, giving Jed a pat on the shoulder: and while Jed, as any boy his age would, remained stoically beside his father, refusing the women's attempts to console him, poor Thirza clung to Jem so hard and was weeping so much they had to prise her from him before he could move off: her screams cut Jem the most, more so than Jed's passive, sorrowful gaze.

As a final act, Jem gave Lizzie Dollery what money he possessed so as to be of some help towards their keep and told her to take anything she needed from the 'cottage.'

There was a sad resignation in the eyes of Ephraim Simms as he stood by the door, holding it open: in that moment, he would not have cared if the two of them had made a run for it: it would have saved him the bother of what he was going to have to do.

Outside, half the village had gathered to witness their departure and they now trailed behind them for a mile or so as they went down the hill towards Hamwyte, all sorry to see Jem Stebbings and Dick Dollery being taken, especially as five others had already been cuffed and marched off to Hamwyte: who knew how many more might be arrested?

Several times poor Ephraim heard his name cursed and he reddened each time on hearing it: some might even have been tempted to seize him and pinion his arms while his two prisoners made their escape across the fields in the darkness: certainly Dick Dollery's wife had half a mind to try.

Just as they reached the small hump-back bridge at the bottom of the long hill, she could contain herself no longer: her girls were all crying, young Thirza was crying, there were villagers all around and her poor deluded rebel of a husband was letting himself be marched out of the parish to the magistrate's house at Hamwyte and a night in the bridewell and goodness knows where after that! She felt that she had to do something: her answer was to throw a stone the size of a chicken's egg, which sailed inches past Ephraim Simms's head and bounced off the road ahead of them.

'No stone-throwing,' Jem cried firmly, whirling round. 'Ephraim is only doing his duty. He has a warrant and he has to carry it out. Dick and I have both agreed to go with him. This is far enough for the lot of you, I think. We would both prefer it if you did not come any farther, any of you. It'll be dark in a half-hour and we still have a way to go. We have to reach the magistrate's house before nightfall. We shall make better time if we go on from here on our own.'

Both men took a last look back after they had crossed the small hump-back bridge, for there the road curves to the right and those standing at the bottom of the hill watching them go were thereafter lost to view.

FIFTY-EIGHT

IN HAMWYTE, Jem and Dick Dollery were taken to the courthouse, where, before the chief magistrate and four others, the warrants were scrutinised as per norm and they were asked to confirm their names, ages and places of abode. The law then specified that some types of offence could be dealt with summarily by magistrates without a jury, but others had to be tried in one of the jury courts, namely Assizes held before judges or Quarter Sessions before a bench of county magistrates: where one of these jury courts was appropriate, the magistrate to whom the suspects were brought could commit them to gaol to await trial if he thought the evidence justified it. In that county, suspects usually went to the next court, whether it was Assizes or Quarter Sessions, unless there was a potential penalty of death or transportation for life, in which case they waited for the Assizes.

The business before the bench completed, Jem and Dick Dollery were marched by the town's two constables to the old bridewell at the bottom of the High Street, a plain building, with barred windows and three cells, each no more than eight feet by eight feet. As it turned out, there were thirty others already there, lads and men from the coastal villages who had been rounded up the previous day for machine-breaking, rick-burning and riotous assembly in their part of the county, rounded up, in fact, by Amos Peakman and his ilk. They had been marched into Wivencaster, put up before a full bench of magistrates sitting in the castle, then sent on to Melchborough for trial at the Special Winter Assizes, which had begun there on the Monday: they had reached Hamwyte as darkness fell and so had been turned into the bridewell to pass the night. Jem and Dick Dollery would accompany them when they continued on to Melchborough in the morning.

The small bridewell was, in fact, so overcrowded that, once they had been leg-ironed and chained to the rest, Jem and Dick Dollery had to squeeze themselves down between the prone forms to find room to settle: not unnaturally, the others were reluctant to move and there were grumbles of protest as the two friends did so. All the prisoners showed signs of having met the yeomanry in the same way as had Jem and Dick Dollery at Burestead Market: for they all had cuts or bruises, some to an arm, some to a leg, or a shoulder or their head. Some had managed to bandage their wounds, but for several, the only cleansing was their own spit and the blood had congealed black upon their cuts.

The actual incarceration did not bother Jem as much as it did Dick Dollery, since, for all his devious ways, it was still his first time: Jem, of course, had been in the House of Correction at Steadleigh as well as Melchborough Gaol and so was at least used to the close confinement: he had, too, spent several storm-tossed days, battened down below, aboard a ship sailing across the Bay of Biscay for Cadiz, so lying close-up amongst a number of other snoring men was not a new experience. He at least slept, though so close-packed were the prisoners in the small bridewell that, when he accidentally turned in his sleep, he pulled at the slashed arm of the man chained beside him, who immediately let out a string of invective and might have caused trouble had not Dick Dollery, still awake, given the man a swift kick with his boot and warned him to keep his silence, using the metaphoric, 'We're all in the same boat here,' which did not go down too well with some of them.

The only thing that truly bothered either of them was their hunger and their thirst: perhaps under orders from the magistrates or just plain forgetfulness, the gaoler did not bring any food or water that evening for his two latercomers: it was not till the morning that he and his assistant placed a single loaf of bread and a jug of water just inside the door of each cell.

'Divide that up amongst yourselves as quick as you can, boys,' he urged. 'You'll be off soon and I doubt you'll get much else today. The yeomanry are here to take you to Melchborough. The whole town is waiting outside to see you goo, though don't expect everyone to cheer, least ways not those at the top of the town. T'is a sad day for England this, a sad day indeed. Some of you'll be lucky to escape the drop, I reckons.'

Outside the day had dawned grey and frosty: the pale winter sun had still not risen much above the town's rooftops when they were all taken out and made to stand shivering in the cold while their leg-irons were removed, though the curb chain through the eyelet of the handcuffs around their wrists was retained to link them together and foil any chance of flight.

As they formed up, Dick Dollery let out a curse. 'Look who is up there!' he hissed, able only to nod towards a figure astride a grey hunter: for there at the head of the column sat Titus Broake, wearing the blue jacket uniform of the old Volunteer Militia, acting as if he had made all the captures himself and was in charge of the whole procession.

Beside him rode a youthful lieutenant of yeomanry, astride a sheened chestnut mare and armed with a brace of pistols, one of which he kept fingering continually as if expecting the prisoners, linked though they were by the curb chain, to make a run for it, while on either side of the column rode four gentlemen of the yeomanry, eight in all, each got up in old Militia uniform, with their sabres drawn and resting on their shoulders, ready to prick anyone who did not keep pace with them. Behind came a further eight special constables, being paid sixpence a mile and lodging expenses for their duty that day, similarly armed and similarly divided on either side so that the whole length of the column was fully covered. Bringing up the rear, each armed with a pistol apiece, were the five Hamwyte magistrates who had issued the warrants and had then committed them to the bridewell: in all, twenty-three armed men to guard thirty-two chained prisoners.

Titus Broake had been informed of Jem's and Dick Dollery's arrest on his return to the Hall the previous evening and had ridden over to Hamwyte especially: there was a look of grim satisfaction upon his face as he rode his mount down the line of prisoners and, pushing between those of two of the special constables, purposely allowed it to bump against Jem and Dick Dollery, chained the one behind the other, sending both stumbling momentarily.

'I warned you, Stebbings, and you, Dollery, that I would hold you responsible for what you did,' he declared. 'I have been waiting for you to return from wherever it is you have been for the last ten days. Now I have you. You will pay dearly for what you did. The full weight of the law will be brought down upon you. I will see to that. I will see the both of you dangling before I am through.' With that, he wheeled his horse away and rode back to the head of the column.

Curiously, by being singled out and addressed so harshly, Jem's and Dick Dollery's esteem rose in the eyes of the other prisoners. 'I see thee has made a friend of the local big-wig,' one of the older men chuckled, which somewhat restored the spirits of those around them. 'Thee must have done something terrible bad to get up his nose.'

The whole town had indeed turned out to watch them leave: as the bridewell was located at the lower end, the labourers and their families were there *en masse* to shout their support for the chained prisoners as they marched up the High Street and to hurl insults and threats at their escort. At the turn-off to Hamwick Dean, the approximate dividing point between the lower and higher ends of the town, Jem and Dick Dollery both heard their names being called: it was Lizzie Dollery, tearful, but waving, standing amid the crowd on the narrow pavement, with her six girls around her, also weeping again: and, thankfully for Jem, alongside them were Jed and Thirza, staring in silent shock at the sight of their father passing chained in line and marshalled by a group of armed and mounted men.

From the more well-to-do inhabitants of Hamwyte, who lined the wider pavements at the top of the town, there were just cold, sullen stares, for they were all owners of fine houses and other property and for a fortnight or so had lived in abject terror of a repeat of the riot and robbery which they had suffered thirteen years before. Some of the younger women even smiled and waved their handkerchiefs at the lieutenant and the riders of the gentlemen's yeomanry and there were even smiles for Titus Broake and the magistrates, though none for the special constables, who were mostly tradesmen anyway.

It took the prisoners most of the day to walk the eight miles to Melchborough: in each village through which they trudged, the people came to stand silently at the roadside to watch them pass, sadness showing in their eyes to see men and lads treated so, especially since they were of their own kind. Halfway there, a steady sleeting drizzle began, which grew gradually heavier, blotting out the landscape on either side of the road. At one point, they were almost run down by a coachman bent on reaching Hamwyte as fast as he could travel: his coach came rumbling out of the afternoon gloom and would have ploughed into the chained line and their escorts had not the young lieutenant seen its lantern bobbing towards them and spurred his horse quickly forward to 'halloo' the coachman into steering his sweating horses to the side of the road.

For Jem and the others it was almost a relief when, in the late afternoon, drenched and cold, they at last crossed the gravelled concourse and approached the gaol's lodge and main gate: the yeomanry, on the command of their lieutenant, halted there and left it to Titus Broake, the five magistrates and the special constables to usher them through into the cobbled yard, where they stood in the sleeting rain as a half-dozen warders, showing no great hurry to receive them, sauntered out to inspect them.

'Special gaol delivery, thirty-two prisoners escorted from Hamwyte. I have the papers here,' declared Titus Broake, somewhat officiously, still mounted, handing down the papers concerning each of them to the head warder, who let out a sigh of exasperation.

'How many more of these damned fools do you intend to bring in?' he demanded gruffly. 'We have had four deliveries this week already. I don't know that the gaol will hold many more. They are coming in from all over. If any more come in, there won't be enough room for our usual villains.'

'You will just have to find room and you may well have a hundred more before we are done,' declared Titus Broake, churlishly, 'for we aim to end what we are about once and for all.'

He motioned to one of the dismounted special constables to release the curb chain which held the men: once that had been withdrawn, the same man went along the line, unlocking their cuffs and handing them to a colleague: the Hamwyte special constables intended to take their irons back with them. It at least allowed Jem and the other prisoners to rub their sore wrists, for the irons had chaffed them all the way and Jem's skin was red and raw from it.

Having delivered their thirty-two, chained and 'dangerous' prisoners without any escaping, the escort party was concerned only with heading off into the centre of Melchborough and the inns there to get out of the rain, for they were as soaked and bedraggled as their charges, and just as hungry.

Titus Broake, however, had a different mission and rode straight to the house of the town's chief magistrate: he had business to conduct with him and the County Sheriff which would concern the Grand Jury sitting the following morning. He meant to have 'his prisoners,' that is, the Hamwick Dean miscreants, Jem Stebbings and Richard Dollery, dealt with quickly at the current Special Winter Assizes: he had no intention of waiting till the Epiphany Quarter Sessions or the Lent Assizes.

Jem and the others, meanwhile, were marched into the gaol. There was the familiar shout, 'Fall in!' and again, without waiting for the bewildered prisoners to comply, the warders pushed and pulled them roughly into line. 'Left turn, up the steps, march!' the cry rang out and once more Jem found himself being herded up the steps, through the door and along the short, dark corridor into the same long, bare room lit by oil lamps as before. The same threat was given that, if they had any letters, locks of hair from wives or sweethearts, or anything that they might have brought in from the outside, they must give it up or, if found once inside, it would be destroyed regardless.

Then came the order, 'Everyone strip! All clothes off for the medical officer's inspection!' with the same reluctance and alarm from those who had not expected it and the same crude chastisement from the warders.

Their clothes were again scooped up and thrown in a pile in one corner: then they were pushed into line again, facing the doorway and sent one by one across the passage to where the same surly medical officer waited.

A different convict was wielding the scissors and the cut-throat razor in the bath room: as Jem sat on the stool, flinching at the scrape of the razor, the barber bent his head close to his ear. 'They mean to make an example of you,' he whispered, sympathetically. 'You lads have been causing them-that-be no end of trouble and they mean to make you pay. Be prepared, squire, be prepared.'

'More of the same, I see, Mr. Hoskins,' was the deputy-governor's surly comment, spoken with a sigh, as he raised a disdainful eyebrow to looked along the line. 'Goodness gracious, how many more of you are they going to deliver to us?'

'Let us hope that it is the last of them, sir,' the chief warder said with a sniff, looking along the line of prisoners himself with a similarly disdainful eye, before reading the rules in the same dull monotone as before.

After that, the chaplain stepped forward and once again, as he spoke, the tears began to well in the eyes of the younger prisoners...

FIFTY-NINE

WHEN THE FIRST of the 'Swing' rioters had been arrested in Kent in the September, soon after the outbreaks began, they had been put up before the county magistrates and had received lenient sentences. Many received only one to two months in the county gaol as punishment, though with hard labour on the tread-wheel or picking oakum: and some of the very young offenders, the fourteen-year-olds, fifteen-year-olds and the like, the boys and 'half-men,' received just a warning from the magistrates. Their part in the machine-breaking was treated as the exuberance of youth, while some of the older youths who appeared before the various magistrates, the seventeen-year-olds and eighteen-year-olds, were considered more in need of correction and were bound over to keep the peace in recognizances of fifty pounds each.

Amongst the labourers, there had always been a belief that their suffering justified their actions, so afterwards there would be no price to pay: indeed, one band attacking the machinery in an iron foundry in Hampshire on a Saturday, feeling that the job was unfinished, announced to the manager that they would let Sunday pass, as it was the 'Lord's Day,' and they would return to complete their destruction on the Monday, such was their belief in the righteousness of their cause.

In the beginning, fortune had favoured the rising and there had been hope early on that the powers-that-be would bow to the labourers' demands and grant an improvement in wages and, at the same time, approve a reduction of rents and tithes for tenant farmers. In places where the decline of the labourer had been watched for years without pity or dismay, magistrates and country gentlemen suddenly began to call meetings to consider the desperate condition of the poor: but as the rioting spread and drew in men other than agricultural labourers, so the authorities became ever more alarmed: and even those landowners who recognised that the labourers were miserable feared that they were witnessing the start of a revolution. Two things frightened them: one was the rapid spread of the revolt and the second was the scarcity of troops to deal with it.

Almost immediately on his appointment, the new Home Secretary, Lord Melbourne, had on November the twenty-fourth called for the yeomanry to be mobilised to go to the aid of the gentry of the shires. Conciliatory methods were to be abandoned and action was to be substituted for diplomacy: firmness and vigour must be used by the lords-lieutenant and the magistrates in quelling disturbances, his lordship declared, and he virtually promised them immunity from prosecution for illegal acts done in the discharge of their duty.

The impoverished, half-starved labourers of southern England were seen as akin to marauding Huns and the mysterious 'Captain Swing' was likened to a second Attila: the Government had come to regard the revolt almost as if a war had been declared against it: indeed, the new Whig Prime Minister, Lord Grey, was to use that very word when he began a speech in the House of Lords with the statement: 'With regard to this war ...'

He went on to declare: 'I can only promise that the state of the country shall be made the object of our immediate, our diligent and unceasing attention...' Later, in the same speech, he added: 'I here declare ... that it is my determined resolution, wherever outrages are perpetrated, or excesses committed, to suppress them with severity and vigour.' His words drew loud cheers from their lordships, their graces the bishops, their honours the judges and the other peers.

Lord Grey continued: 'Severity is, in the first instance, the only remedy which can be applied to such disorders with success and, therefore, although we are most anxious to relieve the distress of the people who are suffering, let them be well assured they shall find no want of firm resolution upon our part – ' More 'hear, hears' from their lordships.

On November the twenty-sixth, the day the Salter-ites attacked the Inworth poor house, *The Times* reported that seventy men and youths had been apprehended near Newbury in Berkshire and that 'sixty of the most forward, half-starved fellows have been taken into custody some two miles from Southampton.'

Thus, by the time of the great meeting at Hamwyte on Saturday, November the twenty-seventh, arbitrary arrests had become the custom in other places: the gaols in some counties were full to overflowing as labourers who took up the cry for higher wages found themselves promptly arrested.

In West Sussex and Hampshire, though the rioting in those counties had lasted little more than a week, three hundred or more prisoners had been rounded up in each to await trial: and in Berkshire, the gaols at Reading and Abingdon were so overcrowded by the end of the month that the Newbury Mansion House and workhouse had to be converted into gaols.

So terrified were the propertied classes by the news of fires that when a group of labourers set light to some straw in a field at Stotfold, in Bedfordshire, when the farmers refused their demand for higher wages, a hundred special constables rode out to the arrest 'ten ringleaders.' Indeed, such was the climate of fear and suspicion that innocent labourers were likely to find themselves being bundled into prison for as little as giving a sour look or making a discontented remark.

'Within a few days from the time I am addressing your Lordships, the sword of justice shall be unsheathed to smite, if it be necessary, with a firm and vigorous hand, the rebel against the law,' the Lord Chancellor, Henry Brougham, told the Lords on December the second.

By December the fourth, even as Jem and the others marched towards Burestead Market, *The Times* correspondent in Wiltshire and Hampshire could report that quiet was restored in those counties. 'The peasantry are cowed and the men who have been prominent in the mobs are being picked out and arrested every day,' he stated.

Where special grievances existed in a village, the labourers were not slow to take advantage of the rising to seek redress: thus at Walden, in Buckinghamshire, in addition to demanding two shillings-a-day wages, with sixpence for each child and a reduction of the tithes, they argued for the restoration of 'Bun Day,' upon which, they claimed, buns used to be thrown from the church steeple and beer given away free in the churchyard and a sermon preached.

On December the sixth, the very day that Jem and Dick Dollery were engaged in the battle of Burestead Market, *The Times* had stated in a leader that never had such a dangerous state of affairs existed in England. 'Let the rich be taught that Providence will not suffer them to oppress their fellow creatures with impunity. Here are tens of thousands of Englishmen, industrious, kind-hearted, but broken-hearted beings, exasperated into madness by insufficient food and clothing, by utter want of necessaries for themselves and their unfortunate families.'

Unfortunately Lord Melbourne's sentiments on the subject were very different: two days later, on Wednesday, December the eighth, the day Jem and Dick Dollery were arrested, he issued a circular, which gave a death-blow to the hope that the magistrates would act as mediators on behalf of the labourers. After blaming those magistrates who, under intimidation, had advised the establishment of a uniform rate of wages, the Home Secretary went on: 'Reason and experience concur in proving that a compliance with demands so unreasonable in themselves, and urged in such a manner, can only lead, and probably within a very short period of time, to the most disastrous results.'

The justices, he added, had 'no general legal authority to settle the amount of the wages of labour.'

The efforts of Jem, Dick Dollery and thousands of others, though they did not know it at the time, had all been in vain.

SIXTY

THE ARRIVAL of Jem, Dick Dollery and the thirty others at Melchborough Gaol had in one week increased the number of rioters held to a hundred and fifty men and youths and had upset all the governor's plans for continuing his silent and separate system: for such was the overcrowding as the new men and youths filled up the cells alongside the other inmates that the chief warder was still complaining in the ale house that evening: 'They keep bringing in fresh ones every day,' he declared. 'God love me, they brought in thirty-two more today! We just don't have the room to put'em. No spare hammocks, no spare cells either. We are supposed to have one man to a cell under this new system. We've had to put the last batch altogether in one half o' the infirmary, right alongside the sick, which ain't exactly healthy. Lord knows what'll happen if they bring in any more of the poor beggars, which I am told they are likely to do. They'll have to goo two to a cell and like it. Maybe even three to a cell, though how they will do that, I don't know! Any more and they'll have to sleep in shifts!'

While the thirty from the coastal villages were taken off together to the infirmary, where they would sleep alongside the sick, Jem and Dick Dollery were taken to cells in one of the radii: the last two empty and separate cells in the gaol, in fact. That night, as Jem lay again in a hammock, he was at least comforted by the fact that he could rely upon his friends not to give him away and heartened, too, by the fact that no one from the villages north of Hamwyte who had set out on the march with him had been amongst those brought to Melchborough that day. Further, wearing the 'peak' going to and from chapel and while in the airing yard would help to hide his identity. Jem was not to know that, at that time, the majority of the men and youths who had initially set out with him on the march and who were still with him at the Battle of Burestead Market were in hiding, except, of course, for the few in Edmundsbury Gaol, who did not know him anyway, and except, too, for Joly Cobbold, who was boldly on his way up country yet again, this time heading for Lincolnshire. The authorities of the next county were still searching for a limping man and a man with a tall hat with ribbons around it, said to be the ring-leaders, but as yet no one had confessed to knowing their names or knowing exactly from where they had come.

As rigidly enforced as were the separate system and the silent system in Melchborough Gaol, if tapping out his message on the cell walls was unreliable as a means of communicating with another, scratching it on the bottom of a tin dinner-can too risky and calling down the water pipes impossible, another way was simply to fling a scrunched note into a friend's known open cell as one went by to or from chapel, which was how Thomas Judd communicated with Jem. Word of the new arrivals and who they were had quickly passed around the gaol by the usual means and Thomas Judd also recognised Jem's distinctive limp twenty inmates ahead of him as they passed in single file down the stairs to the chapel the following morning: on his return, Jem found the screwed up piece of brown paper on his cell floor and Thomas Judd's near intelligible capitals scrawled upon it, reading: *'NAT NEWMAN HAS TURNED ON US.'*

Three days before Jem and Dick Dollery had arrived at the gaol, Nathaniel Newman had been visited in his cell by the same round-faced chaplain, the Reverend Hunt, who addressed all prisoners upon arrival. 'In view of the seriousness of the charges against you,' the puffy-cheeked chaplain began, 'have you thought how you might help yourself? I hope the court will favour you, but I think they will not. While you may have considered yourselves in the right to act as you did, you have caused a great deal of panic throughout the whole of England. These are capital offences and I believe the authorities mean to make an example of you and others like you. Amongst some, there is a belief that the very life of the country itself is threatened and they are not yet persuaded that England is tranquil again. Their first consideration will be the danger which they perceive this country is in – ' He paused to allow the words to sink in. ' – I will do my best for you, but I have to warn you that the length and nature of the events has minded the powers-that-be to deter others from your example. That means they will regard severity as the only remedy which can be applied to such disorders with any success.'

He paused again: the fifty-year-old blacksmith was staring back at him open-mouthed: he had not expected such an approach from a chaplain.

'If, perhaps you were to promise to give the magistrates information concerning various others involved in the machine-breakings which you witnessed and whom you can identify, as well as those involved in any robberies and acts of incendiarism which you may also have witnessed, you would be well rewarded,' said the chaplain, quietly. 'Fifty pounds is being offered as a reward for anyone who gives information leading to the conviction of a rioter and five hundred is being offered for the apprehension and conviction of an incendiary. You would also find great favour with the magistrates. Your own punishment would be far less severe if you were to become an informant for the Crown prosecutor and, after a while, after a lesser sentence, which might be of only a month or two's duration, you would be able to go home to your wife and family.'

'You should not ask a man to do such a thing,' Nathaniel Newman protested: he was almost trembling, but whether with anger or fear, the chaplain could not tell. 'No man worth his salt would betray his friends in the manner you ask and I cannot betray mine and you should not ask a man to do it. I would rather suffer any punishment than do that. No decent man who has any respect for himself would do it.'

However, the chaplain's words remained with Nathaniel Newman and he passed a restless night: images of his wife and the five children of his large brood still living with him, all sitting mournfully, cold and hungry in their cottage beside the forge while he languished in a dark gaol cell, filled his mind's eye and he could not get rid of them. He had already heard whispers of what was happening in other places, of the sentences being given there. The warders had told them all on their arrival of how the magistrates of other counties were treating the rioters far more severely than they had in the beginning: if things went badly for him, he could well spend months – years even – in gaol: and he did not want that.

In the daytime, the inner door of the cell was left open from nine till five so that inmates were not denied all semblance of communication with the world: at night, however, the inner door was closed or 'bolted up,' as it was termed, though, the prisoner could be viewed by the gaoler through a small vertical slit in the wall.

The next day Nathaniel Newman pulled the hand-spring by the door linked to the bell which caused the small metal rectangle bearing his cell number to project from the wall: he then informed the answering warder that he would like to speak to the chaplain and, in consequence, the chaplain spoke to the governor. At precisely two o'clock in the afternoon of the Wednesday, even as Jem and Dick Dollery were trudging down the hill towards Hamwyte beside

Ephraim Simms, the burly blacksmith was taken from his cell and escorted by two warders to a room in another part of the prison, where five magistrates sat in a line at an oak table awaiting him: at one end sat a clerk with a pen and ink with which to scratch down the prisoner's testimony.

This duly done and the deposition sworn to and 'marked' by Nathaniel Newman, it was then placed on to a pile of other depositions which had been taken from the other witnesses: Titus Broake, Parson Petchey, Amos Peakman, Marcus Howie, Joshua Godwin, James Heginbotham, Joshua Jaikes, William Mussett and Ephraim Simms.

'You have done the right thing,' said the chief magistrate. 'You have eased your conscience and assisted the law. You will not be forgotten...'

SIXTY-ONE

HIGH UP on the east face of Melchborough's 'new' Shire Hall, at the head of the wedge-shaped High Street, overlooking the market place, the figures of Justice, Wisdom and Mercy, in bas-relief, looked down upon the inhabitants passing below: for it was in the two purpose-built courtrooms on the ground floor of the Shire Hall, either side of the main staircase leading up from the foyer, that the Assizes were normally held each spring, summer and winter by the judges of the Home Circuit: there, too, the Quarter Sessions were conducted on the Tuesdays of the usual session weeks and there also the petty sessions were held every Wednesday and Friday.

The 'new' Shire Hall had been built forty years before to replace a small and cramped timber-framed Sixteenth Century sessions house, which a hundred and forty years before had witnessed the examination of some of the two hundred and fifty so-called Eastern Counties 'witches' brought there by the infamous 'Witchfinder-General,' Matthew Hopkins. Indeed, the old building had been so greatly in need of repair, so small and noisy and so open to the sounds of passing carriages and carts on the gravelled street outside that it had infuriated all circuit judges who had ever sat in it: they had complained long and bitterly that on busy days the crowd so encroached there was scarce room for them to conduct their business, that witnesses had to struggle through a host of onlookers, lawyers and others just to reach the bar and that even then their words were often drowned by the noises outside.

The 'new' Shire Hall was altogether different: a handsome three-storey building of light-grey Portland stone, rusticated on the lower half where three central archways gave access through a portico and a high arched doorway: rising from the basement half were four threequarter Ionic pillars supporting a pediment, below which were five large windows of an elegant assembly room which extended the whole length of the building's upper storey, some eighty-five feet in length and forty-five feet in width, with a stuccoed ceiling ornamented by plaster acorns and oak leaves, from which hung eight cut-glass chandeliers: at one end was a music gallery and, at the other end, a sculptured marble chimney-piece, either side of which in small niches stood two elegant Grecian female statues.

It was in the magnificent stuccoed and chandeliered assembly room that the great and the good of the county gathered at Christmastime and Easter to dance across its polished beechwood floor at their charity balls to raise funds for the relief of the county's wretched poor: it was there, too, that, in view of the fact the new gaol on the Hamwyte road was near to bursting, the Queen's serjeants decided to press the assembly room into service as a larger courtroom for the coming trials of the clod-hopping labourers who had caused so much riot and aroused so much fear over the past fortnight. Only the assembly room was sufficiently large enough to accommodate not only the expected number of prisoners who would be put to the bar before their honours but also the great number of the county's gentry, who for the past week had been clamouring to be seated at the Special Winter Assizes. So for the whole of the Saturday of December the fourth, the sound of banging reverberated throughout the building as carpenters dismantled the judge's bench and jury's bench in the smaller of the two lower courtrooms and manhandled the sections up the stairs to reassemble them in the grander assembly room.

Late on the afternoon of the Monday, while Jem and Dick Dollery lay amid the roots of an ancient oak north of Burestead Market, two judges had arrived in Melchborough and had proceeded to the Shire Hall, where they had opened the Special Assizes.

On the Tuesday morning, even as Jem and Dick Dollery were creeping through the fog and lying in ditches on their way back to Hamwick Dean, the honourable judges, Sir Lionel Lingley Launceston and Sir Bernard Grebbleton-Hove, accompanied by the County Sheriff, the mayor and the aldermen, several magistrates and the various prosecuting lawyers, deans and canons were at divine service in the town's old restored cathedral church, a short distance from the Shire Hall, seeking 'His divine wisdom' in their deliberations to come.

For his sermon that day, the Sheriff's chaplain took his text from Romans: Chapter thirteen, Verse five, *'Wherefore ye must needs be subject, not only for wrath, but also for conscience,'* in which he reminded them of the necessity of proper obedience to the laws of the land, not merely from the fear of punishment, but for conscience sake also. 'While the laws are in existence,' he declared, 'it is the duty of every man to obey them and not to set up his own individual opinions of them as the standard of right and wrong. It is also a duty incumbent on all persons in times when the peace is disturbed to exert themselves for the restoration of tranquillity.' Their honours were seen to purse their lips and nod their heads in agreement.

At noon, the procession of judges, aldermen, clergymen and lawyers then returned to the Shire Hall to begin the two sessions, Mr. Justice Launceston presiding in the Ordinary Criminal Court, that is, the specially prepared assembly hall, and Mr. Justice Grebbleton-Hove in the Nisi Prius Court below (nisi prius translating as 'if not before'). Twenty gentlemen were then empanelled as the Grand Jury, amongst them the County Sheriff himself, who, being a viscount, considered the Grand Jury's deliberations on the matters of the moment too important to be left to people of a lesser status. As such, he had taken it upon himself to lead the Grand Jury at Melchborough as its foreman: after all, look what had happened in Kent when such matters had been left to the ordinary magistrates: the dammed asses had let the malcontents off!

The Grand Jury having been sworn in and the proclamation against vice and immorality read, Mr. Justice Launceston then proceeded to inform them of the statutes which covered the specific charges which they were to hear, particularly concerning matters of riotous assembly and acts of incendiarism and machine-breaking, for which, he noted, a number of men and youths had already been brought into Melchborough Gaol specifically to be dealt with at the Special Winter Assizes.

'Those ignorant and misguided men who may be guilty of outrages, in setting the property of their fellow subjects on fire, who may be guilty of riotously and tumultuously assembling and, when so assembled, extorting with force and violence money and victuals or any other thing from persons whose habitations they may invade, who may destroy the useful machines appropriated to agriculture and manufacture – I say that those persons should learn that, in such instances, if they are apprehended and brought to justice, they must undergo the penalty of the law and that they are liable to pay for the infraction and violation of the laws by the forfeit of their lives and the loss for a long period of time of their native country by transportation to foreign parts.

'I regret to say,' he went on, 'there are persons who exaggerate the distress and raise up barriers between different classes – who use the most inflammatory language – who represent the rich as oppressors of the poor. It would be impertinent of me to say anything to you as to your treatment of labourers or servants. That man must know little of the gentry of England, whether connected with the town or country, who represents them as tyrants to the poor, as not sympathising in their distress, and as not anxious to relieve their burdens and to promote their welfare and happiness. Some will have hit upon the theory that the tumults have arisen from distress and there I have to admit that it might be partly true, but every man possessed of the feelings common to our nature must deeply lament it and endeavour to alleviate it – as you gentlemen no doubt have done and will continue to do – by every means which Providence has put within his power.'

He then informed them of the statute passed in his late Majesty's reign providing that: '*If any person shall unlawfully and maliciously set fire to any church or chapel, house, stable, coach-house, outhouse, warehouse, office, shop, mill, malt-house, hop-oast, barn, granary or to any other building...the person convicted of it shall suffer death...The same punishment is inflicted for setting fire to other articles of property, not buildings or habitations, or erections, for the same statute provides that unlawfully and maliciously setting fire to any stack or corn, grain, pulse, straw, hay or wood shall be punished also with death.*'

Further, '*...riotously and tumultuously assembling together, to the disturbance of the public peace and unlawfully and with force demolishing, pulling down or destroying or beginning to demolish, pull down or destroy any church or chapel, house ... or any building used in carrying out any trade or manufacture ... is an offence amounting to felony and punishable with death... Unlawfully and maliciously cutting, breaking or destroying or damaging with intent to destroy or to render useless, any threshing machine, or any machine or engine...is liable to be punished by transportation for seven years or imprisonment and in cases of imprisonment, hard labour, solitary confinement and with whipping.*'

The petit juries were then sworn in, twelve good men and true in the two courts, and, sitting in their separate courts, their lordships dealt with the first cases, the normal crimes of robbery, burglary, assault to the person and the like, though amongst the first five before Mr. Justice Launceston in the assembly room was a girl of twenty whom he sent to the House of Correction for three calendar months for unlawfully disposing of and attempting to conceal the birth of a female child of which she had been delivered. A twenty-year-old male was gaoled for three months for stealing goods worth ten shillings and sixpence, and a twenty-one-year-old had the sentence of death passed upon him for breaking and entering a dwelling house and stealing goods to the value of nineteen shillings and threepence.

Meanwhile, in the Nisi Prius Court below, Mr. Justice Grebbleton-Hove recorded judgments of death against four men, one aged twenty-four, two aged nineteen and one aged eighteen, though each would later be reprieved and sentenced, one to gaol for a year and the others to transportation for life.

The hearings against persons charged with the normal run of offences continued on the Wednesday, when Mr. Justice Launceston passed a sentence of death upon a labourer found guilty of robbing an old man while drunk, then jumping on him and kicking him into a ditch: he also recorded judgments of death upon two others for robbery.

In the Nisi Prius Court, Mr. Justice Grebbleton-Hove recorded judgments of death against six men, two aged only eighteen: in fact, in that one day alone, their honours blithely doomed nine men, though in time eight would be reprieved and sentenced to transportation for life.

Only four judgments of death were recorded on the Thursday, as the hearing of the normal cases reached its conclusion, two each by their honours, all of whom, thankfully, would later be reprieved, though of those, one would be sentenced to transportation for seven years and another sentenced to transportation for life, while the others would receive two years in Melchborough Gaol.

As yet, no rioter or machine-breaker had appeared: they were due to be put to the bar from the next day, Friday, with the business likely concluded by the evening of the Saturday: indictments were being added even as the Assize was under way, so keen were the authorities to have done with these matters.

Indeed, such was the interest in the actual trials of the machine-breakers that, from the Wednesday onwards, a steady stream of people flowed into the town: the public intended to be there to see them when the first of many who had terrorised the countryside proceeded by 'fly' from the gaol to the courthouse, some to sympathise with them, having themselves suffered as they had suffered, others to stand and stare and to look in awe upon those who had caused them such fear and misery. By the Thursday, the town's five-and-a-half thousand inhabitants had been swelled by a further thousand, the greater number of them gentry from the surrounding Hundreds: and the total of names on the court calendar had grown from eighteen at the start of the Assizes to fifty-four.

Fortunately, Melchborough, being not only the county town and the location of a large weekly market for the surrounding villages, had a half-dozen large inns and taverns along and around its High Street and market square, each well served by coaches from the capital: by the Wednesday evening, there was not a room to be had at an inn or a lodging house. In fact, the landlords, determined to make the best of a windfall, doubled their charges for bed, food and drink and, it being the middle of winter, added three shillings a day for laying a fire in the bedrooms and, as it was dark by four o'clock in the afternoon and the sun did not rise till after eight o'clock in the morning, charged extra for tallow candles.

In certain of the inns and taverns, too, water was surreptitiously added to the home-brewed ale in the hope of it being a thirsty few days for all who had come to view the proceedings and, similarly, a farthing was added to the price of a pint pot. Even the ancient Half Moon, which then projected out and obstructed the High Street at its entrance and was an inconvenience to all carriage and wagon traffic and due to be pulled down, had let out all of its musty rooms to curious lesser personages from the provinces, while, on the Thursday morning, the day of the first transfer of the prisoners from the gaol to the Shire Hall's cells, the side streets off the High Street were so choked with coaches, carriages, post-chaises, traps, gigs, carts and carriers' wagons, it seemed that half the county had come to town.

SIXTY-TWO

THE FIRST machine-breakers and rioters were eventually put to the bar before Mr. Justice Launceston in a crowded assembly room at nine o'clock on the Friday, Melchborough's normal market day. Ten men, the oldest sixty, the youngest sixteen, others seventeen and eighteen years mostly, were brought up and charged with having riotously assembled on a heath near Wivencaster on the Monday of that very week, even as their honours were arriving in the town: they were further charged that they did, by threats, compel their employers to sign an agreement for raising the rate of their wages. All were found guilty by the jury, after due evidence had been given, and all were sentenced to the gaol, two for twelve months with hard labour, one for nine months, four for six months and three for three months.

His lordship, however, had not softened: the next man put to the bar, indicted on a charge of having set fire to a barn and several stacks of corn on the night of November the fifth in the south of the county, though not involved in any machine-breaking, was convicted after the jury deliberated all of ten minutes and was sentenced to death, though he never expected the sentence to be carried out and, questioned the likelihood of it as he left. 'They won't hang me, will they?' he asked: two weeks later, he was to learn that they would.

Meanwhile, in the Nisi Prius Court, Mr. Justice Grebbleton-Hove heard his first case of actual machine-breaking: three labourers from the coastal village of Chudland – three out of a hundred present – were indicted for breaking a machine, valued at forty pounds on the Saturday, six days previously. All were found guilty within the hour. 'It is now my painful duty,' intoned his honour, 'to pass such a sentence upon you as will make you a public example and be the means of deterring other persons from committing the offences of which you have been found guilty.' He then sentenced all three to transportation across the seas for seven years.

No sooner had they been taken down than nine other labourers from the coast were ushered up to the same bar, indicted with destroying a threshing machine, also valued at forty pounds, in the parish of

Marsey. Though most admitted being amongst the hundred there and received good character references from their vicar and others who spoke up for them, the jury immediately found all guilty and they received varying sentences, three of transportation across the sea for seven years, two of hard labour for twelve months, one of six months in gaol and three of three months in gaol.

After that, two robbery cases were heard, which resulted in a man of thirty-five being sentenced to eighteen months in gaol and a nineteen-year-old and twenty-six-year-old being found not guilty, which was a surprise to everyone.

Next up were seven men charged with riot along with fifty or sixty others in the parish of Clipping, again on the coast, only four days previously: all were found guilty, again within the hour: one was sentenced to three months with hard labour and the others to six months with hard labour.

On the Saturday, it was almost ten o'clock before proceedings got under way due to their honours rising late. Put to the bar first was a well-known pugilist from Wivencaster, a true 'bruiser,' with a flat nose and scarred eyes, who had 'accidentally,' so he said, struck a special constable in the face with his fist in the execution of his duty during the fracas on Mile End heath. For his inability to control his temper, he received six months' imprisonment, as much for drawing-out the case unnecessarily and wasting a good hour of the morning with his foolish attempted cross-examination of witnesses, who were all special constables anyway, especially since in the view of a wearily sighing Mr. Justice Launceston, the man was clearly guilty and only using the court as a stage to display his own cockiness.

There was just time before lunch to try two youths from one of the villages to the south of the county town who had been part of a group of twenty rioters roaming the countryside and doing mischief who had knocked upon the door of a wealthy gentleman at two o'clock in the morning: two groups had already visited him that evening and night and each time he had given them beer. This third band was a party of stragglers and the gentleman was wearying of the game: to deter them, he had stationed ten of his servants in the portico and, when the mob arrived, he asked them: 'What do you want, my lads?'

'Money,' was the answer.

'Money you shall not have on any account,' the house owner had replied firmly.

One of the band then made the mistake of threatening the houseowner with an iron bar: instead, he was himself seized by the gentleman, while his servants sprang forward and knocked down several of the others, who then fled. 'Such outrages make one wonder whether one is living in a civilised country,' snorted his honour and proceeded to raise its moral tone by sentencing all the prisoners to transportation for life.

More rioters were brought up in the afternoon: first after luncheon before Mr. Justice Launceston were three men from the south of the county, who had threatened a farmer because he would not raise their wages as they asked: they were each convicted and sentenced to three months of hard labour, with ten days of it to be on the tread-wheel. Unhappily, as they retreated from the bar to allow the next batch of prisoners up to it, one amongst them showed his displeasure with a reference to his honour's legitimacy, or otherwise, and was called back for a further three months to be added to his sentence.

The next three to shuffle forwards were, in fact, the very men to whom Jem and Dick Dollery had been chained on their way to gaol: they were said to have been amongst a hundred and forty who had smashed a threshing machine valued at thirty pounds and a chaff-cutter valued at eight pounds in Great Accleton on the Tuesday and to have also demanded two shillings and threepence a day in wages. It was said that, in order to get that sum, they had told those farmers who had agreed to pay it that they would go to the tithe feast and force the gentlemen who received the tithe to give the farmers back half of their money. 'Extortion,' his lordship declared it and sentenced them all to seven years' transportation.

When those three had been taken down, six more were brought up to replace them, again men from the coast, who were all charged with having destroyed a threshing machine at Nokes Lawton, again only three days previously, when a mob of three hundred had assembled in the centre of that village before marching. The prisoners said a farmer named Baker had given them leave to break his machine – indeed, they said he had also incited them to break that of another farmer named Wilson and had followed them to ensure that they did it. The first farmer, of course, denied it: the proof against them was deemed so clear and the jury so 'perfectly satisfied' with the veracity of the evidence against the men that they told his lordship it was unnecessary to trouble him to sum up and, without leaving the box, the jury immediately returned a verdict of guilty on all prisoners. The judge sentenced each of the men to transportation for seven years.

Three of the men were then kept at the bar and further charged, along with a fourth brought up to join them, with breaking the second

368

machine, saying still that they had the sanction of the first farmer to do it, but the jury again found all prisoners guilty and, in a repeat of the circumstances previously, they were each sentenced to seven years' transportation, thus, in the case of three of them, doubling their sentence to fourteen years' transportation.

Immediately upon the conclusion of the sentences, a number of women, seated behind the prisoners, set up a dreadful shrieking: transportation was as good as a death sentence to the wives and families of the men: the removal of the bread-winner would leave them destitute: they knew, too, that the sentence was most likely a final separation: everywhere there was a frenzy of consternation and grief.

More than one man's voice was heard to exclaim as he was led away, 'Farewell, my love, I shall see you no more.'

'Let me take my child into exile with me,' cried one man. 'He is only eight months old and its mother died giving him birth. He will be left without kith or kin.'

'You should have thought of that earlier,' snapped the judge.

Such anguish and despair had seldom before been witnessed in a court of justice, certainly not in the memory of those present: even the counsel seated at their own tables were moved by it. Mr. Justice Launceston, however, had witnessed such scenes before: by then it was late afternoon, almost evening, and he did not intend to remain to watch: he called the adjournment for a half-hour and slipped quietly off his seat and went through a door behind into his chamber, where a meal of bread, butter, jam, scones and cream, and a pot of tea had been laid. After tea, he still had one indictment to hear that day against two youths also arrested at the melee on the heath at Wivencaster: his honour had long ago resigned himself to the fact that it was unlikely he would finish before eight o'clock that evening at the earliest.

It was not the prospect of the late finish which had upset him: he was used to those at Assizes: he had been in an ill temper since the lunch adjournment. Normally, at that time, the foreman of the Grand Jury, the County Sheriff, would, in accordance with custom, make the usual presentment, made at the end of every Assize, that the Grand Jury had nothing further to present and to request they be discharged. It meant that he and Mr. Justice Grebbleton-Hove had completed the calendar and could depart.

However, since the start of the week, he had had to suffer indictment after indictment being added almost daily against those cursed machine-breakers: and that very morning they had added yet another and this one looked as if it would take longer than the others, at least four or five hours, whereas he had been able to dispose of most of the other cases he had heard in less than an hour apiece.

It was true that before he and Mr. Justice Grebbleton-Hove had set out from the Inns of Court, the Attorney-General had sent him a letter in which he insisted that as many cases of machine-breaking and riot as the county authorities were able to put up before him be dealt with as time permitted – 'These damned reprobates,' as his lordship had referred to them, 'must be dealt with abruptly, consistently and severely. I intend to have this insurrection stamped out once and for all.' – So Mr. Justice Launceston felt almost obliged to accept when he found his old friend, the County Sheriff, waiting along with the town's chief magistrate and mayor to inform him that they had added yet another indictment to his calendar that very morning which they would be pleased if he would consider dealing with as a matter of urgency.

'It would go a long way towards restoring peace in the district if these particular fellows were dealt with as soon as possible,' the County Sheriff had informed him.

For some reason, the County Sheriff was in the company of one of the two Members of Parliament for Hamwyte, a gentleman named Sir Titus Broake, who was of the same party as his lordship and, it appeared, had been one of the victims of a particular group of men and was anxious, for the peace of the Hundred, that they be dealt with speedily at these Assizes rather than have their case held over to the Epiphany Quarter Sessions in the New year or even, God forbid, the Lent Assizes four months off!

Thumbing through the depositions which they had brought, the judge saw immediately that there was little chance of the case, if started, being completed that day unless he sat till midnight and he had no intention of doing that. So, reluctantly, with a sigh, since the Attorney-General had requested it and his old friend wished it, he agreed to remain over the Sunday and to take the final indictment, as a matter of urgency, from the start on the Monday. It meant that the Special Winter Assizes would not be concluded as he had hoped: it would mean, however, he would be expected to attend divine service at the cathedral church on the Sunday, which did not please him overmuch either, though a day's delay before he headed on was not such a hindrance as the next Assizes, up in the next county at Edmundsbury, were not due to begin till the Wednesday.

Even so, his last indictment was something of an imposition, even for an old friend, and he said so: whoever were the new miscreants who were to be put to the bar on the Monday morning, in Mr. Justice Launceston they would find themselves facing a very irritated judge.

As he sat eating his tea, the usher crossed to the window and raised the bottom of it slightly to let in some air because smoke from the fire was blowing back down the chimney and swirling about the room. However, by doing so, he allowed in the sounds from the street, where the 'fly' for the removal of the last prisoners was at that very moment surrounded by the weeping and wailing mothers, wives, sisters and children of the convicts. As each prisoner stepped into the cart, he found his hands seized by a dozen others: for some, it was the last touch of a loved one: then, as the sound of wheels rolling away across the cobbles towards the gaol was heard, the screams of despair and anger took over again.

'Damnable racket!' exclaimed Sir Lionel and, rising to his feet, he slammed the window shut himself.

SIXTY-THREE

WHEN Titus Broake had ridden away from the gaol after delivering Jem and Dick Dollery and the thirty other prisoners, he had gone straight to the house of the town's mayor, who as the chief magistrate also served on the Grand Jury: the two had then gone in a post-chaise to the home of the County Sheriff, as the current foreman of the Grand Jury, in his mansion just outside the town: in consequence, the Grand Jurors were presented with a further bundle of depositions to read the following morning.

As it happened, five of those serving on the Grand Jury were the same five magistrates who had committed Jem, Dick Dollery and the others from the court at Hamwyte and so had it on the word of one of their own that, of the thirty-two prisoners who had been brought from the Hamwyte bridewell to Melchborough Gaol two days previously, one was the very ringleader of the mob which had broken the threshing machines on his estate and had also attempted to set fire to his barn and the other was his second-in-command. Further, he was positively able to identify all the Hamwick Dean rioters by name and face. He was most anxious, therefore – indeed he insisted upon it – that six of the latest batch brought in should be put up at the Special Winter Assizes rather than be held over. 'Speedy justice,' he exclaimed, 'speedy justice. Make an example of them once and for all!'

The depositions, which had already been taken from himself and other witnesses in Hamwyte were then perused: there was much sniffing and wreaths of tobacco smoke clouded the air. As it turned out, seven-and-a-half minutes after the viscount had picked up the first of the depositions, he came across a single page of a witness statement from a blacksmith by the name of Nathaniel Newman: what he saw there convinced him that it was more than sufficient to return a 'true bill' on the six at least whom the local lord of the manor was keen to see brought to justice. 'All agreed?' the viscount asked in the manner of one who had made up his mind and did not expect any contradiction. 'We have more than enough to bring charges and we have the witness statement of this man Newman as well.'

'Agreed,' said the other members of the Grand Jury, some raising their hands to signify it, others just grunting their acquiescence.

Titus Broake left the chamber where the Grand Jury met wth a sense of elation: he had his main antagonists, Jem Stebbings, the man Dollery and four others, and that was all that mattered to him: and when their trial was over, he would make a point of ensuring that the farmers who had given in to them on wages would go back on their pledges and the parson's tithe, too, would be returned to normal or the next thing they would want was for the tithe he received as lord of the manner to be reduced as well.

Thus, it was late in the afternoon of the Saturday that Jem, Dick Dollery, Enos Diddams, John Romble, William Stubbs and Thomas Judd were assembled in a line in the yard of Melchborough Gaol, ordered to turn up their cuffs and to put out their right wrists, which then had a handcuff snapped on them. The long curb chain was again reeved through the eyelet of each cuff so that, though linked together, they might ride reasonably comfortably in the empty 'fly,' which was returning to the Shire Hall threequarters of a mile away, having brought back twelve others, escorted by four warders and a small group of mounted yeomanry in case the populace should take into their heads to attempt something foolish.

'T'is by a special request of one of the gentlemen who serves on the Grand Jury sometimes,' the chief warder at the gaol was to explain that evening to his wife. 'A fellow by the name of Sir Titus Broake, from Hamwick Dean, lord of the manor there, wants all six of them put to the bar on Monday first thing. Revenge, if you ask me. It seems his machines were broken by them and his barn was set on fire. He wants them got rid of and quick. Poor beggars! If you ask me, he wants them tried, convicted and hanged before Christmas or I'm a Dutchman. At the rate they're still bringing them in, the January Quarter Sessions will be even busier.'

Despite Saturday not being a market day, peering out the 'fly's' back flap as they made their way through the town, Jem saw that the pavements the whole way up the High Street to the Shire Hall were lined three and four-deep with people eager to see the comings and goings of the machine-breaking prisoners. Not unexpectedly, on the faces of the on-looking gentry and the wealthier tradesmen of the town, for Melchborough had many fine houses with gardens leading down to its two rivers and, therefore, many well-to-do inhabitants – on their faces were looks of obvious satisfaction. However, it also had the same percentage of poorer inhabitants as any other town, living in the same unsanitary and dirty conditions down alleyways and around refuse-layered yards: and from them there were the same murmurings of sympathy and sad faces as the inhabitants of the lower part of Hamwyte had shown only a short while before.

In the market area in front of the Shire Hall, where the street was wide enough to be called a square, the crowd stood ten deep in a great semi-circle around the Shire Hall's archways, leaving only a narrow path for the yeomanry to escort the 'fly' through and round the back of the building where the prisoners dismounted. Once inside the Shire Hall, Jem and the others were ushered down the same small flight of steps as Jem had been pushed down at his trial a year and more before, at the bottom of which was the passageway he had trod and the line of five black doors on one side. There, he again answered to his name, as did the others: the chains were taken off and Dick Dollery, Enos Diddams and the three others were all pushed into one cell. Hardly had their door banged shut than two other cells were unlocked and a dozen prisoners, downcast, abject and already handcuffed, who had already been convicted and sentenced that day, were brought out and lined up, ready for the curb chain to be reeved through so they could be taken back to the gaol in the same returning 'fly.'

Jem, meanwhile, was kept standing, till one of the warders gave him a push towards a door farther along the passageway. 'This one is for you,' said the warder, laying a hand on his shoulder in front of the farthest door. 'Orders of the magistrates from Hamwyte, especially your Mr. Broake. You are to be put by yourself till Monday.' And with that, he threw back the door to reveal an interior which was absolutely pitch black: it was the refractory cell. Not a thing was visible in the cell, not even the fact that a second grill lay between the first door and the interior till the warder lifted his lantern and shone its light into the darkness: and though the cell was the same size as the other cells, it was utterly devoid of furniture, neither table, chair, nor bed or hammock.

'There's room enough for the others in the one cell if they bunches up a bit,' said the warder, giving Jem a push, 'but you have your own special cell all to yourself.'

As the door clanged shut, the utter darkness of the cell was like a tomb: not one chink of light was detectable: Jem felt as if he had been buried alive. Only by feeling his way round the walls did he eventually come upon a small raised platform with a sloping headpiece in one corner, his bed: further exploration revealed a damp rug folded on it, his only covering.

The strain of trying to peer through the enveloping darkness and to exercise his mind soon produced a sense of mental fatigue in Jem: in the end, he just lay down upon the wooden bed and stared up into the darkness which cocooned and oppressed him. Mercifully, the weariness of the past few days caught up with him and he fell asleep, relieved from his stress and despondency by a dream of Mary-Ann, Jed, Thirza and himself, all at home in their old cottage, the four of them together again as a family.

Things were better for Dick Dollery and the others: even though they were in irons and guarded by the warders, they were together and were allowed to sit and talk: they were even given a meal of badly cooked gruel, the kind of stirabout Jem used to eat in the army, with a slice of bread added and a flagon of weak beer to share. Jem, however, dozing alone in the darkness for the whole of the Sunday, received none of it, just a lump of stale bread and a dish of water on the following morning.

'Orders,' said the warder again with a shrug, closing the grille and leaving him to the darkness.

The news of their unexpected trial, meanwhile, was carried to Hamwyte by a coachman pulling into the yards of the Black Bear at noon and taken on to Hamwick Dean in the early afternoon by the old wagoner, Daniel Gate.

SIXTY-FOUR

THE TRIAL process then placed defendants at a distinct disadvantage: a guinea fee was required to hire an attorney from amongst those who consistently followed the Assizes around on its travels in the hope of picking up work: the drawback was that, if a prisoner could not afford the guinea, then he or she or they would have to defend themselves against the whole weight of the court and the prosecution without the benefit of legal assistance, overawed and uneducated as they generally were when compared with the university educated men who inhabited all parts of the justice system. Even had a defendant been able to fee a defence lawyer a guinea, he would not have been able to speak *for* them: defence counsel could only cross-examine prosecution witnesses as they appeared at the bar and as such perhaps even to question their motives for bringing the prosecution, obvious though that might seem to those who had heard the charges. This, it was thought, was the best way of ascertaining the truth of a matter and would put the accused in a better light in the eyes of the court and in the opinion of the jury if he or she or they responded spontaneously to what witnesses said. Since none of the Hamwick Dean six could pay the guinea fee, they found themselves entirely at the mercy of the court.

It, of course, made it all the more difficult for an unlearned man to contest the case brought against him, perhaps woven into a coherent and convincing tale by a skilled lawyer while he himself languished in a dark cell: if he were innocent of a charge or if the interpretation of it was at odds with his belief, perhaps bewildered by his strange surroundings, he had only his own memory and his own imagination to pick the lawyer's story to pieces, to change black into white and apparent guilt into manifest innocence. The principal argument against reform of this miscarriage of a system was that, to allow persons the aid of counsel in putting their statement of fact would make justice slower, more expensive, and more theatrical: it was the contention that the judge did, in point of fact, represent the interests of the prisoner.

Just before nine o'clock on Monday, the thirteenth of December, Jem Stebbings, Dick Dollery, Enos Diddams, John Romble, William Stubbs and Thomas Judd, late of Hamwick Dean in the Hundred of Hamwyte, were put to the bar together in the spacious assembly hall, guarded by a dozen warders and special constables. As Jem was led from his black cell, the unexpected brightness of the day was as blinding as had been the darkness: and such was the dilation of his pupils that he had to keep his eyes closed for a good half-minute, like one newly wakened from sleep, before he could carefully open them.

At first he sensed rather than saw his five friends waiting in the same passageway: still dazzled and bewildered, without being ordered, he extended his wrists to have them cuffed and waited while the link chain was again reeved through: in that fashion, with much clanking, the six Hamwick Dean men mounted the back stairs. Only as they were brought shuffling into the main assembly room were the handcuffs and the curb chain removed: the chief warder did not wish to incur the wrath of his honour a second time by presenting prisoners before him still manacled as he had inadvertently done when the first half-dozen from the coast had been put up.

'On no account will I have prisoners brought before me manacled,' the judge had stormed. 'They are free men till they are convicted.'

As they shuffled into the hall, Jem became aware of lines of faces staring at him and people whispering to each other: fingers pointed, but whether they were pointing at him or the others he neither knew nor cared. Every seat in the assembly room was again taken, as they had been for all the machine-breakers' trials: there must have been upwards of three-hundred people seated in rows immediately behind the counsels' benches and yet more standing along the side aisles and along the back. In fact, so many had been unable find a seat in the body of the hall that the musicians' gallery over it was packed to overflowing. Indeed, such had been the concern of the usher regarding the great number of ladies present in that balcony and so crushed amongst the males were they likely to be that he had allocated the whole row of front seats to them, with their men folk jammed behind and having to crane their necks over hats and feathers to see yet more of the 'poor, misguided, rebellious wretches' come to their doom.

A great 'Oooh,' like a sad sigh, went up as they entered, almost as if the onlookers were anticipating the verdicts: Jem knew that there was unlikely to be any sympathy found amongst any of them: and, if by the remotest of chances the sympathies of any person in the room were with them at all, the constitution of the jury was decidedly against, just as it had been for the trials of the other men.

Normally, the County Sheriff and the chief magistrate would have compiled the men of the jury panels from amongst the town's tradesmen: but, at the actual commencement of the Assizes on the Tuesday, it had been reported to Mr. Justice Launceston that some of those summoned to the town to be selected to be empanelled had been overheard, while travelling in a coach, to say that, if they were chosen for any of the machine-breakers' trials, they would not convict in cases where the labourers had been driven to excess by poverty and low wages. Consequently, his lordship had discharged a good number of those empanelled on account of there being 'a strong likelihood' that they would be reluctant to convict. In their stead, the jurymen who stared at the prisoners as they were brought into the dock and arraigned at the bar comprised a baronet, three knights of the county, two honourables and seven others of substantial means who might in time aspire to a title of some kind, all of them large landowners and men of leisure: for the petit jury had been selected from the Grand Jury itself, the very same twenty-three gentlemen of the county who all during the previous week had been compiling the charges, the same men who had read the depositions of the witnesses and, after discussing the matters concerned, had returned for each the very 'true bill' which had placed them at the bar of the Special Winter Assizes.

As he regarded the faces and the looks directed at them, Jem's heart sank: such esteemed jurors, he knew, were likely to be more severe than others, quite apart from the fact that they would be particularly hostile to any case of arson against property, for he assumed they all owned something somewhere. Poor William Stubbs seemed to be affected by the moment and fell to snuffling tearfully till Dick Dollery, beside him, kicked him unseen by the warders: Dick was his normal surly self, glaring back at the host of spectators like one angered by being put on show for the amusement of others. As for Enos Diddams, John Romble and Thomas Judd, they had entered with their heads bowed in the manner of the contrite and now stood there the same, as if hoping to extract sympathy from the jurors as well as from the watching public.

As it was the custom then for the prosecutor to pay the expenses of witnesses whom he called to support his case, Titus Broake had made sure that not only was his bailiff, Heginbotham, to be called but so were Caleb Chapman, Ephraim Simms and Joshua Jaikes: he would have added Parson Petchey to his list had not the hook-nosed

Reverend Doctor refused his offer and stated, with a certain contempt when waylaid at his gate, that he would attend himself by his own means to ensure that justice was done against such ungrateful malcontents as had accosted him and his wife: it was his duty to do so. 'God would expect no less of me,' he declared.

Thus, when Titus Broake walked into the Shire Hall on the morning of the trial, having stayed overnight at the Spread Eagle Inn not fifty yards from it, he believed that he had all the evidence he required and was most particularly pleased with deposition of the turncoat, Nathaniel Newman. That was the final touch, the irrefutable evidence of one who was a friend of all the accused, who had witnessed their desperate acts and had, he said, been so appalled by the wantonness of some of them that he had cut himself off from their company. He would most probably get the fifty pounds which the Government had offered, though he doubted the blacksmith would get the five hundred: the Grand Jury had baulked at recommending that, as they had on whether he should be offered the free pardon. What would happen to him afterwards was not the lord of the manor's concern: indeed the question had not even crossed his mind. It was quite obvious that a witness who lived amongst a community and gave evidence against others in that community would be foolish to go back and live there: relocation to another part of the country was the only recourse: but that was not his concern either. Of the other victims of the rioters, Amos Peakman, Marcus Howie and Joshua Godwin, all had stated their determination to obtain their own justice for the indignities they had suffered: so it was in a cheery mood that Titus Broake mounted the steps to the assembly room early that Monday morning,

At precisely a minute past nine, his honour, Mr. Justice Launceston, banged his gavel to silence the murmuring amongst the crowd and, when Jem and the others had all answered to their names, the crier read the first three of the indictments to be heard that day, in that they were '...*charged on the oaths of the honourable Sir Titus Broake, MP, lord of the manor of Hamwick Dean, Justice of the Peace and landowner, with having on Thursday the twenty-fifth of November last, with divers other persons unknown, unlawfully, riotously and tumultuously assembled together, to the disturbance of the public peace, on the premises of the said Sir Titus Broake, of the said parish, in the said county, and feloniously were present aiding, abetting and assisting divers persons to us yet unknown with feloniously and unlawfully destroying certain machinery used in the threshing of corn and the cutting of chaff and turnips on the said manor farm and on the premises of the said complainant, in the county aforesaid, against the form of the statute in that case made...'*

'Further, m'lord,' went on the clerk, *'...on the oath of Sir Titus Broake ... on the twenty-fifth of November last, they did wilfully with malice and aforethought set fire to and attempt to destroy his barn with the consequent damage and loss of much property within it to the sum of several hundreds of pounds...'*

Much to the irritation of the judge, Dick Dollery, awed by the magnificence of the room, was too occupied in looking about him, staring up at the plaster oak leaves and acorns which adorned the ceiling and so did not hear the clerk's question, 'How do you plead?' when it was addressed to him first and it had to be repeated before he thought to answer: 'Not guilty, sir.'

They were further charged *'...on the combined oaths of Amos Peakman... Marcus Howie... and Joshua Godwin... farmers all in the said parish ... that on the twenty-fifth of November last, also, they did unlawfully riotously and tumultuously assemble together, to the disturbance of the public peace, and did feloniously aid, abet and assist divers persons, to us yet unknown, with feloniously and unlawfully destroying certain machinery used in the threshing of corn, the cutting of turnips and chaff and the drilling of seeds ... and did feloniously aid, abet and assist ... in the firing of two ricks ... and together also did feloniously threaten, abuse and resort to menace to steal from each of them various sums of money to the total of four pounds, two shillings, and further did assault the said Amos Peakman, farmer, and his wife, and break windows at his home with stones ...'*

The next charges was read solely against Jem and Dick Dollery, that *'... on the oath of the Reverend Doctor Wakefield Petchey, rector of the said parish of Hamwick Dean, Jem Stebbings and Richard Dollery together are charged that they did on the twenty-second day of November last, unlawfully, riotously, and tumultuously assemble with divers others together, to the disturbance of the public peace, at the parsonage of the said place and did together feloniously threaten, abuse and resort to menace in demanding an abatement of the tithes due the said person, from five hundred and fifty pounds sterling per annum to three hundred pounds sterling per annum, with consequent loss thereof.'*

There were gasps amongst the watching public: they had not expected that the six men at the bar could have done so much: what could possibly have driven them to such madness?

At that point, the county's prosecuting attorney rose to his feet, straightening his wig which had become lopsided when he had sat down heavily earlier. Hooking his left thumb in the folds of his robe and, with a slight bow to his honour, Charles Semblage, a short, puffy-faced lawyer from the same chambers in Lincoln's Inn Fields which earlier had produced Tobias Grint for the enclosure negotiations five years previously, rose to his feet to begin his outline of the case against Jem and others for their deeds at Hamwick Dean. He had been able to plan his case against the six over the weekend, whereas they were somehow expected to assemble their defence themselves while they faced him: the death of Mr. Able had indeed come at an inopportune time for them, though whether the aged and friendly lawyer could have done them any good at all in that hostile place would have to remain a matter of conjecture amongst those who witnessed the events there.

'On Monday, the twenty-second of November,' declared Mr. Semblage in a clear, strong voice, which belied his short, rotund stature, 'an assemblage of peasantry at Hamwick Dean, near Hamwyte, in this county, numbering at least three hundred, proceeded to the parsonage at Hamwick Dean, where they conducted themselves in a riotous manner and by threats and menacing conduct demanded a reduction of tithes. Their object, m'lord, was a belief that this would have enabled their employers, most particularly a number of farmers of that district, to pay better wages. Three days later, on Thursday, November the twenty-fifth, a numerous gang, upwards of three hundred, appeared at the residence of Sir Titus Broake, of Hamwick Hall, and there demolished two of his threshing machines and various other implements and attempted to burn down his barn, which, I am told, mercifully, they failed to do, though not for the want of trying. They then proceeded to the farms of the other prosecutors, namely, Mr. Amos Peakman, of Goat Lodge Farm, Mr. Marcus Howie, of Smallponds Farm, and Mr. Joshua Godwin, of Milepole Farm, all within the said parish, and did likewise demolish threshing machines and various other implements at each and, by threats and imprecations, demand money which they received and took away, ostensibly to buy beer at the village's inns.'

So many indictments having been read out, the judge's sole enquiry, made with raised eyebrows, was simply which of them was to be taken first.

'The machine-breaking at Sir Titus Broake's manor farm and the other farms of the parish, lumped together for expediency, if it pleases your lordship,' said the prosecuting attorney.

'It does not please me at all,' snorted his honour, for it necessitated a certain shuffling of papers as he had them in the wrong order from his reading of them. With a weary sigh, he added: 'But press on, Mr. Semblage, press on and let us be done with this business as quickly as we can.'

SIXTY-FIVE

TITUS BROAKE was called first and came stamping into the witness box, confident that his status in the village, his past four years as a magistrate, his knighthood and his new position as a Member of Parliament would count for more than anything the defendants might say in their defence: he gave the six a cursory glance, but other than that, when he spoke, confined himself to looking at either the judge, his friends the jurors, the prosecuting counsel or the great body of on-lookers.

His testimony was to the point: 'I am Sir Titus Broake. I live at Hamwick Hall. I am the lord of the manor and a Member of Parliament for Hamwyte and a Justice of the Peace at Hamwyte. On the twenty-fifth day of November, I was at my estate, Hamwick Hall, in the parish of Hamwick Dean, when I observed a large body of men and youths and others approaching. I estimated them to be three hundred or more in number and I recognised many of them as being from the village over which I hold the lordship. They were carrying hammers and other iron weapons and were all chanting bloodcurdling threats, "Bread or blood" or something. They came on to my estate and confronted me at the Hall. They said they had come to break my threshing machines and they demanded the right of permanent employment and said I must agree to pay a wage of two shillings and sixpence a day in the summer for all labourers I employed and two shillings and threepence a day for the labour they did in the winter. They asked me to sign a petition to that effect, which I refused. They then broke into my barn, which was locked as I would not fetch the key, broke up my two threshing machines and a turnip cutter which they found there and other implements, then set fire to it. All the defendants in the box were present. The man Stebbings seemed to be their leader, for he was the one who made the demands of wages and work for them. Stebbings was at the front when they came on to my land, leading the chanting, and when I refused them the pay they asked for and the conditions they sought, it was Stebbings who shouted for them to go the barn! When the barn was set afire, I saw

Stebbings in the doorway. He was encouraging them. He was in the barn when it was set alight. It was only by Providence that it did not burn down completely.'

The judge asked two questions: 'How much of the barn was lost?' and 'What was the defendant, Stebbings, shouting, if you say he was shouting?'

'A good part of the barn internally was burnt,' answered Titus Broake, still indignant at the memory of his loss. 'I lost upwards of forty quarters of wheat, oats and barley as well as certain implements and machinery, notwithstanding the loss of two threshing machines, smashed to smithereens. When I heard Stebbings he was shouting, "Off to the barn! Break the machinery and burn it down." They were all there, all six of the defendants, when my barn was set alight deliberately, then they had the gall to say it was an accident and that they had actually helped put it out.'

To ensure that all knew how insult had been added to injury, the lord of the manor added, as if incredulous at the mobs' audacity: 'When they had done all that, they had the temerity to go up to the Hall while I was in the barn and to demand five pounds from my wife as their "fee"!' It produced the anticipated intake of breath from the onlookers.

Jem did not bother to protest: the words 'To the barn!' had been shouted by Dick Dollery, but he could not say so: and he had only learned later of those who had visited the Hall: by then he was almost indifferent to it all and had long since decided that a defence was futile. Titus Broake meant to have his pound of flesh and Jem was more amused by his desperation to obtain it, his willingness to say anything to achieve it: he just sighed and maintained his silence.

The prosecuting attorney then produced from amongst his papers the letter Jem had written and which he had read out to the farmers at the Saturday meeeting, asking them if they would agree to raise the men's wages in accordance with the demand stated, two shillings and sixpence a day in summer and two shillings and threepence a day in winter, for six days of work, and permanent work to be given, which they were to sign or make their mark: he passed it to the clerk who read it out to the judge and jury. It was the same letter he had taken to the Anchor at Inworth: the last he had seen of it was when he had passed it to Thomas Judd for safe-keeping on their return to Hamwick Dean late that same evening and had not thought about it since: now here it was produced in court.

'I consider it one of the most violent and dangerous papers I have yet seen,' declared Titus Broake with the pomposity of one who believes himself, when handed the letter to peruse before the clerk passed it on to the judge. 'Unfortunately, it had already been assented to by too many occupiers of land before I obtained hold of it. It was discovered in the home of Thomas Judd, a cordwainer, when he was arrested on the Tuesday evening last. It is my belief that it was to be carried round the adjoining parishes of Salter, Cumvirley, Cobwycke and Gledlang on the Tuesday to foment mishchief there. I had Thomas Judd arrested and charged by the magistrates at Hamwyte and he was committed to the bridewell there and then to the gaol at Melchborough for trial here, along with others before you. I believe, by my swift action, I succeeded in repressing a likely tumultuous action and, by subsequently calling together the occupiers of land to form a yeomanry and a special constabulary, I had the satisfaction of restoring tranquillity at that place and other places.'

His honour smiled, thankful that at least he had before him a man who was forceful and who was willing and not afraid to act promptly: not one of those damned hand-wringers who seemed to want to find excuses for these malcontent machine-breakers, barn-burners and rick-firers, who seemed to think a riot was an occasion for fun.

'I commend your action, sir;' he said, with a slight nod of the head in acknowledgement: then, turning to Jem and the others, he asked with a sigh: 'Have you any questions for the witness?' He busied himself with shuffling his papers as he did so, as if anticipating they would not: Jem simply shook his head: he did not see the point of drawing out more information from Titus Broake or having the same information repeated, both of which would count against them: the others looked at each other blankly: they could not think of any questions either, especially as it seemed to attempt it would incur the wrath of his honour, who was keen to press on.

Heginbotham was next into the witness box to give his version of what had happened at the Hall and to answer what questions were put to him by the prosecution counsel and the judge, who frequently interrupted to ask questions of his own: indeed, it was in reply to the judge, impatient to establish recognition, that Heginbotham identified Jem as having been at the front of the men marching along the drive towards him, who declared it was Jem and Dick Dollery who had done all the talking and also identified each of the other four as having been present on his master's estate and prominent in the actions there.

Jem himself had no disagreement with the greater part of Heginbotham's testimony, though Dick Dollery growled and muttered under his breath at every answer, particularly when the incident of the barn fire and Jem's position in the doorway were described. No one had noticed whether Heginbotham was there or not so none could say for sure since they had been occupied with other matters at the time. Heginbotham had, in fact, been on his way to seek out Ephraim Simms: by saying what he did, he was only attempting to preserve his employ: to have done otherwise would have put himself out of his newly-built tied cottage on Hall Lane and his family with him.

One by one, the three farmers followed: Amos Peakman was the first and gave the same evidence exactly as he had given in his deposition to the magistrates, describing all that had happened to him: it took all of three minutes. He concluded: 'I had received a letter from this Captain Swing fellow a week or so before. It was pushed under my door in the night, warning me, if I did not break my thrashing machine myself, a mob would come and do it themselves. I didn't see why I should do what they wanted so I did nothing, just locked my barn and waited for them to come. Thought I might talk some sense into their heads since I knew most of them. When they came on the Thursday, all the six defendants in this court were at the front of the mob, like they were leading it.'

'Did you keep the letter from this Captain Swing fellow?' the judge asked, hopefully. 'Perhaps we might ascertain who wrote it.'

'I did not, your lordship,' said Amos Peakman, sheepishly. 'I burned the damned thing as soon as I received it, more's the fool me.'

Dick Dollery, however, did not see it that way: he was feeling quite important, standing in the box, looking out over the whole assembled court – the spectators, the lawyers, the solicitors who followed the Assizes and who had seated themselves in the body of the court, the clerks who sat in their seats. When he realised he was able to put questions which at other times would have been put only by one of the bewigged learned counsel who were paid a guinea to do it, he thought to himself 'Why not ask a question and put this damned man in his place? Show the people what type of man he truly is.'

The judge was as surprised as everyone when, to his same question, put in the same bored fashion, and anticipating the same mumbled refusal, Dick Dollery spoke up: 'I have a question. Was I among those who put thee on the dung heap, Amos?'

'No, I did not see you among them,' was the farmer's careful reply, his face reddening at the mention of the dung heap and the ripple of laughter which went around the courtroom.

'And was I one of those who would not let thee off it and forked it all over thee?'

'As far as I know, you were not either,' replied Amos Peakman, wishing he would ask him something else or not at all.

'That's because I was somewhere else, Amos, in the barn smashing up thy threshing machine,' declared Dick Dollery, almost proudly.

It was a foolish remark which the judge, the jury, the prosecuting counsel, most of the people in the courtroom, the warders and even the other prisoners recognised as such, but to Dick Dollery it was a sensible one, for it cleared him of any assault upon the farmer's person: and breaking a threshing machine, to his way of thinking, was not half so serious as assaulting someone, so he was quite pleased with himself for his cleverness and, from the many smiles all about him, others had seen it, too.

Dick Dollery was still not yet done. 'Did thee not lay a dozen village men off afore all this come to pass, Amos, and tell 'em to go on the parish?' he asked.

'I did,' replied Amos Peakman, sourly, with a slight cough of embarrassment now that his deed was being exposed in open court.

'Even though thee knew they all had families to feed and would be scarce able to pay their rent?' continued Dick Dollery.

'Aye,' answered Amos Peakman, 'but some things can't be helped. I only took half of the mowers and gavellers on because I needed as many hands as I could get to get the harvest in quick. In better times, I wouldn't have done that. It was against my better judgment to take some of them on at all, if you want to know. Same as I wouldn't have taken on that poor woman that got killed if I had known.'

Jem felt a sudden coldness come over him at the mention, even if obliquely, of Mary-Ann. Dick Dollery, however, had not noticed and simply ploughed on, dismissing the farmer's remarks as simply the usual grousing of his kind.

'And did thee not keep on the Irish?'

'I kept on the Irish because they were used to working a threshing machine and the others were not,' declared Amos Peakman, sharply. 'Some I took on just for the gathering-in. After that, there was no more work so I let them go.'

'As winter was approaching?'

'Aye,' he answered, then after a pause, 'aye' again.

He left the box more red-faced than when he had entered it and did not look up to meet the eyes of the next witness, Marcus Howie: in fact, the two avoided their eyes meeting, almost as if there was an antipathy between them.

Just as Amos Peakman had done, Marcus Howie gave a reasonably accurate account of what his wife had told him of the events concerning the machine-breaking on his farm, the condition in which he had found it on his return and the value of his loss, but there was something hesitant in the way he did so, as if he were unhappy at finding himself there at all.

'My wife dealt with them,' he said, matter-of-factly, 'as I was away at the time. And, though they broke my thresher, they were polite to my wife in doing it, she says, not threatening like.' As he said it, Marcus Howie looked across at Jem and there was almost an apologetic look on his face: it was as if he had been influenced by the women of the house. Other than his wife and daughter giving the men and youths beer, nothing else had been mentioned in the deposition of what had happened so at least his daughter was spared the indignity of what had happened to her becoming public knowledge, which would have mortified them all.

When Joshua Godwin gave his evidence, which again lasted all of three minutes, he also did not speak too ill of them, saying, apart from breaking his thresher, winnowing machine and two seed drills and being in a mob of several hundred, he had not been concerned for himself and his family from any of the Hamwick Dean men and had only feared for his life when a group of youths whom he did not know came back and threatened him with an iron bar.

The only question Dick Dollery asked of him was: 'Was I or any of us amongst those who came back to threaten thee, Joshua?'

'No, you were not one of them,' replied the farmer, emphatically. 'You were only there at the machine-breaking and when I handed over the two sovereigns and the beer and cheese to thee.' He reddened and shifted uncomfortably, for, in trying to be helpful, he had condemned his questioner further, not that he bothered one bit. 'You were there for that, Dick, I am sorry to say,' Joshua Godwin went on, spreading his hands, 'but I have sworn an oath to tell the truth. What is in my deposition is all truth and nothing but.'

'And the other defendants?' asked the judge, looking up from scratching with his pen, 'Were they all upon your farm as part of the mob when your threshing machine was broken?'

'They were, m'lord, all of them,' replied Joshua Godwin, but not vindictively, uncomfortable at having to make the admission so publicly.

John Romble asked what was the value of the property he had lost? 'You are a well-to-do man, Joshua,' he said, 'why have you prosecuted us over such a small thing?'

'The value of what was damaged might not amount to much,' declared Joshua Godwin, surprised by the question, 'ten pounds or so for the threshing machine, for it was an old one, already well used, and a few pounds for the loss of the two drills and the winnowing machine. But I had to prosecute to protect myself. If I did not, I might well find myself subject to further losses. I would not have proceeded against you had I not found it impracticable to do otherwise.'

Then, for some reason, he looked across at Titus Broake, sitting in the body of the court, as if the reason for his being there at all was some form of pressure from him: Titus Broake simply sniffed, shifted in his chair and retained his stony-faced composure.

Something must have deterred the farmer, too, when asked the same questions by the judge about the leadership of the mob: tactfully, he did not pick out Jem or Dick Dollery or Enos Diddams or any of the others as having actually been the ones who led the mob. 'There were too many to know who was their leader,' he said. 'There were upwards of two or three hundred. They were all milling about all over so I could not rightly say who was what at the time, except those who were there.'

When he referred to the letter he had received, warning that his ricks would be set on fire if he did not stop using his machines, it was hurriedly rustled from amongst his papers by Mr. Semblage and handed, via the usher, to the judge.

'Has it been ascertained who wrote the letter?' Mr Justice Launceston wanted to know.

The answer was given later – by Nathaniel Newman.

SIXTY-SIX

WHEN Jem and the others had been led upstairs to the assembly room, one of the cells had immediately been taken over by Nathaniel Newman, brought in chains and under guard from the gaol to await his call to give evidence. Such was the fury on Dick Dollery's face when the blacksmith came into the box that, if there had not been warders close at hand to step forward and grip his arms, he might well have jumped over the bar and attempted to throttle the blacksmith there and then, regardless of the lawyers seated on the benches in between. As it was, as soon as Nathaniel Newman came into the court, the warders closed upon them all to prevent any such disruption and they had to content themselves with icy stares and muttered oaths.

After the blacksmith had mumbled a reply to his name, he sheepishly sneaked a quick sideways look at them to see how his one-time friends now regarded him: Dick Dollery and Nathaniel Newman had been drinking friends of a kind for years, though there was a difference in their ages of several years: but that friendship dissolved the instant their eyes met.

Nathaniel Newman's evidence was as damning as would be that of anyone who had been a witness to all their actions and deliberations and who had been a willing part of it all, too. He was with them at the times the offences were committed: there was no denying that, though he began by attempting to exonerate himself from everything: 'I was working in my forge on the day of the farmers' meeting when Jem Stebbings, Dick Dollery and Enos Diddams came to see me,' he began, 'and I had to turn out for the meeting at the Wayfarers' very much against my will.' It was true that he had turned out against his will, but only because he was in the middle of firing a batch of horseshoes and did not want to stop: indeed he had said, 'I'll be with you as quick as I can. It's about time we did something.' It was hardly the refusal he implied.

'Jem Stebbings, Dick Dollery, Enos Diddams, John Romble, Thomas Judd and William Stubbs were all at the meeting,' he continued. 'Jem Stebbings was our leader. He sort of elected himself. I don't know whether he was asked or not. At the Wayfarers', Jem Stebbings agreed to speak for the village men to the farmers, which he did. He got them to sign the letter for the wages and he also led us to the parsonage, where we got two-hundred-and-fifty pounds off the parson's tithe. He was also the leader in the ill treatment of Mr. Jaikes, the overseer, though he did not fetch the cart they put him in. Three days after, he led us to the four farms at Hamwick Dean, the Hall and the three others, which had threshing machines and told us to smash them up. He was at the front all the time and, to my knowledge, it was he who first suggested that we break the threshing machines. In the Wayfarers' in my hearing, he definitely said, 'We should smash the machines! Smash every one on'em!' I heard him say so in the yard. I believe he did so more because his dear wife was killed while working on one of those machines, on Amos Peakman's farm while he was still in Melchborough Gaol for poaching. He had only come out of prison towards the end of October and, immediately after he come out, I first heard the men talking about breaking the machines of Sir Titus, Mr. Peakman, Mr. Howie and Mr. Godwin. So I assumed it was him who had started it. I admit that I was with the mob that helped to break the machines of the four gentlemen. When we went to the Hall and on to the other three farms, some amongst us I did not know – I supposed they had come from Lower Rackstead and Merchant Staplers – they set fire to the barn at the Hall and to ricks at Mr. Peakman's. I do not know whether they was told to do it or just did it off their own back. What I can say is that Jem Stebbings did not set the fire, but was one of those who helped put it out. On the matter of the letters that were sent signed "Captain Swing," they were written in the Shoulder of Mutton ale house. I admit I wrote one and Thomas Judd wrote another to Mr. Godwin. Everyone would have written one, but three on 'em who was there can't write so well so Jem Stebbings wrote the most – three – to Sir Titus, to the Reverend Petchey and to Mr. Peakman. My letter was the one sent to Mr. Howie, for which I am very sorry. I stuck it in his gate so he would find it. I was also there when Jem Stebbings led us all up to the parsonage – and got Parson Petchey to sign the paper to reduce the farmers' tithes. Jem Stebbings and Dick Dollery even told the parson how much he was to get, which, I thought, was not the thing to do to a man of the cloth and a reverend doctor, too.'

The only question came in the form of an outburst from Dick Dollery when the blacksmith had finished his evidence: 'Thee was with us, weren't ye, Nat? Thee was with us all the way, doing what we did. Why turn agin us?'

There was an embarrassed silence from Nathaniel Newman as the judge called for 'Silence!' and the witness was quickly excused.

The crowd had realised from the start that a turncoat was giving evidence and Jem and the others were cheered to see that Nathaniel Newman was surreptitiously hissed by a more vociferous section of the public as he was escorted from the courtroom: down below, he was put back in a cell on his own to await the afternoon resumption.

The last witness called by the prosecuting counsel and paid by Titus Broake to be there was a surprise: it was Caleb Chapman, looking old and wearied for his sixty-three years: he entered the witness box decidedly uneasily, with his shoulders drooped and his head lowered and raised it only in answer to the crier and to give the six at the bar a brief, friendly smile, but then quickly lowered it again as if fearing the judge might think he was up to something.

By giving his answers slowly and deliberately, he managed, nevertheless, to give a favourable account of the fairness of the meeting in the Wayfarers' when the rate was settled with the other farmers, though he had to acknowledge that the two men who had attended the meeting as the representatives of the labourers had been Jem Stebbings and Dick Dollery. He had, he said, known nothing about the treatment meted out to Joshua Jaikes or the march on the parsonage or the traipse to the four farms until after the events: when they had all gathered outside in his yard, he had thought it was 'just another meeting.' It was as if his inability to help his old friends – and old customers and members of his one-time tithing group – troubled him, for, before he left the box, it prompted him to speak up for them.

'I would like to say, m'lord, I have known Jem Stebbings for a dozen or more years as a husbandman and a customer of my inn and I can say honestly, having been the parish constable for a time, that I have always found him to be an upright and honest man, hard working and to do what he did, or what is said he did, was out of character and the act of a desperate man. In my view, your honour, the men had no option to do what they did. They were starving – '

There was a hiss of anger from the judge. 'These men are being tried for breaking threshing machines,' he interrupted, sharply. 'Such evidence is scarcely regular. If there is anything to be said on that matter, the court will hear representations of it later.' To him, extenuating circumstances were irrelevant as to the cause of why they had smashed the machines. 'We have not come here to inquire into grievances,' he declared, waspishly, 'we are here to decide law.'

Caleb left the witness box sadly shaking his head at the fact that the judge should refuse to allow him to give evidence about wages and distress and yet, at the same time, did not hesitate himself, as Mr. Justice Launceston did not, to make known his own views and to question in a disbelieving manner the conditions which had produced the disturbances.

They then moved on to the third charge concerning Parson Petchey: evidence was given, which Jem could not deny, first by Parson Petchey himself, that a mob had appeared at the front door of his parsonage and had demanded that he reduce the tithe and, further, that he sign a letter stating so and that he had done so only because he had been menaced by them: the leader of that mob he identified as Jem Stebbings and Dick Dollery, for they had done the talking, even though some three hundred of the villagers had been there also.

The only question asked of him was by Dick Dollery: 'Did we threaten thee with any violence during our conversation with thee, Reverend?'

'I was menaced by you and by the others,' declared Parson Petchey testily. 'I would not have signed the paper had there not been so many of you present. I felt insulted and belittled and I am not a man to be insulted and belittled.'

It was his final comment. 'Quite so, quite so,' said Mr Justice Launceston as the parson left the box.

He was then followed somewhat unhappily and sympathetically by Joshua Jaikes, who told in detail the ignominy of his departure from the village and drew laughter from some of the onlookers and even a smile or two from the lawyers and clerks sitting at the tables.

'A most unfortunate day, Mr. Jaikes,' commented the judge, drily, 'I trust you are recovered?'

'I am, your honour,' replied Jaikes, pleased by the judge's solicitation and leaving the box with the beginnings of a smile upon his face.

The only light moment came when Mr. Justice Launceston somewhat wearily again asked if any of the prisoners had anything to say in their defence to the members of the jury: none had: Thomas Judd, not understanding procedure, sheepishly replied: 'But I don't know any of 'em!'

The cases concluded, the jury went into a huddle in one corner: this was not unusual: such was the nature of justice then that sometimes a jury at an Assize court did not even bother to leave their box in finding their verdict. In a single day, a jury might hear upwards of twenty cases and pass judgment on them all: a jury at a Quarter Sessions, on the other hand, was quite likely to hear upwards of forty cases a day in the same courtroom and pass 'guilty' and 'not guilty' verdicts on them all: to depart to another room to deliberate upon each was a waste of time.

The jury did not discuss the evidence in their huddle: they simply allowed the views of the bewhiskered baronet in a royal blue topcoat and yellow waistcoat to predominate, supported by the three knighted gentlemen and the two honourable gentlemen: after two minutes, they returned to the box and announced their verdict: 'Guilty, my lord, all six on all charges!'

'A good time to adjourn for luncheon, gentlemen,' said Mr. Justice Launceston, sweeping up his papers and making for the door as the crier shouted loudly: 'All rise.'

The members of the Grand Jury, being gentlemen of the county, had excelled themselves over the six days of the Assizes in laying on luncheons, teas and suppers for their honours and themselves in a side room behind the main hall: this time they had laid on a spread of cold hams, pork pies, cold beef with pickled onions, cold Italian sausage, potatoes, peas, gravy and Scotch eggs, with jam tart and custard and trifle to follow.

As well as his honour and themselves, that day the Grand Jurors had also invited other guests who had attended court over the past few days to see the rural wretches put to the bar: amongst them that morning was Mrs. Philomela Sloane, wife of Captain Charles Sloane, retired, late of the 73rd of Foot, who lived in a large mansion in a fine park at Nadbury, not five miles from Melchborough, himself one of the Grand Jurors and also a juror on the opening days in the Nisi Prius Court of Mr. Justice Grebbleton-Hove below.

Jem and the others, meanwhile, were herded from the court by the warders, manacled again in the corridor outside and taken back down the steps to the cells below for their meal: a pint of cocoa and a lump of bread.

SIXTY-SEVEN

IN THE EYES of the authorities, the attack on the Inworth poorhouse was the most heinous of all the crimes committed around Hamwyte during the two weeks of insurrection. As it happened, three of the Hamwyte magistrates who had committed the six Hamwick Dean men to the Special Winter Assizes also served as Grand Jurors in the proceedings against them. Thus, when casting around for someone, anyone, to take the blame for the damage to the Inworth poorhouse, the authorities seized on the deposition of an Inworth labourer. In it, he clearly cited one Richard Dollery, whom he knew by sight, as having taken part in the destruction of the poorhouse and the other, Jem Stebbings, whom he also knew, as having been at the scene. Since both were in custody on other charges and they could not as yet apprehend the ringleader of the Salter mob, one Thomas 'Tater' Sack, it made sense to the Grand Jury to draw up a fifth indictment, charging the said Jem Stebbings and the said Richard Dollery that they did *'...on the oaths of William Clarke, with divers others unknown, riotously and unlawfully assemble in the parish of Inworth on Friday the twenty-sixth day of November and, when so assembled, did feloniously begin to pull down and attempt to demolish the poorhouse of the united parishes of Inworth, Hamwick Dean, Lower Rackstead, Merchant Staplers, Salter, Greater Tottle...'* This had been the fifth indictment read out.

Two Salter-ites had, in fact, been apprehended and taken to the old Norman castle at Wivencaster, which served as a gaol, but at that time neither had been brought on to Melchborough as neither was a likely ringleader, one being the village idiot and prone to fits and the other blind in one eye and crippled in one leg. Both, in fact, would later be charged with assisting in the part demolition of the Inworth poorhouse at the Lent Assizes, though still in the absence of 'Tater' Sack, his pint-sized lieutenant and two others who had fled abroad.

In the case of the county prosecutions, the clerks of the committing magistrates first took the depositions and then got up all the prosecutions in their capacity of solicitors to the same magistrates, prosecuting as county authorities, to the exclusion of solicitors of the individual prosecutors. Whereas the county authorities had taken up the less serious charges against the rioters, through Mr. Semblage, the Government had decided it must prosecute on the more serious ones, that is, those which might lead to the death penalty being pronounced, such as conviction for arson or the destruction of certain properties. Normally, this would have been done by the Attorney-General, but, it was decided, his presence would be required at the Special Commissions of Assize being set up to prosecute the many hundreds of rioters and machine-breakers in those counties where the outbreaks were deemed more severe, namely in Hampshire, Wiltshire, Dorset, Berkshire and Buckinghamshire. In his stead, he had sent a senior barrister, a tall, handsome Welshman, Sir Roderick Llewellyn-Roberts, who had spent the greater part of his life prosecuting at the Old Bailey as well at various Assizes: he would prosecute the said Jem Stebbings and the said Richard Dollery for 'their role in the part demolition of the Inworth poorhouse.'

Thus, it was, as Jem was sitting in the cell with the others, the door was unexpectedly opened and he and Dick Dollery were brusquely called out by the warder and taken to a small room at the end of the basement passageway, where the warders normally gathered: there, at a table sat a thin, diffident-looking man with a sheaf of papers spread before him, a small jar of ink on the table and a steel-tipped pen in one hand.

'My name is Williams,' he declared, brusquely, as if none too pleased to be there when he should have been seated in an inn, eating his lunch and drinking his ale. 'I am an attorney at law. I am here at the request of his honour, Mr. Justice Launceston, who is trying you. As a matter of conscience as much as justice, his honour is reluctant for the prosecution upon so serious a matter to proceed without some counsel for the defence assisting you in some small way. I have to tell you also that his honour does not like men to plead guilty on such charges as it restrict his variety of sentencing. I hope that is understood?'

Jem and Dick Dollery nodded, though both were unsure as to what it meant exactly.

'I have the depositions of the witnesses here,' went on Mr. Williams. 'I will do my best to read them over the recess. All I can say to you is I will do my best for you. We have a quarter of an hour. I have to tell you I am here only by chance. I was in court on an entirely different matter when I was approached. This is entirely unexpected.'

'But we cannot fund you. We have no money – ' Jem began, but Mr. Williams waved his protest away.

'That will be taken care of,' he said as if it were no matter and then proceeded to take down what Jem and Dick Dollery related, asking them also their 'Occupation, if any? Married or single? Children? Ages? Parish of residence?' Both answered the questions clearly and calmly and waited as the man scratched each reply noisily with his pen on a sheet of paper before him: it took no more than ten minutes of his time: then he was gone and the two bemused friends were returned to the cell to finish their cocoa and dry bread.

At least, with Mr. Williams to cross-examine any witnesses, Jem and Dick Dollery had some hopes when they were again brought up into the brightness of the assembly hall: but those hopes were soon dashed: for no sooner had the judge taken his place and the court been called to order than Mr. Williams rose.

'M'lord,' he said with a heavy sigh, 'due to the fact that the defendants, Stebbings and Dollery, have no money to pay for an attorney, I have foregone my lunch to go down to the cells under the impression that I was assigned by this court to act for them. I was briefed on the understanding that the court would pay my guinea fee. However, the court has seen fit to refuse to assign and, therefore, to pay me. I regret I have now to inform you, m'lord, that I must decline. In short, regretfully, m'lord, I must refuse to act for the prisoners.'

Jem's heart sank and Dick Dollery let out as low groan: the fact that a learned man was to question witnesses on their behalf had given both of them a decided lift: now their hopes were dashed.

Even the judge was taken aback. 'Do I take it, Mr. Williams, that you are abandoning these men at the time of their peril?'

Mr. Williams shrugged. 'I am m'lord,' he said, spreading his hands in the gesture of one who could do nothing else. 'They have no fee for counsel and the court refuses to assign or to pay me.'

'Most irregular,' said the judge, 'most irregular. I cannot have this.' Then, as if an idea had come to him, he fixed his eyes upon the only other occupant of the lawyer's benches, a florid-faced, several-chinned man of considerable girth who was idly sitting in the well of the court, twiddling a silver toothpick.

'Mr Samuels, would you oblige me?' the judge asked, with a gracious smile.

Mr Samuels was a King's Counsel from London, one of the many who followed the Assizes court on its journey around the country, though, it seemed to Jem and the others, he was not an overly successful one, for his robe was well worn and frayed and his wig was grey and in need of washing and was perched lopsidedly on his head as though placed there as an afterthought. While most of the others attorneys and barristers, save for the prosecuting counsel, had left for the next Assizes, he had remained out of idle curiosity, but also in hope of gleaning some knowledge of the cases which would serve him well when the rest of the wretches were put to the bar in the months ahead.

Mr. Samuels scowled as he rose, clearly not keen to take part in the proceedings. 'Without a fee, my lord?' he enquired in surprise.

'Without a fee, Mr. Samuels, as a kindness to me, if you will. We will enter a not guilty plea.'

'With respect, m'lord,' said the startled Mr. Samuels, 'I have no knowledge of these men's cases. I have not read the informations and, therefore, I am reluctant to act without an attorney,' He gave Mr. Williams, who sat petulantly on his seat, a withering look. 'The men's lives should not lie at my feet.'

'If you require time to consider the case or read the informations, I can give you a few minutes,' said Mr Justice Launceston, wishing to resolve the matter

'Thank you, my lord,' said Mr. Samuels with the customary polite bow, though the actual sentiment was absent, 'I shall endeavour to do my best for the prisoners, but I hope it will be recognised, my lord, that I act under a great disadvantage.'

Once he had read the depositions and pulled at his nose several times, Mr. Samuels rose to thank the judge for the three minutes he had been allowed: and, as he sat down, Mr Llewellyn-Roberts rose to summarise the 'dastardly deeds of that day' which had led to 'a set of desperate savages marauding through this hitherto submissive and peaceful county.'

'Yes, yes, press on, press on,' said the judge, sighing.

Lemuel Mussett was first into the box and gave an honest account of what had happened to him and his wife. 'A half-dozen on'em come to the door and told me I had a half-hour to pack my goods on a barrow and get out of there because they was going to wreck the place,' he declared. 'I remember two on'em because I know 'em – I know 'em to be from Salter. They said they would look after the old folks and the sick orphans, but they were going to demolish the place come hell or high water, begging you pardon, m'lord.'

'Are any of those men in this court room?' enquired Mr. Samuels. 'Do you recognise either of the defendants, there in the dock, as being amongst those who issued the ultimatum?'

Lemuel Mussett studied Jem and Dick Dollery for a moment and then slowly shook his head. 'I can't say for sure,' he said, actually telling the truth: he had been so startled by everything that happened to him that day that he had been unable to recall in his mind's eye anyone other than the rough 'Tater' Sack and his pint-sized lieutenant, who had been standing beside the Salter leader when the ultimatum was given.

'Did you see the accused Stebbings and the accused Dollery at the poorhouse at any time?' Mr. Samuels asked.

'I don't recall seeing either there,' he replied, which was again the truth, 'If they come, they come after I had left, though I did see Jem Stebbings up at the Anchor before it all started, so he was round about at the time, but I can't say that I saw him exactly as you ask.'

When he left, a solemn-faced, somewhat bewildered, burly farm labourer, in his mid-forties, from Inworth, came into the box and Mr. Llewellyn-Roberts – 'With your permission, my lord' – read out his deposition for him since he could not read himself and it would have taken too long to extract the same information from him all over again by questioning alone and time was pressing, as Mr. Justice Launceston had already reminded him. Jem recognised him immediately: it was the man he had pushed aside.

'My name is William Clarke,' read the barrister, with a somewhat embarrassed sigh, 'I am a farm labourer. I live in the parish of Inworth. I am employed by a Mr. Tate and had taken the day off to be at the meeting with the farmers at which my master was also present. I witnessed the destruction of the Inworth poorhouse, though I did not take part myself. There was a fair crowd just looking on and only fifty or sixty doing the actual breaking. I was standing just near the gate alongside a group of others, who had come up from the Anchor, and we watched together while the mob was engaged in doing what they were doing. Most of them I did not know. They were all strangers to me from villages other than Inworth. The only two I did recognise were Dick Dollery of Hamwick Dean and Jem Stebbings of Hamwick Dean. Dollery was on the roof breaking off tiles. I know him because I have seen him walking about his own village. I distinctly saw his head come through a hole in the roof and saw him pushing tiles off. I knew Jem Stebbings because he had been at the Anchor earlier, talking with the farmers and was made known to us. He came rushing up to join in when the breaking started. I saw him go into the poor house and he was about the yard, shouting up to those on the roof, one of whom was Dollery. He was waving his arms a lot. He appeared to be urging them on. I later saw him standing by the railings watching as they piled the furniture and things on to a bonfire and set it alight. He was talking to Dick Dollery as they walked away. They seemed pleased with what they had done. Dick Dollery seemed particularly so and the others with him were all smiling. I do not know who the others with them were.'

At the conclusion of the reading, the man simply confirmed it was what he had told the Grand Jury, though he hung his head when he did so and mumbled his reply as if hoping that all those behind him listening would not hear it.

'What did he say?' demanded the judge.

'He said it is as it was stated, my lord,' counsel replied.

'Good. Any questions, Mr Samuels.'

The man's evidence had done for Dick Dollery, of course: there was no point in Mr. Samuels bothering to defend him. So when he rose slowly, it was to ask in a solemn manner: 'You say you saw one of the defendants pushing tiles off the roof, what was the other one doing?'

'He was talking to people who were doing the destroying and carrying things out. And, like I said, he went into the building while it was being demolished and was in there several minutes afore he come out again so I suppose he was doing the same as all the others,' the labourer replied.

'You did not yourself go into the building?'

'No, it were too dangerous with bits flying about everywhere, tiles off the roof, floorboards and broken bits of furniture and the like.'

'So you did not see what the defendant Stebbings did inside the poorhouse?'

'No, not for certain.'

'A witness, the Reverend Coleman, will say he had asked Stebbings to stop the destruction at the poorhouse. Could he not have been doing that?'

The labourer merely shrugged. 'I don't know anything about that. I didn't hear what he said. All I know he was shouting up to those on the roof.'

'Is it not strange that of all the others there, perhaps amongst them people from your own village, you cannot recall any of them, but you clearly recall these two?' Mr. Samuels asked, suspiciously.

'There were too many of them for me to remember the lot on'em,' the labourer replied indignantly, 'but I remember Dollery because I knew him and I knew the other one because I had seen him on the green and he pushed past me to go through the poorhouse gate. Shoved me out of the way, he did. That's why I remember him.'

'Did you see him at any time actually joining in the destruction of the poorhouse?' Mr. Samuels persisted.

'No,' admitted the labourer, somewhat reluctantly, 'not actually breaking anything, but he was in the yard when others was doing it and he was talking to everyone who was coming out, too, like he was urging them on. And he went inside. I saw that.'

In his heart, Jem knew that it was futile to protest: the judge had heard the facts from an 'independent' witness who worked for one of the yeomen farmers of Inworth so would believe him whatever else was said. Clearly, his actions in attempting to stop the men had been misconstrued: neither would the man have been able to hear what he had shouted up to Dick Dollery as there had been far too much noise at the time.

Nathaniel Newman was then brought back, but this time he did not even look at his old friends, but kept his head lowered and damned Dick Dollery even further by recounting how the mob from Hamwick Dean had been led by him, how they had detoured to the Green Man at Lower Rackstead to recruit others on their way to Inworth and how, when they had arrived at the poorhouse, several had rushed forward to take part in its destruction, though he maintained, when questioned by a disbelieving Mr. Justice Launceston, that he had no idea who else from Hamwick Dean had taken part.

'There was so many people milling about, breaking up everything by then,' he replied. 'I can't be sure who was doing exactly what.'

Mr. Justice Launceston raised a sarcastic eyebrow. 'Really?' was all he said, but he did not pursue the matter.

He reluctantly admitted in cross-examination by Mr. Samuels that he had taken part and believed that he should have, and would have, been, prosecuted himself had he not promised to give evidence against Jem and Dick Dollery: his only concession to Jem was that he had not seen him in the building and he had not actually seen him taking part in the destruction and that was all.

'Did you not hear me shouting for you to stop?' Jem asked him later as his only question.

'I did not,' was the blacksmith's reply. 'There was so much noise going on all around, banging and crashing, like, I did not know you was with us till I saw you talking to Dick afterwards.'

The Reverend Coleman's deposition was brief and not really helpful: he confirmed that he had asked Jem to intervene, but had not followed him to the poorhouse: he had intended to do so and had set off, but had hardly gone a hundred yards when he was accosted by several villagers. 'I was told not to intervene and to mind my own business by several persons,' he said. 'What I took to be threats of violence against my person and against my family were implied if not actually made. Instead, I went into the church and knelt and prayed for God to forgive his straying sheep.'

The word of a clergyman would have been Jem's best hope, at least if Mr. Samuels had held out any hope for either of them: but he seemed to give up at that point and collapsed back on to his seat with an exapserated sigh and a shrug to his fellow lawyers: he had done his best: he could do no more: after all, it was not really his case.

None of the Inworth farmers who had negotiated with Jem and the labourers at the Anchor gave evidence: since no one was willing to pay their costs for the day, they had remained in Inworth. Besides, to have given evidence of their agreement would most probably have laid them open to the criticism of the law and the Establishment, for it was known that some of the judges considered farmers who negotiated with rioters or who put their threshing machines out into fields so that they could be broken by a passing mob should themselves be put to the bar.

Again the jury did not retire to give their verdict, but went into a huddle in one corner near to the judge's bench for three or four minutes, with much nodding of their heads, before returning to the box, where the bewhiskered baronet stood again and, in answer to, 'What say you?' replied, not expectedly, 'Both are found guilty, my lord.' The trial had lasted exactly one hour.

SIXTY-EIGHT

AT THE END of the session, it was common for those prisoners who had been found guilty to be brought back to hear their punishments: thus, Enos Diddams, John Romble, William Stubbs and Thomas Judd were again brought up from below to join Jem and Dick Dollery at the bar: the shrug which Jem and Dick Dollery gave as the other four came up communicated the expected outcome of their case.

It was also expected that defendants who had been convicted of capital crimes were given a chance to address the court before they were sentenced. 'Anything to say?' his honour asked, in the tone of one who considered that there was nothing they could say which would alter anything: they were all guilty as charged and that was that, in his view.

'I leave my defence to the counsel,' said John Romble boldly.

'Your counsel cannot speak for you, you must speak for yourself;' snapped the judge. Being as ignorant of the workings of the law as the law itself, none had known that a man accused of a felony, whatever his condition of mind or body, had to answer the speech of the prosecuting counsel himself.

At that, John Romble mumbled his refusal: 'Nothing to say, m'lord' as did William Stubbs and Thomas Judd in turn: it was as if the three of them had resigned themselves to whatever punishment was to be meted out and did not wish to say anything which might encourage the judge to be more severe than he intended or more scornful, since all during the session he had interrupted both witness and counsel alike to make his own comments.

Enos Diddams at least tried. 'Begging thy pardon, m'lord,' he began, 'we meant no harm to no one in what we did. We was told a magistrate himself had told farmers they ought to set aside their threshing machines off their own backs to help the common labourer because of all the misery they was creating, begging your pardon again, m'lord. I am a farm labourer myself and I have found it too difficult to get work in my own parish for the last three years. I have had to get work wherever I can. I was able to find some work this summer, at least for the harvesting, at a place three miles from my cottage – and glad I was of it – though I earned only seven shillings and sixpence a week. But I stuck at it because the poor rate paid only three or four shillings and then only for road work. It were low enough as it was and they was a-gooing to lower it again, so I heard. I had to walk three miles to my work and three miles back each day. Because of all the walking, my boots were so wore out they needed mending ready for the winter. The week the troubles started I didn't have a shilling for iron for them. I only had six shillings to support my whole family and that's why we decided to ask for more wages, begging your pardon agin.'

The judge almost snorted with derision. 'That is no excuse for the actions you have perpetrated,' he declared. 'Your master paid you the wages which had been agreed between the two of you, did he not? Did you not stop to think, when assembling a mob to demand higher wages, that your action could be construed as one of combination, of combining together illegally? A crime is no less a crime because the man who commits it is poor.' It silenced poor Enos and he lowered his head again, reddening at the rebuke and did not look up again.

Dick Dollery, however, was not one to remain quiet at any time: a simply countryman he might be and unschooled, he was going to have his say and damn them all, but not about himself, instead about his friend, Jem, as much as because of his friendship but also because of a troubled conscience since it was his action which had brought the two of them there, as the ringleader of the mob which had marched in support of Jem and had allowed themselves to be diverted from it to take part in the attack on the poorhouse.

'I have known my good friend Jem Stebbings here since we were boys together, m'lord,' he declared, turning to look at Jem. 'He is a veteran of the Peninsular war, who became a sergeant in the service of the old Iron Duke himself. He was a soldier at Waterloo with the old Duke with this county's own regiment, the Forty-Fourth, and has his medal for it. In our village of Hamwick Dean, he did the negotiating for us with the farmers. It is because of him that we were able to have tithes and taxes down, so that the farmers – even the unwilling ones – could pay us the wages we asked. None of us could live on six shillings a week. No man can. The man who spoke up for us was my good friend here.'

It was a well-meant attempt, but the wealthy men of the jury were not much impressed and it showed upon their faces.

His honour saw it almost as a vindication of everything they had heard that day: it also gave him a further chance to offer a rebuke to these 'damnable upstart rioters.'

'If a man has been a soldier, then all the more reason for expecting that he should have had the discipline to stand against all that happened,' he snorted. 'Being a soldier makes him doubly responsible. The others were simple agricultural labourers. He was a man in whom discipline should have been ingrained!'

Till then Jem had not intended to say anything: like John Romble, William Stubbs and Thomas Judd, he had not wanted to risk encouraging the further scorn of the judge. As a distraction to himself, he had kept his eyes focused on the darkening sky showing through one of the tall windows: however, his lordship's disdainful manner irritated him. What he thought and said would not alter the verdict or ward off their punishment, but his words might well be remembered by those who heard them: it would show that he was not one to be brow-beaten into silence, even when in front of an array of lawyers more learned than himself or an audience of town and county gentry.

'We did what we did because we saw no other way,' Jem declared boldly when the judge turned to him. 'It was not our intention to do harm against any person. All we wanted were decent wages. Our object was solely to raise the wages of the ordinary labourers who work for masters who think nothing of spending as much on a new silk waistcoat or a gown for their wives or a new hat for their daughter as they do on a man's money to feed his family for a week. These same men spend as much money, if not more, taking care of the horses they ride to chase foxes than they do on the labourers who toil for them.'

The judge did not seem to care much for Jem's comment. 'I am convinced that one of your victims, the Reverend Doctor Petchey, does no such thing,' he reprimanded, 'yet you proceeded as a mob to his house and, according to the depositions of witnesses which you have not disputed, demanded that he reduce the tithe and the annual amount from it which is his by right. It was highly insolent of you to demand that the tithe be reduced by your rector, a gentlemen, who had by an expensive education qualified himself to discharge the sacred duties of a minister of the Gospel, asking him to descend from that station and reduce himself to the situation almost of a common labourer.'

Somehow, Jem managed to retain a quiet and respectful tone. 'As far as the tithes go, I am not aware that God expects any man to give his hard-earned wages in tithes to keep another man in luxury while others around him go hungry,' he said, which produced an intake of breath amongst the women in the court and coy smiles of admiration from some, too. 'It was our thinking, your lordship,' went on Jem, 'that gentlemen who wear clerical garb might do with a little less salary and a deal more piety. It is my belief that both God and Jesus would have said, "Keep the tithes if you cannot pay them and feed your families".'

His lordship did not see how matters appertaining to tithes and wages should concern a common labourer. 'That is an impertinence, You presume too much,' he declared, peering down at Jem over the top of his rimless spectacles. 'I cannot for the life of me see why you should all be so discontented as to seek to foment revolution as the French peasantry did. I do not understand why you are so discontented, why you should want to ruin your master by breaking their machines? In some respects, you are better off than your masters. You do not have the worries that beset them day to day from each waking morning. You have fewer worries and you pay less in taxes.'

'All we ever asked was that those above us would look down kindly upon us and would begin to relieve us,' said Jem, refusing to be cowed. 'When we made our application to those you call our masters, it was to be hoped that, through them, it would reach right up to the head, to Parliament itself. It did not. Instead they put out the yeomanry against us and swore in as special constables every man of means who had a grudge against our rising. As to farmers being worse off than ourselves, when my wife and our two children were evicted from our cottage because the vestry would not pay her rent when she had no money to pay it herself, they lived in a so-called cottage built by some squatter from what he could find in the hedgerows and the woods and abandoned by him when it was no longer habitable. Yet it was all my dear wife could find to shelter herself and our children. She is dead now, may God rest her soul. In heavy rains, the roof leaked, for it is made of turf cut from the verge. On cold days, fearful draughts come whistling through every crack and there are a dozen of those which I have had to fill with clay from the ditch. And when the wind blew too strongly, I feared always that the whole thing might be blown down about our ears. Yet there are farmers in our parish who keep their animals in dry stables, their cows in dry byres, their pigs in dry sties. I eked out my living from day to day. Some days I had no money to buy food and was forced to go to the parish and to beg for relief and what I got from the parish was a pittance, barely enough to keep the soul in the body of one let alone the souls of four of us, yet I was expected to go to church and touch my forelock to the same parson who preached the Christian truth with one breath and encouraged a reduction in the poor relief with the next. When my dear wife was alive, she would give her food to our young kiddies before she would eat herself and you ask me why we did what we did! Because we were hungry! We were just hungry, our kiddies were hungry, our families were hungry, we had no hope and the country closed its eyes and its ears to us. That is why we did what we did – for our wives and our young kiddies!'

Jem's anger was not likely to deter a judge: he had heard the angry tirades of a thousand men: what concerned him was that it was already mid-afternoon, he had heard them out and he had read again the sections of the Act under which men could be hanged for assembling riotously and breaking machinery. He had to admit that the man, Stebbings, for a country labourer, was as eloquent a man as he had come across at the bar all year: it never ceased to surprise him how so many of the 'lower order,' though half of them were not even able to write their names, could speak so well.

However, he had a duty to perform: these men had all been found guilty and he must pass sentence upon them. It was late afternoon and tea was waiting.

SIXTY-NINE

JUDGES THEN had considerable flexibility in choosing punishments, which ranged from the death penalty to a small fine, though the specific punishments available in each case depended upon the specific offence for which the defendant was convicted: felonies, for example, were not punished by a fine.

Mr. Justice Launceston, however, had come to a firm decision: if the law ceased to be administered with due firmness and men looked to it in vain for the security of their rights, then that was the road to anarchy and the end of order. The nation's wealth and power would be at an end, its capital and industry would move to a more peaceful country whose laws were more respected or better enforced: it was his duty, therefore, to ensure the continuance of the laws and statutes of England, for the good of the whole nation.

It irked him particularly that, by the very Act under which a man could be hanged for riotous assembly, by another section of it seven years was fixed as the maximum penalty for breaking a threshing machine: he chafed under this restriction. Had Parliament foreseen such crimes as men going into a neighbouring parish to break a threshing machine, then he was convinced it would have enabled the courts to give them a more severe sentence: as it was he was bound by it.

One thing was for sure, these men before him would find none of the leniency of earlier months in his court, especially those who were not agricultural labourers and had had no real cause to riot, to break machinery, to burn down barns and set ricks ablaze: there would be no giving them a month in gaol or discharging them as had been done in Kent.

His first address was to Enos Diddams, John Romble, William Stubbs and Thomas Judd. 'Prisoners at the bar,' he began, shuffling his papers and drawing himself up so as to look down upon them from an inch or so higher than his normal seated height, 'prisoners at the bar, whatever may have been the perceived rights of your cause, there is no small feeling about the land in high places that you were wrong in the manner in which you conducted it. You may well have considered your actions a mere protest and justified to relieve the distress which unhappily existed in so many parts and still exists despite all you have done. You may, too, have anticipated only a token punishment for your misdemeanours. It is my duty to disavow you of any such thought here and now – '

He paused to allow the meaning of his words to be understood and for the poor wretches before him to prepare themselves.

' – It is my firm conviction that the notion that machinery which facilitates the means of procuring subsistence can be injurious to the lower classes is an absurdity. If individuals are so aggrieved by privations and injuries, they must apply to the Legislature, which alone can afford them relief, but it can never be tolerated in any country which professes to acknowledge the obligations of municipal law, that any man or body of men should be permitted to sit in judgment upon their own wrongs, or to arrogate to themselves the power of redressing them. To suffer that would be to relapse into the barbarism of savage life and to dissolve the very elements by which society is held together – '

Another pause as his cold eyes ranged along the line of men at the bar. 'Enos Diddams, John Romble, William Stubbs, Thomas Judd, you have all been convicted on evidence satisfactory to the jury of crimes the nature of which the security of this country and the maintenance of the law upon which it depends makes it indispensable to pass the sentence which the law points out. Of you all, only Enos Diddams is an agricultural labourer by need. You, William Stubbs, are a harnessmaker by trade. You, John Romble, are a wheelwright by trade and you, Thomas Judd, are a cordwainer by trade – you make boots and shoes. None of you has or should have anything to do with threshing machines. They do not interfere with your labour. Their destruction does you no good – '

Again a pause while he gathered himself to introduce the solemn tone of sentencing: 'Therefore, having deliberated well and seriously on what it is my duty to pronounce upon you, I feel I have no discretion in a case of this sort, but that I am bound to pronounce the punishment of the law, which the Act of Parliament has provided, and accordingly the sentence is that each of you shall be transported across the high seas for seven years – '

The four men were stunned: transportation was tantamount to exile for life: they had always regarded the machine-breaking as a legitimate form of protest, since it was the destruction of mechanical machines which took away men's work and their ability to feed their families and so was justified by that. The three tradesmen had not stopped to think that the threshing machines did not affect them: each had in his time performed some labour on the land as their trade declined and in that they regarded themselves the same as any field labourer: but each was still first and foremost a journeyman and would willingly have returned to his trade. What they had done was to help their friends, to add strength to their numbers and their cause: they had treated their arrest almost as martyrdom.

The realisation that he would be separated from his wife and his young children, the youngest of his six being only five years, was too much for poor William Stubbs: he let out a cry of anguish and tears formed in his eyes and he stood at the bar shaking.

'You will leave this country, all of you,' continued his lordship, 'you will see your friends and relations no more, for, though you will be transported for seven years only, it is not likely that at the expiration of that term you will find yourselves in a situation to return. You will be in a distant land and it is likely, through your foolishness, that you will be parted from your loved ones for ever in this world and the land which you have disgraced will see you no more.'

The judge turned next to Dick Dollery. 'As to you, Richard Dollery, I can give you no hope of remaining in this country either. It is my duty to state that, for the violent and disgraceful outrages for which you also have rightfully been found guilty on the evidence, you should be sent out of the country and transported across the high seas for fourteen years. Public justice would not be satisfied without that being done. The peace of the country and the protection of the property of peaceable individuals require it. I, therefore, hope and trust that, in whatever situation you may hereafter be placed, whether part or the whole of your life shall be spent in another country, separated from those friends and connections which are dear to you here, you will conduct yourself as an honest and industrious person and endeavor to secure you own peace of mind and the mercy of God, which will render you worthy of His acceptance whenever it may please Him to call you from this world.'

With a wave of the hand, his lordship brusquely added: 'Take them down.'

Quickly, the warders came forward and pushed the five towards the door: in the corridor outside, they were surrounded by eight or nine of the uniformed guards, their wrist were again manacled, the chain reeved through and they were hurried almost at a stumbling run down the steps. The severity of their sentence had so shocked Dick Dollery and Enos Diddams that they seemed unable to comprehend the enormity of it: their minds for the moment were concentrated upon remaining upright, though there was little strength in their legs.

SEVENTY

EVEN AS DICK DOLLERY and the others were taken out the back of the Shire Hall, where a 'fly' waited to take them back to the gaol, Jem was joined by two of the coastal youths of seventeen and eighteen who had been brought back from the gaol at noon and lodged ready in the cells below. They had been tried before Mr. Justice Launceston late on the Saturday evening and convicted after the affray on the heath at Wivencaster, but it had been so late in the evening that his honour had reserved sentencing, most particularly because, during their trial, the youths had severely tested his patience by treating the courtroom as their stage and had maintained a proud and defiant attitude to whatever adversity might befall them. In consequence, Mr. Justice Launceston wished to be fair and had ordered them to be brought back after he had pondered the matter of their sentencing over the Sunday.

The seventeen-year-old, by the name of Francis Tutter, had also been convicted of the theft of two sovereigns from a farmhouse, rather than wait for them to be given by the farmer on request: but, more tellingly, he had wielded a sledgehammer during the later fracas with the yeomanry and special constables on the heath and had knocked off the hat of one of the magistrates with his sledgehammer when he was, in fact, aiming to smash in his skull. The eighteen-year-old, named Charles Hodgson, had been found guilty of 'riotous assembly,' theft of money along with his friend, machine-breaking and extorting money from two persons he had met on the road on the way to the heath, one of them, it turned out, a baronet. He had also gained a certain notoriety as the self-styled leader of the mob from his own village which had broken several threshing machines: he, too, had struck at one of the yeomanry on the heath with an axe, breaking his arm.

Whereas, apart from his remarks at the end of his trial, Jem had remained silent for most of it, the two youths, as if to impress the watchers, had showed scant respect for anyone and, whether questioning witnesses or being addressed by judge, counsel or others, they had assumed a manner which they would not have dared to use before had their cause not already been lost.

The seventeen-year-old Tutter, facing the charge of 'felonious assault' against the magistrate had, when first committed, summoned the chaplain and made a full written confession in the hope that his honesty and penitence would mitigate in his favour, with the chaplain as a friendly witness. The confession, however, was made in the presence of one of his gaolers: and, by the rules of Melchborough Gaol, of which the chaplain had been ignorant and had never dreamed such a practice existed in any gaol in the country, he had been compelled to submit the confession, on which the youth had made his mark, to the gaoler for inspection. It was then shown to the governor and a copy of it made and given to the prosecuting barrister: so that when poor Tutter was called up for trial, such was his extreme poverty, that he could not raise the necessary guinea to fee counsel and so had had no legal advice or assistance.

The judge spent a short period glancing up and down a piece of paper through his spectacles before nodding to himself and placing it aside, apparently satisfied that he had read the right information: only then did he reach down with one hand to a drawer alongside his seat. When his hand reappeared, it was holding a square of black cloth: which he placed upon his wig: immediatelyt, there were gasps around the court room and a hub-bub of noise arose. No machine-breaker or rioter had yet been sentenced to death or even had a judgment of death recorded against him, though fourteen other poor souls at the same Asisizes had. No one save the authorities had ever considered the crimes warranted such severity.

'Silence!' ordered the judge, sternly, turning to look at the prisoners in the dock, but without an ounce of compassion in his eyes: he had a duty to perform, according to the law: now he must carry out that duty: it was as simple as that.

The meaning of his placing the black cloth on his wig dawned slowly upon the two youths: they stood open mouthed in disbelief as first their names and then their sentences were delivered. They gripped the rail and began to tremble as others had done before them: now there was no trace of the bold demeanour which had impressed the watchers during their trials: they were stunned by the catastrophic vengeance being extracted from them.

At their arrest, they had anticipated only a token punishment for their involvement, perhaps six months or a year in gaol at the most: that was why they had had their hour of jest and bravado and playing to the gallery: now they faced oblivion jerking on the end of a rope. Tutter began to weep, while his friend stood stoically shaking his head as if in disbelief at the severity and finality of the sentence. At the end of it, unable to think of anything else to say, he looked at the judge and said in a polite manner, as if actually grateful: 'Thank you, m'lord.'

It was some time before the judge, still with the black cloth upon his wig, turned to address Jem alone: holding the piece of paper before him and in as solemn a voice as any had ever heard, he declared dispassionately: 'Jem Stebbings, it is with the same painful consideration I address myself to you as well as the two others. You are an older man, a man of forty-three years, one who led rather than was led, a former soldier in His Majesty's service, a veteran of the great wars against the tyrant Napoleon, a soldier who fought both on the Peninsula and at the great battle at Waterloo. You are also one, it has been clearly shown, who was a prime mover in many of the incidences which have been ascribed to you. You were the leader for the machine-breaking mob in your own village, you were the leader also of the mob which accosted the Reverend Doctor Petchey over the tithes, and who coerced the farmers into signing an agreement to raise wages. You were present at both the attempt to burn down Sir Titus Broake's barn and at the part destruction of the poorhouse at Inworth, though there is some doubt, rightly so, as to whether, in fact, you did assist at either. However, you were a principal in the events which led up to both. Therefore, I feel it is my duty to pronounce the awful sentence of death upon you also. Having been convicted of the offences named, you, too, must forfeit your life to the laws of the country...'

There was a sudden emptiness in the pit of Jem's stomach, a fluttering of his heart and he felt himself sway before he managed to grip the wooden bar and prevent himself from collapsing: it was several seconds before he managed to recover himself in time to hear the judge again, saying to all: ' ...I hope that the fate of these three will serve a warning to others, that this court will deal harshly with any who seek to foment revolution. Take them away.'

Jem, the tearful Tutter and the shocked Hodgson were handcuffed and chained again and hurried out of the back of the Shire Hall, where the 'fly' containing Dick Dollery and the others was waiting.

'T'is the vengeance of the upper classes they have given out, not justice,' Dick Dollery managed to whisper, before he received a sharp blow on the arm from the guard and the curt command, 'Silence! Hold your tongue or it will be the worse for you!' How it would be worse than transportation for fourteen years, he did not know.

The scenes outside were a frenzy of people: news that three of the machine-breakers had just been condemned to death brought more of the townsfolk swarming round to join those who had been waiting there all afternoon, eager to see the doomed prisoners make their last journey through the streets of their county town.

This time, Jed and Thirza were amongst the throng who waited: word had been got to them at Hamwick Dean during the Sunday that their father was to appear in court on the Monday with the other Hamwick Dean men and they had been brought by Dick Dollery's wife, Lizzie, along with his six girls in the company of the wives and families of the other Hamwick Dean men: the wagoner, Daniel Gate, had waived his fee to bring them all together. There, too, were the mothers, fathers, brothers, sisters and in-laws of Tutter and Hodgson, weeping and wailing and calling out their names.

As the lumbering 'fly' pulled out into the High Street, the crowd all surged forward and had to be forced back roughly by the yeomanry and special constables: even so, a hundred and more followed it all the way to the gaol, a long straggling line of them, running ahead to get to the two bridges first where they knew the cumbersome wagon would have to slow so that they could call out to those riding inside.

Several times Jem managed to see out when one of the warders lifted the flap to peer out himself in case danger threatened, danger of a rescue, that is: in the deep gloom of the winter afternoon, Jem thought he saw Thirza and Jed running alongside two of Dick Dollery's older girls: he could not be sure, but so desperate was he to see them one more time, to fix their images in his mind one last time, that he allowed himself to believe it was them.

All Jem could think, as the 'fly' trundled towards the gaol, was that the severity of his sentence was due entirely to the machinations of Titus Broake: it could not have been anyone else: he was a magistrate at Hamwyte, he was a Grand Juror, a Quarter Sessions magistrate, friend of the County Sheriff and now a Member of Parliament. 'He has done this to me,' Jem said to himself. 'If I had not been in gaol, Mary-Ann would not have been killed. Titus Broake is responsible for that. Now he seeks my end as well.' He could not forget the taunts the lord of the manor had made when they had been lined up outside the Hamwyte bridewell: how he had ridden down the line especially to confront him and Dick Dollery: how he had sworn evidence against him which had sent him to Melchborough Gaol.

It was he who had denounced Jem as the ringleader of a violent mob when he had simply been their spokesman, asked by them to speak on their behalf simply to obtain better terms from all the farmers: he had tried to do it with courtesy and without menace, merely putting the men's case. True, he had led them in smashing the threshing machines, but that was vengeance for Mary-Ann's death: but he had never once chanted 'Bread or blood!' That had been left to the younger ones amongst them, the hot-headed ones like the two Lower Rackstead youths. It could only be as a result of Titus Broake's falsified evidence of the burning of his barn and the evidence of the Inworth labourer, William Clarke, that had led to him being the only one from Hamwick Dean sentenced to death, for no other evidence had been presented against him, nothing from the march, nothing from Burestead Market, if indeed the authorities in the next county knew who he was and where to find him…

Meanwhile, it being late in the afternoon, the learned judge and the jury had retired for a prepared tea in one of the ante rooms: even as the 'fly' carrying Jem and the others trundled into the gaol yard and the lodge gates clanged shut behind them, Mr Justice Launceston was standing with his back to the fire in the sideroom of the assembly hall, warming his back while he sipped his cup of tea and ruminating on the fact that, from the more than thirty Assizes at which he had sat, he had yet to receive a pair of white gloves: for it was a tradition of the Assizes, that had he been able to deliver a 'maiden session' – that is, one in which no one was condemned to death – he would have been presented with a pair of white gloves by the jurors. He had to console himself that he and his honourable colleague had left seventeen for hanging and most of the others to be transported for what most probably would be the rest of their natural lives.

On the morrow, he was off to the next Assizes at Edmundsbury and from there up into the next two counties: there was still plenty of work to be done, plenty of machine-breakers and arsonists to be tried and convicted and 'left for hanging' when he moved on.

Once inside the gaol, the warders instantly separated Jem and the two other condemned and marched them along various passageways to some steps that led down to cells in the bowels of the gaol, the condemned cells. Once there, the name and sentence of each was called out and they were handed to another gaoler. 'Everyone strip,' the new warder ordered and Jem was forced to take off his suit of black clothes and, when he had done that, he was given a grey suit, consisting of a jacket, waistcoat, and trousers, and a sort of Scottish cap, and a pair of woollen stockings: he was, however, allowed me to keep his boots. As soon as he had put on the grey suit and had made a bundle of his old clothes, they were taken from him; the only hopeful; sign was that a ticket was pinned to them before they were thrown into a cupboard. Each was then led to a separate cell, the door was unlocked and they were pushed inside.

A more wretched place in which Jem found himself could hardly be imagined: the cell was barely five feet wide and seven feet long, with a window high up on the wall, washed over with a grey paint to block out half the light so that the place was in almost perpetual gloom: the nail-studded door had a small iron grate in it, the walls were lime-washed and the floor flagged. There were two shelves in the cell, one to stow the hammock, sheet and blanket in the daytime and the other to hold a tin pannikin, a copper bowl, a wooden spoon, a wooden saltcellar, a brush and a piece of soap, which was to be taken away at night and returned the following morning. A wooden flap hinged to the wall and propped with an iron crutch served as a table, with a crude wooden stool set before it being the only seat: on the table were a Bible and a prayer-book, as if the condemned needed to prepare themselves to meet their Maker.

As Jem sat in his cell, in an inn across the market place from the Shire Hall, Titus Broake was in the process of counting out five guineas before the greedy eyes of William Clarke, the Inworth labourer, as promised for the evidence he had given over the demolition of the poorhouse.

At the same time, Nathaniel Newman sat in a separate wing from that of his former friends, his cell door locked against any who might have heard of his betrayal: even the warders shunned him, called roughly to him, barked their orders at him: and spat in his food and his cocoa, while other prisoners, when all were locked in for the night, shouted their threats at him.

Fearful of those as he was, for he knew men would carry out those threats if given the chance, what troubled him more was that a part of his deposition had been omitted, struck out, though he did not know it, at the request of the lord of the manor when it had been read by the Grand Jury: '...What I can say,' he had clearly stated, 'is Jem Stebbings did not set the fire in the barn, but helped to put it out...'

He was still troubled by it when he was put to the bar at the Epiphany Quarter Sessions, for the authorities, had not pardoned him as he had expected they would and as he had been led to believe that they would.

SEVENTY-ONE

AS THE OLD YEAR approached its end, more than nineteen-hundred men and youths were lying in county gaols and improvised lock-ups throughout the south of England: the movement was crushed: the time for retribution was at hand.

Outside Melchborough Gaol, weeping and fearful mothers, wives, sisters and children clamoured at the gates of the lodge, pleading to be allowed inside to see their menfolk, both those already sentenced and those yet to be tried, for the gaol was full to overflowing. Even the warders who turned them away admitted that the scenes were truly heart-breaking, especially when upwards of two hundred waited all day through a heavy fall of snow on the Christmas Eve, a Friday, in the hope that, as an act of compassion at a time of great rejoicing for others, the governor might allow them through. All day, they stood in huddled groups about the gravelled concourse, pallid-faced, as if all the blood had ebbed from their features, speaking in whispers as though bereaved already, amongst them Dick Dollery's wife and his whole brood of adolescent and grown-up daughters, Enos Diddams's wife and his grown family of four, William Stubbs's wife and children, all of whom had walked the eleven miles to Melchborough to be there, only to be told yet again, as the afternoon deepened into dusk, that the prisoners had already been locked away for the night.

Retribution came at Melchborough on a frost-covered morning two days after Christmas when, soon after seven o'clock, Dick Dollery, John Romble, William Stubbs and Thomas Judd, and all the other capitally convicted prisoners still in the gaol and those awaiting trial at the Epiphany Quarter Sessions, were taken out into the yard and made to stand in chained rows of twenty before the lodge: high above them stood the black scaffold with its black chains hanging down from the beam.

Just before eight o'clock, as the sun struggled to rise above a dark bank of cloud walling the eastern horizon, four figures in the dark uniform of the prison, with their shirts unbuttoned at the neck, their hands cuffed in front of them, were brought out on a reeved chain, led by a tall man in black, with a high black hat, followed by the Ordinary, reading aloud from a prayer book. Alongside the four prisoners were four warders, each carrying a stout embossed truncheon, while behind them came four militiamen, each with a bayonet fixed to his musket and glinting in the cold light of the morning.

Two of the condemned were youths of no more than seventeen or eighteen: both were weeping and begging their gaolers, 'Please, please, please!' even as they passed by the serried ranks of the watching prisoners and went through the doorway and up the steps of the lodge: the two others with them simply hung their heads, looking at no one, as if not wanting to be known themselves at that drastic hour.

The sheer cold-bloodedness of it all, the warders grim-faced but pulling on the chain, walking the four to their doom, the militiamen determinedly ushering them up the steps with their bayonets, was too awful a sight for some of the younger convicts: realising what they were about to witness, they began weeping quietly to see youths like themselves mount the scaffold, knowing the certainty of their end within a matter of minutes.

As the first of the doomed four appeared on the roof of the lodge where the gallows were set, he stood for a moment looking about him, as if bewildered to find himself there: and for a moment, it seemed as though he was contemplating jumping down and making his escape through the crowd of several hundred which had gathered on the great concourse below. Instead, he turned away and placed himself under the beam at the farthest end, with his face towards the throng: the three others meekly followed in their turn. Immediately, a man in black went quickly along the line, twisting each round to face inwards, at the same time drawing nightcaps from his pocket and pulling one tightly over the heads of each. Thus did Francis Tutter and Charles Hodgson look upon the world for the last time.

As the clock on the Shire Hall threequarters-of-a-mile away began to strike eight, a great murmur rose from the crowd on the concourse: the Ordinary began to read the Lord's Prayer, retiring from the drop as he did so: a signal was given, the bolt was drawn and a sudden, horrific shrieking of women and the deeper groans of men reached the ears of the prisoners in the yard. It was all too much for poor John Romble and William Stubbs: they could not look and lifted the fronts of their jackets over their faces, while Thomas Judd, and many of the others, turned their heads away and, if able, leaned for support against the wall of the yard, shocked to witness the awful spectacle as the four dropped in unison. Dick Dollery was too far back in the yard to see properly, particularly as the bandage which protected his wounded sightless eye covered half of his sole seeing eye: everything was a blur to him and only the whispered commentary of the man next to him revealed what was happening. For some two minutes, there was a dreadful jangling noise of chains, then silence: it was over. Almost as if that in itself were a signal, the women outside began to wail again.

One hour earlier, the door of Jem's cell had been pulled open, even before the dark had turned to light: three guards had entered, one at the rear carrying a lantern. As Jem stood to receive them, the senior guard with the lantern ordered him curtly to step into his boots and not to bother tying the laces. There was a brusqueness about them that they would brook no delay or protest: what they had come to do was to be done quickly and no fuss was to be incurred.

As he pulled on his boots and stood up again, Jem was determined that he would face the ordeal with as much dignity as he could muster, praying that his courage would not fail him at the last, the nearer they approached the gallows: for many a man has walked towards the gallows confidently till the sight of them caused his collapse: it takes a brave man indeed to go knowingly to his death without trembling and without his legs buckling.

Jem, however, managed to control his shaking limbs and no sooner had he stood up than he was spun round by the two guards, his arms were pinioned behind him, cuffs were rapidly fixed around his wrists and he was taken roughly by the upper arms and, as the third guard stepped aside, he was propelled out into the passageway. Curiously, no one else stood outside as he had expected: no other guards, no other prisoners: no priest: but then he had cursed the Church and particularly one Parson Petchey often enough in their hearing that the absence of a clergyman did not surprise him. They must have decided he would not welcome the Ordinary to give him absolution: or perhaps he was waiting outside with the others and he was the first they were to collect, he thought to himself: or else it was to be just him and no one else.

He could not prevent the thoughts which flashed through his brain: 'These are my last sights on this earth, my last memories. I am to be hanged before even the sun is up, without so much as a sight of the dawn or the new day. In ten minutes or so I shall be dead!' It was a dread he thought he had left behind on the battlefields of the Peninsula, before the fortress at Bergen-op-Zoom and again on the morning before Waterloo: but there, in Melchborough Gaol, it had returned.

The two guards had such a firm grip on Jem's arms as they hustled him along the passageway that, restricted by his leg-irons, it was all he could do to put one foot in front of another: even so, he made no protest and neither did he resist, but allowed himself to be hustled, dragged almost, as they went up the stairs. The two guards holding him did not utter a single word, neither to him nor to each other or to the senior guard with the lantern who led the way, almost as if to speak would be to alert others to what was happening.

They took him up a second stairway on to the first landing, then, curiously, up the stairs to the gallery above that and finally to the third gallery above that. Halfway along the third gallery, they stopped before one of the heavy iron doors: the senior guard with the lantern pushed it open and Jem was roughly bundled inside – into an empty cell.

'You're lucky, his Lordship, the Home Secretary, has changed his mind. You're not for the drop after all,' said the chief warder with a sneer. 'You're being boated to Australia for fourteen years instead. You're off to Van Diemen's Land – to build roads.'

At that, they all laughed uproariously and slammed the cell door shut, chalking up his number on the board outside: they were still laughing to themselves when they went off.

Jem just sat upon the chair at the hinged table top and shivered uncontrollably: although he had been spared the gallows, he did not know why: for when sentence had been passed, his mind had reeled and it had been several seconds before he had managed to recover himself. So he had not heard the judge's next words: ' ....I must, however, add that it has been a matter of most deep and anxious consideration to me to see whether I could distinguish between your case and that of the others. The sentence of death will, therefore, be recorded against you, instead of being formerly passed, the meaning of which is that it will be for His Majesty, and not for us, to determine whether your life will be spared and on what terms.'

SEVENTY-TWO

THE SENTENCES of the machine-breakers were such that they were discussed almost daily by everyone, rich and poor alike, in humble cottage and grand mansion, in the Wayfarers' Inn, the Carpenters' Arms, the Bull at Merchant Staplers, the Green Man at Lower Rackstead and a host of other places – and, most particularly, as it turned out, at Nadbury Hall, a Second Georgian mansion situated a few miles outside of Melchborough, owned by Captain Charles Sloane, retired, of the 73rd of Foot, now a gentleman of the county with an estate of eight-hundred acres: indeed, they were discussed at dinner by himself and his wife, Philomela, the very evening that Jem and the others were sentenced.

Philomela Sloane had been present on all three days of the machine-breakers' trials: so many others of the county's society had been there whom she knew that it was almost a social occasion: a person dare not miss it. Her husband being one of the Grand Jurors, she had been able to get a seat near to the aisle each time, only five rows behind the lawyers' benches: influence counted. It had pleased her, too, to be so far forward, with none other than her ladyship, the dowager duchess of Melchborough, seated with her two daughters only one row in front: they had exchanged nods: recognition mattered.

She had attended first on the Friday morning when the first of the machine-breakers had been put up, again on the Saturday morning, missing the afternoon sitting due to other commitments, but had returned to sit with her husband on the Monday morning in the spacious assembly room (he having completed his jury work) to see the last six put up, the six from Hamwick Dean – an extra trial, she had been told – and also to have tea with the rest of the Grand Jurors and his honour, the judge, congratulating themselves on a job well done, the calendar completed, before he departed.

She had sat through the hearing that morning, feeling the same sympathy for the poor wretches standing at the bar as many others. and had returned after lunch to hear the later indictments against two of the rioters. So many accepted their punishment with a stoicism that she found entirely unexpected, almost touching, though she had objected when one or two had made disparaging remarks about their King and their country, which she had not expected to hear.

However, she had to admit, she had experienced a pang of guilt that first day when the members of the jury had arrived at their very first 'guilty' verdicts so quickly: she hoped her husband, Charles, in the Nisi Prius court below, was deliberating more before announcing the verdicts there. Not that she disagreed with them: it was just that all the terrible crimes of which everyone spoke had been committed mostly against property rather than the person of the farmers or the landowners themselves: and, further, they had been committed by men and youths driven to desperation by neglect of their needs and open hunger.

The terrible sentences of transportation had shocked her: so many of them were young men, no doubt with young families whom they would leave behind to fend for themselves as best they could. Then had come the sentences of death against the three, the two youths and the older man: she had not expected that the judge would consider the crimes of which they were convicted warranted such an extreme punishment.

When she heard the dreaded words of the judge – 'The sentence of death will be recorded against you...' – spoken to the older man standing with the two youths, she had let out a loud gasp, the same as many others: surely, they could not resort to capital punishment for such crimes as these men were charged?

Something else troubled her, too, about one of them, the older man: it had troubled her ever since she had heard him speak when he had made his response to the scorn of the judge: for a common countryman, he had been almost eloquent. His voice, she felt, she had heard before somewhere, but where? Was it on her husband's estate perhaps? No, he had never been employed there. In Melchborough itself perhaps? Hardly, she and her daughters only ever went into the shops there by carriage and always pulled up outside them: and, if they needed to go from a milliner's, say, to a couturier's, they simply got back into the carriage and drove there, even if they were within walking distance of each other. For the life of her, she could not recall when she had heard his voice and the phrase, that phrase, '...your young kiddies.'

'Your young kiddies...your young kiddies...!' The same phrase kept going round and round in her head: she could not understand why her brain should have stored the memory of it so deep within its recesses and then suddenly to have brought it forward again: why? It was not a phrase she herself had ever used or was ever likely to use: it most assuredly came from the 'lower orders.' A maidservant might have used it in her hearing perhaps? But no it was a man's voice with which she associated it: a man's voice. But whose?

'The soldier who was in the dock today,' Philomela Sloane began, 'the man who fought at Waterloo – the one whom the judge said was a veteran of the wars against Napoleon, surely such a man should not have to face such a horrible end as hanging, not a man who has fought for his country with the great Duke himself?'

Captain Sloane forked the piece of beef into his mouth and regarded his wife in some surprise. 'Yes, it is very sad, my dear,' he agreed with a sigh, adopting his old army habit of speaking before he had finished chewing properly, 'but it appears from all the evidence and the witnesses that he was as guilty as the rest of them and was involved just as much in the breaking of threshing machines as the others. Whether he was one of those who set the barn afire was, I grant you, not established, but he was singled out as one of their leaders by one who was one of them. As a leader then, he must pay the full forfeit to the law.'

A younger voice, more contemptuous, now piped up. 'Surely mother, you are not taking up the cause of a bunch of rebellious clod-hoppers? They are just a bunch of country yokels. Peasants! They did what they did and now they must pay the price for it.'

Philomela Sloane's cheeks reddened: she had not expected her fifteen-year-old son to challenge her so openly and in such a derogatory fashion.

'It is just that the sentence seems too harsh,' she protested. 'I know threshing machines were broken and a barn was set on fire, but did they not say, in the case of this man, that he had helped put out the fire in the barn and that in the destruction of the poorhouse only that he was there and not that he actually took part in any of the destruction? Did not the vicar say in his evidence that he had asked him to stop the destruction? Surely that would exonerate him? That gave him a reason for being there? That was what he was doing?'

'It was all contained in the depositions which we read and which were presented, dear,' her husband replied with a shrug, somewhat puzzled by his wife's insistence on pursuing the subject and wondering if he were right to have allowed her to attend at all: women never did have the degree of detachment needed for such matters as ordering floggings or capital punishment and bringing wrong-doers to justice: only men had the wherewithal to do that. But then he had wanted her to see how the Grand Jury had done its work in bringing these country wretches to the bar of justice to face the full majesty of the King's law.

'Remember, dear,' he went on in a placatory tone, 'the owner of the barn was the lord of the manor, a magistrate himself, a Member of Parliament, an honourable man. He knows this man. They live in the same village. He swore on oath that he had seen the man in his barn when it was set ablaze. I do not think that you can have a better testimony against a man than that he was seen to be doing it. I know Sir Titus. I cannot say I like him, but I have sat with him on the Bench at Quarter Sessions on occasion. It is true, he is a belligerent man, I will grant you that, but he swore an oath upon the Holy Bible before he gave his evidence, and, if a man does that, then you and I and his lordship have to believe that he is telling the truth, the whole truth and nothing but the truth, so help him God! The fact that the fellow was a soldier at Waterloo, in the King's service with the old Duke, should make no difference to this case. It is sad but – ' He shrugged. ' – I myself was at the battle before Waterloo – at Quatre-Bras, at the cross-roads – and would have been there at the final battle, too, if I had not been wounded earlier, by golly, as well you know. But I have not gone about wrecking half the kingdom!'

The others fell into silence: they expected a further comment from their mother, but there was silence instead. It was her youngest daughter who noticed first, looking up from cutting her meat the twenty-year-old saw her mother was seated frozen, unmoving, as if as in a state of catatonic shock.

'Mother!' she cried, which made her husband, her son and her two other daughters, one twenty-two, the other twenty-three, seated at the table with their husbands, look towards her: then 'Mother!' again: but still Philomela Sloane sat there, mouth open, her fork, with a slice of potato upon it, paused halfway to her mouth.

'Charles, I have it! You have given it to me! That is where I heard it! That is where I heard him. After the battle! After the battle!' She let her knife and fork fall with a clatter on to her plate and clapped her hands in her joy. 'It was him! I know it, I know it! I am convinced! It was him!'

She was beaming now: indeed, such was her exuberance that had she not been perfectly composed a few seconds before, her husband and family might well have supposed she had been unexpectedly overtaken by some form of delirium.

It was not only the voice of the condemned man which had come to her, but also the words of the lanky, round-shouldered man who had been standing beside him at the bar of the court: '… a sergeant in the service of the old Iron Duke himself,' he had said, '…a soldier at Waterloo with the old Duke … with the Fighting Fours, the Forty-Fourth … in our village of Hamwick Dean …'

She had something to say and was determined to say it before she forgot it. 'After the battle, after the fighting was over, you remember, Charles, I told you, I went looking for you,' she blurted out. 'I had been told you had been wounded, but I did not know where you were. I have not told you this before, but I actually went looking on the field itself where all the fighting had been, where the battle was actually fought. I had the children with me. They were so young, I doubt that they remember it. After all, it was fifteen years ago, I do not think they even realised where they were or what had been happening. I could not shield them from the horrors and the dead men and the dead horses. My goodness, I shudder at the memory of it even now! But I was looking for you, dearest. I had to go – '

Her husband, indeed the whole family, were looking at her as if she had lost her reason: she ignored them and plunged on. ' – We went right through the middle of it. Oh, I was not the only one. There were many other women – wives of officers and non-commissioned officers, who went looking for their husbands that night and the next day – and, sadly, many poor creatures found them.'

Here she paused, allowing them to catch up with her racing thoughts and to picture their mother walking across a field of battle at night, peering into the faces of dead soldiers. ' – I remember I came across a picket of English soldiers. I had lost my way. I had gone too far down the hill when I should have gone along the ridge to the right and the sergeant who was in charge of the picket helped us – the children and myself. In fact, he told me where you might be. It is perhaps because of him that we are together now – for the fighting had been so fierce and there were so many dead and so many wounded, I do not think I would have found you but for him.'

The whole scene had come flooding back to her: the horrors of the field, the piles of dead, the moaning wounded, the threatening Prussians, her walk back through the Forest of Soigniés and the sights she had seen: the road one long, uninterrupted charnel-house of unburied horses, with pieces of broken carts and harness scattered about everywhere: the remains of tattered clothes which had once been soldiers' uniforms, strewn everywhere or thrown amongst the trees: shoes, belts and scabbards, infantry caps, broken feathers and Highland bonnets covered with mud, which had belonged to the wounded who had attempted to crawl from the field and who, unable to proceed farther, had lain down and died upon the ground. With them were the bodies of the wounded who had died in the wagons on the way back to Brussels and had been tipped out, to await a hasty burial.

When she had returned to Brussels itself, the streets had been choked with cartloads of wounded, their clothes stained with blood, hundreds of them, lying on their backs in the long wagons, while others on horseback and on foot made their way slowly and painfully past, many almost sinking with fatigue and loss of blood, seeking a hospital of some kind.

'At first I could not find you. There were so many wounded arriving,' she went on. 'The roads were crowded with them. The regular hospitals were soon filled and barracks, churches and convents were opened up and turned into temporary hospitals. Even tents were pitched on the open ground near the citadel and many of the wounded were taken there. There was such a multitude of wounded continually entering the town that many of the poor sufferers were just lying on the hard pavement or on the steps of the houses, waiting for assistance.'

Her husband, of course, did remember the fighting, only too well, in fact, but not the fighting at Waterloo itself: on the evening of the sixteenth, two days before, when the troops had retired towards Brussels, back towards Waterloo, he had been lifted on to a cart with other wounded and trundled back partway along the road, where he had spent the night lying on the cart before it was taken on the morning of the great battle a short way back from the lines to some buildings at the Mont-St-Jean farm, where the surgeons had set up for operating. Being an officer, he was one of the first to be seen: a naval surgeon had probed with forceps for the ball in his chest, fired by a cuirassier's carbine, and thankfully had pulled it out by hooking his finger underneath it in the usual fashion: then he had opened up the wound to let it bleed itself clean, before putting leeches on it to cleanse it further. After that, while the great battle was fought a mile or so away, he had lain all day in a state of fever with these gnawing at his putrefying flesh, not knowing night from day or life from death, before the assistant had sluiced the wound clean with water and sewn it up with twine. That night, Captain Sloane, of the 73rd Regiment of Foot, had again been loaded on a cart, so intermingled with a dozen or so others from that day's fighting that it was difficult to see which limb belonged to which man. The five men alongside him had died from the shock of their amputations: so that when the women coming out of Brussels, whom they had met it upon the road, on inspecting them for their own husbands, had presumed them all to be dead, too: neither his uniform nor his face and form had been recognised in the darkness. In Brussels itself, after the dead had been off-loaded, he had been taken to a school being used as a hospital and there, late the following day, his wife and three young children, returning from their battlefield search, had found him and she had spent the next two weeks by his bedside nursing him back to health.

'There were some Prussian soldiers looting the dead,' his wife continued, 'evil-looking fellows. They tried to stop us, but the sergeant of the Forty-Fourth came to my rescue, mine and the children's. He escorted us past them. He saved us, Charles! He saved me and the children! I believe they – ' She paused, seeking the right delicate words. ' – I know one of them who came towards us intended harm. I have no doubt he would have robbed me and perhaps harmed the children, for they were very surly fellows, being Prussians. The sergeant pointed his musket at them and that deterred them, sent them packing. Then he escorted us back towards Brussels. He left his post to do it. I firmly believe that the man I saw today is the same man who saved us, Charles! I am utterly convinced of it, utterly convinced of it. That man saved us and they are going to hang him! Oh, no, Charles, no. We must do something to help him, we must. A reprieve, Charles, a reprieve…!'

Around the table there was a stupefied silence.

SEVENTY-THREE

IT IS A MATTER of historical record that, of the near two-thousand men and youths of the Southern Counties brought to trial, two hundred and fifty-two were sentenced to death, of whom, in time, nineteen would be hanged and the sentences of the other two hundred and thirty-three commuted to transportation. The full number transported was five hundred, the greatest number from Wiltshire, a hundred and fifty-one, with a further hundred from Hampshire: others came from Berkshire, Buckinghamshire, Essex, Dorset, Gloucestershire, Huntingdonshire, Kent, Norfolk, Oxfordshire, Suffolk and Sussex. A further six hundred and forty-four were imprisoned, seven were fined and one was whipped.

In Jem's county alone, almost a hundred and fifty men and youths from the northern part had been arrested, of which forty-seven had already been tried at the Special Winter Assizes along with him and his friends, the others being left to the January Quarter Sessions or the Lent Assizes. At those, they would be put to the bar eight to ten at a time, batch after batch, for a brief trial, most lasting barely an hour.

The harshness of the sentences, particularly the death sentences against so many of the 'Swing' rioters, brought a storm of protest from all classes: clergy, doctors, lawyers and tradesmen of every type and status: almost before the trials were over, petitions were being organised by individuals and the inhabitants of numerous towns and villages throughout the country in an attempt to save those sentenced to death and to put in a plea for a reduction in the sentence of the others.

The only means of obtaining mercy then was to petition the Crown for a Royal Pardon: and, since no expenses were provided for the process of petitioning for a reprieve, it was confined to those suspects who knew about it or could afford it. Proof of previous good character might also be influential in securing a reprieve and a changed sentence and the public was well aware of that and so the wording of petitions tended to dwell on that aspect of a condemned man's character.

The concept of the Royal Prerogative of Mercy, that is, reprieving people who had been sentenced to death, dates back a long way in English law. At that time, the reigning monarch had the power of life or death over all his or her subjects and sat with the Privy Council in disposing of capital cases. In London, the Recorder of the Old Bailey would submit his report in person to the monarch and Privy Council with his recommendations for each prisoner. Outside London, the judges would send their report and recommendations to the Secretary of State after each Assize held in the county towns.

In March of 1782, the Home Office came into being and the Secretary of State for the Home Department, or the Home Secretary as he came to be known, became a member of the King's 'Hanging Cabinet,' which decided the fate of each person sentenced to death. The punishments imposed by the court, however, were not always carried out, since judges could temporarily suspend them until the case was heard by the King and his Cabinet, who had the power to award free or conditional pardons. In Jem's county, it so happened, over a five-year period, a quarter of those found guilty of felonies were sentenced to death at the Assizes, though, thankfully, nine out of ten were reprieved.

In the case of the 'Swing Rioters,' however, such submissions for leniency by counsel were likely to be in vain: the authorities, the establishment, the landowning gentry, were determined to take a hard line to discourage any further outbreaks of civil unrest in the New Year, a stand which had the support of both King and Parliament.

In general, however, public sympathy seemed to be with the rioters, though a motion moved in Parliament for a general pardon was heavily defeated by the House of Commons. The hope was that the sentences would be commuted to varying degrees of punishment, with the young, in particular, treated with leniency: though even the petitioners knew that, while their lives might be spared, the majority of them would not be permitted to remain in this country: in short, they would be transported.

Thus it was, one morning in mid-December, a letter, one amongst a hundred others, arrived at the London residence of the great Lord Melbourne, the Home Secretary, written in the untidy hand of Captain Charles Sloane, retired, late of the 73rd Regiment of Foot, to inform his Lordship that one of the condemned was a sergeant who had served with gallantry in the Peninsular War: an account of that 'gallantry' and 'his bravery' towards his wife and children on the night following the great battle at Waterloo was included.

'...*as a captain (retired) with the 73rd of Foot, who had the honour of serving with His Grace, the Duke of Wellington, at Quatre-Bras before the Battle of Waterloo,*' the letter began, '*I beg to inform Your Grace that the man so named, Jem Stebbings, late of the parish of Hamwick Dean, at present held in Melchborough Gaol under sentence of death after trial at the Special Winter Assizes, is a former soldier, like myself, who served as a sergeant with the 44th of Foot at both actions and, while on picket duty the very night following the main battle, was most helpful and courteous towards my dear wife, Philomela, and our three children, showing gallantry and great bravery at a moment of great peril when he came across them on the field seeking my wounded person. He personally interceded and escorted them to safety from the field when they were threatened by some of the Prussian ghouls who pilfered from the dead on the field after the battle. I have to say, Your Grace, that it is with a feeling of horror I record that one who is not the most guilty of the rioters should be the one to suffer the extreme penalty while some of the most guilty and of far worse character escape with comparatively no punishment. As a member of the Grand Jury of this county, I am, fully cognisant of the facts presented in the case against Jem Stebbings and, respectfully, would urge Your Grace to consider some other sentence more fitting. Although not knowing the man in whose cause I intercede, I can say with all honesty that I would hesitate to take away the life of such a man on the evidence presented, but rather would seek to banish him to Van Diemen's Land. I accept that many of those brought to justice, by their very deeds, are not worthy to live in England, but I fear carrying out the extreme penalty on him will do more harm than good in the village of Hamwick Dean and indeed in the county as a whole and humbly beg Your Grace to grant him leniency as I believe that such a man should not suffer the severe penalty which has been imposed upon him...*'

His was not the only plea for clemency: the day after the sentence had been pronounced, for time was of the essence if a reprieve were to be secured, Caleb Chapman had toured the village in a blustery wind and driving rain to obtain affidavits and testimonials from anyone who could write a sentence, anyone willing to say that Jem Stebbings had always borne an excellent character and outlining the events of November the twenty-second, twenty-fifth and twenty-sixth more accurately as he knew them and thus more favourable to Jem, all of which he then posted in a bundle to Lord Melbourne's Home Department himself.

Caleb Chapman even wrote to the vicar at Inworth, the Reverend Coleman, to solicit his support: *'Dear Sir, I have taken the liberty of wrighting to you about Jem Stebbings, who is under the penalty of death in Melchborough gaol, to ask, Sir, if you can speak to do any good for him it. A witness has sworn again him for being a part of the Inworth poorhouse riot, but there are nine out of ten people that will come on their oath that he was thear only to do good. As you may know, Sir, he was at the inn talking with the farmers when it all started up and could not have been a leeder. So, dear Sir, if you can make it convenient to send me a few lines, I will endever to satesfy you for it. – Your obedient servant, Caleb Chapman, now retired from churchwarden and parish constable, keeper of the Wayfarers' Inn at Hamwick Dean.'*

Reverend Coleman willingly responded and got the curate of St. Barnabas's Church, Higher Rackstead and the curates at Merchant Staplers and Lower Rackstead to sign it, too, so it contained four clergymen's signatures: *'We, the undersigned, beg leave to represent to your Lordship the case of Jem Stebbings of the said parish convicted at the Special Winter Assize held last week at Melchborough of breaking threshing machines and sentenced to the ultimate penalty of hanging. Jem Stebbings was found guilty with five others, yet while the others were sentenced to transportation of seven and fourteen years, he alone of them is sentenced to suffer the extreme punishment. We understand that he received a more severe punishment on account of his appearing at the trial as the instigator of the troubles in the parish when, in truth, Your Grace, we know that he was requested to become a speaker for the labourers in their meetings with the local farmers and that he competently and peacefully conducted negotiations successfully at which one of our number, Reverend Coleman, was present. We beg to state also that he is to all intents and purposes a farmer's labourer and that he has received parochial relief during the last and preceding winters as a distressed pauper and such has been the distress around us that he has been one of those frequently employed in what is called parish work on repairing the roads and performing related coppice work, and we, therefore, earnestly hope that your Lordship will consider that a commutation of his sentence into transportation with his associates in the guilty transaction will be sufficient to answer the justice of the case. – Yours obediently, Reverend Finias Coleman, vicar, St John's Church, Inworth: Reverend William Waters, curate, St John's Church, Merchant Staplers: Reverend George Snetterton, curate, St.*

Cuthbert's Church, Lower Rackstead: Reverend John Travis, curate, St. Barnabas's Church, Higher Rackstead.

There was even a change of heart by two of the farmers: Marcus Howie and Joshua Godwin both wrote leters to accompany the reverends' letter and, along with almost everyone in the village and the two hamlets, including all the farmers, signed the petition which was got up: only Amos Peakman refused point blank, but then he had been flung on to the dung heap by them: Titus Broake and his wife and Heginbotham, his bailiff, were not asked.

Though Jem's petition was the most pressing cause, the other Hamwick Dean prisoners were not fogotten and other petitions, suitably signed by all again, were sent to the King and to the Home Office on their behalf: Dick Dollery was described by his two petitioners – Caleb Chapman and Jack Tickle, mine hosts of the village's two inns – as, 'a sober, steady, civil, peaceable and industrious man…' and '… he has ever been a most kind husband and a most indulgent father to six daughters living.'

Three of Enos Diddam's previous employers in his latter roamings around the parishes looking for work gave him a character reference, describing him as an 'honest, trusty and faithful servant,' while Samuel Thorn, the baker, described him as 'honest, sober' and 'worthy of credit,' adding somewhat meanly: 'His father was in confinement as a lunatic for several years and a very small portion of liquor is known to produce a very similar effect on the mind of his son at times and so could be given as a reason to account for his rash behaviour of late.'

Henry Romble, brother of John Romble, who lived in the hilltop market town of Maydun, gathered a number of testimonials on behalf of his brother there, and managed to get his own employer to describe him as 'an honest, sober inoffensive man who had maintained his own business as a wheelwright till he was forced to go labouring during the recent time of distress…'

The seventy-nine-year-old Widow Judd petitioned the Home Secretary on behalf of her son, declaring that he had always 'borne an excellent character for sobriety, diligence and peaceable behaviour,' had always kept himself in work and provided for her, adding: 'If he is to be transported, I shall be deprived of his succour and assistance.' Reverend Coleman also wrote to Lord Melbourne himself that 'Thomas Judd has had shown constant attention to the duties of the Sabbath' and evinced 'quiet, peaceable and steady conduct at other times, and his kind and exemplary attentions to his mother, who from her age will probably never see her son again after his removal from this country.'

Even the mayor of Hamwyte got up a petition: '*My dear Lord, At the request of the clergymen of the parishes of Hamwick Dean, Lower Rackstead, Merchant Staplers and Inworth and many of their parishioners, I, Thomas William Poultney, mayor of Hamwyte, have undertaken to intercede on behalf of Richard Dollery, Enos Diddams, John Romble, William Stubbs and Thomas Judd, all of the parish of Hamwick Dean, near to our town, who were sentenced at Melchborough Winter Special Assizes on December the thirteenth to transportation over the seas, and also on behalf of Jem Stebbings, sentenced to the ultimate penalty at the same Assizes...*'

Five-hundred and forty-nine signed it, a few with their names, but most with their mark.

Petitions for the Hamwick Dean men were also sent to the Home Office from several other towns in the county, including one signed by all the clergy of the low church at Wivencaster, some of the bankers in the High Street at Maydun and every trader in that town and the same in Shallford and Levendon.

SEVENTY-FOUR

THE ACTUAL COST of the damage for the rioting across the Southern and Eastern Counties, when the final estimate was eventually brought in by those who tallied up such things, was estimated to be in the region of a hundred and twenty-one thousand pounds sterling, of which arson accounted for a hundred thousand of it as farm property, some industrial workings and poorhouse property went up in flames. Machine-breaking by itself, though counted in hundreds of broken threshing machines, added up to no more than eight thousand pounds, while general riot damage, the breaking of windows and doors and the like, totalled six hundred pounds.

Apart from the breaking of the machines and the odd barn and rick fire, the greater majority of the machine-breakers had regarded all that they had done as a relatively non-violent form of protest: thus, they were devastated by the severity of the penalties they received. The judges seemed not to care that, in punishing the men's wild fling of folly, as some called it, they also passed sentence not only on the men and youths before them but pronounced a doom equally as terrible on the wives and mothers and children and babes-in-arms who would be left behind. The judges were particularly down upon the number of men who, though not agricultural labourers, threw in their lot with them, that is, the wheelwrights like John Romble, the harnessmakers like William Stubbs, the cordwainer like Thomas Judd and the carpenters, joiners, smiths, bricklayers, shoemakers, shepherds and smallholders: where the law permitted, they were sentenced to transportation for life.

In one case, two husbandmen brothers, one thirty-two, with a wife and child, the other twenty-four and unmarried, supporting a widowed mother, still renting three or four acres, keeping a cow, and working for the neighbouring farmers as well, were also sentenced to transportation for life, notwithstanding the fact that their characters were exemplary. However, evidence given against them was that their opinions were dangerously radical and that they subscribed to William Cobbett's inflammatory *Register* and had been heard reading it aloud to twenty or thirty other villagers. Further, the youngest had carried on foot a petition for the reform of Parliament to the King while he was at Brighton, signed by a hundred and seventy-seven 'persons belonging to the working and labouring classes' of the area in which they lived: he was reported to have given some trouble to the King's porter by an importunate demand for an audience

Amongst those tried at the Epiphany Quarter Sessions at Melchborough were six others from Hamwick Dean, rounded up by a dejected Ephraim Simms, but only with the assistance of a dozen special constables from Hamwyte on warrants sworn to by Titus Broake, Amos Peakman, Marcus Howie and Joshua Godwin, though to their credit, the latter two farmers did try to withdraw their warrants, but the Hamwyte magistrates would not allow it. Thus, Thomas Thickbroom, the old ploughman's son, Job Stokes, Matthew Loather, Daniel Brady, the shoemaker's son, Richard Owers and John Harkness, not one above the age of twenty, began the New Year incarcerated in Melchborough Gaol, the only difference being there was no sworn evidence in any of the depositions against them that they had participated in the actual breaking of a threshing machine, or had attempted to fire any property, only that they had been present at the farms as part of the mob. On the day of the Epiphany Quarter Sessions, neither Marcus Howie nor Joshua Godwin appeared to give evidence

By then the mood of vengeance of the landed classes had abated somewhat: consequently, several of the younger labourers from that county, not then in their twenties, brought up at the same Quarter Sessions, though found guilty of machine-breaking, escaped with just two years' and one year's imprisonment with hard labour, respectively. The dismay of the public against the harshness of the sentencing manifested itself when eight-hundred would find themselves acquitted or bound over at the following Quarter Sessions and Assizes.

At the Melchborough Epiphany Quarter Sessions, Nathaniel Newman, having admitted his part in the machine-breaking at Titus Broake's, Amos Peakman's Marcus Howie's and Joshua Godwin's farms, was tried singularly for safety's sake and received twelve months' penal servitude in Melchborough Gaol, which was for his good conduct in turning informant. The turncoat blacksmith spent six months in Melchborough Gaol before a petition was got up by the magistrates at Hamwyte, including Parson Petchey and Amos Peakman, Marcus Howie and Joshua Godwin, as well as his wife, on account of the fact that he was ill: in consequence, he was released after eight months, though he did not return to Hamwick Dean, but went somewhere else. There were some who tried to find out where, but learned only that it was in the North, in one of the smoky cotton mill towns of which none knew the name.

Parson Petchey was not asked to sign the petition which the four other clergymen signed and did not agree to his curates signing their letter, though he did not prevent it: he simply remained aloof to it all: if his curates wished to sign a petition, then they did so of their own volition. Instead, Parson Petchey sat for two nights in his study, still with the gouge in the ceiling above his head to remind him, and composed a prayer, which, when he had completed it to his own satisfaction, he read it to his wife and then posted it to the Archbishop of Canterbury, supposing it might be spoken in as many churches as possible.

By coincidence, it fell in precisely with the Archbishop's plans: for, he had, at the request of the Privy Council, begun to give great consideration to preparing a form of prayer to Almighty God that would help to calm the troubled state of certain parts of the kingdom. Parson Petchey's composition arrived two days later and so was published and sent out under the Archbishop's signature to churches all over the kingdom, even as the scores of men and boys were being sentenced to death and others to transportation for life or fourteen or seven years. In Hamwick Dean at least, it was recited with genuine feeling by its author who had already broken his agreement to surrender part of his tithe.

'Restore, O Lord, to Thy people,' Parson Petchey recited to a near empty church the Sunday before Christmas, 'the quiet enjoyment of the many and great blessings which we have received from Thy bounty. Defeat and frustrate the malice of wicked and turbulent men, and turn their hearts: have pity, O Lord, on the simple and ignorant, who have been led astray, and recall them to a sense of their duty; and, to persons of all ranks and conditions in this country, vouchsafe such a measure of Thy grace that our hearts, being filled with true faith and devotion and cleansed from all evil affections, we may serve Thee with one accord, in duty and loyalty to the King, in obedience to the laws of the land, and in brotherly love towards each other.'

Other clergymen in other parishes, who were about to break their agreements, also spoke it equally as fervently.

SEVENTY-FIVE

FOLLOWING the Assizes, the keepers of the various gaols throughout the kingdom were required to transmit to the Secretary of State for the Home Department a list of prisoners who had received sentence of transportation and the terms of their sentences, as well as other details known. An order was then forwarded, directing to which of the hulks moored in the Thames or at Portsmouth they were to be conveyed to await transportation: for the latter purpose, three ships were being made ready in the roads at Portsmouth, specifically to convey the 'Swing Rioters' on the hundred-and-twelve to hundred-and-twenty days' journey to the other side of the world: the *Eleanor* for New South Wales and the *Eliza* and the smaller *Proteus* for Van Diemen's Land.

Early in the New Year, one week after his reprieve, Jem Stebbings was called from his cell and told to prepare for a journey to Portsmouth: irons were put on his legs, the lodge gates were pulled open and he was taken into Melchborough market place and locked on a coach for London, accompanied by a warder named Gossett and the clerk of the prison, a friendly and somewhat sympathetic man by the name of Edward Bean. He had hoped that he would be reunited with Dick Dollery and the others, but he was told that, for this journey, he would travel alone.

'The powers-that-be want you sent on your way across the high seas as soon as is possible,' Edward Bean informed him with a shrug. 'There is too much feeling against what has happened. Many say the sentences are too harsh by far for what you men did, but it seems someone has it in for thee and wants thee out of the way before the country goes soft and asks the King to pardon the lot of you.'

The journey to London was uneventful: it was only at the changeover, where the three of them had to walk from Aldwych across London Bridge to take another coach from Southwark, that the clerk unexpectedly, noticing his limp was more pronounced, offered to take the irons off Jem's legs, though leaving on the curb chain and the handcuffs. 'We have to walk across the bridge and the rattling of the chain will cause people to look at us,' he explained.

Jem did not care if people did stare at him. 'Do you mean to put them on again when we have left London?' he asked.

'Aye, we are obliged to put them back on you,' said Gossett.

'Then I will keep them on,' declared Jem proudly. 'I am not ashamed to wear the chain. If people wish to stare after us, they will. And if they ask who I am, tell them I am one of those who rose up against those who would starve us and who is being punished for it.' Bean and Gossett merely looked at each other and shrugged

There was much fussing at the inn where they took the coach to Portsmouth and many sympathetic comments were heard when it was learned that he was indeed one of the poor unfortunate rural rioters.

They arrived at the Gosport docks in Portsmouth late in the evening, well after dark: at least thirty other convicts were lined up at the reception point on the dock. Most had, unlike Jem, been forced to walk there over two days from one of the western counties and, like him, most had received the stiffer sentences of transportation, for life or fourteen years. It was as Jem joined the line of prisoners shuffling along the dock in their clanking irons, marshalled by the pushes and shouts of the accompanying warders and soldiers holding lanterns, that his spirits reach their lowest, particularly as men cursed and stumbled till they were all ordered to put their hands on the shoulders of the man in front so that they could move properly. Eventually, they descended the dockside steps and, six together in small boats, were rowed out under guard to the *York* hulk, an old dilapidated naval ship, still with two masts, but with her gun ports blocked and accommodation on the top deck for the warders.

Even to reach the high deck of the hulk, they had to climb laboriously up the nets thrown over the side, with no consideration being given that they were all still wearing their gaol irons. Once on deck, they were pushed and pulled into line by soldiers of the same regiment as those on the dockside and a posse of hulk guards: only when all were aboard and the row boats had departed for the shore were they unchained and ordered to strip off their clothes, which were then thrown overboard. Despite the night cold and the lateness of the hour, each man in turn had two buckets of cold seawater thrown over him and their skin scrubbed by two of the hulk warders with a long-handled brush till it was chaffed and smarting and, in some places, such was the warders' disregard for the torment they inflicted, even bleeding. Their hair was snipped as close to the scalp as scissors would allow by a barber from the town and they waited naked and shivering in line till all were done: then they were given their hulk clothing, a two-colour 'magpie' suit, one half of which was black and the other half yellow. A blacksmith then pumped up a small forge on deck and new wider iron rings were riveted around their ankles, connected by eight links to a ring in the centre, to which was fastened a strap reaching up to a leather waist belt which supported the links and kept them from dragging on the ground.

It was well after ten o'clock before they were ushered down into the lowest deck of the hulk, which was the darkest and most foul-smelling part of the ship. No fire was allowed to heat the cages in which they were herded, twenty to a cage, and, though issued with a blanket apiece, the night was so cold that, by morning, their shirts and the blankets were damp from the frigid air: everywhere men were coughing and spitting out phlegm, but no hot drink was given, neither coffee nor tea nor cocoa, only water. A quart of water was provided in a tin basin, but six were expected to wash themselves in it without soap: for that, they were charged a penny a piece: consequently, there were few takers.

The daily diet allowed a pound and a quarter of bread, but no butter, a quart of thick gruel, morning and evening, while on four days meat was added, but no greens or potatoes, with a quarter pound of cheese given on the other three days in lieu of meat.

What fresh air there was in the crowded quarters was provided by three air pumps, which had to be hand-operated day and night, which meant that each man was detailed at a certain time to take his turn at the handle, even if awakened from sleep: punishments for talking or supposed insolence would see the stint doubled. For one hour each day they were allowed a brief respite on the deck and then only to attend divine service, conducted by the hulk's chaplain from the poop deck, though all were still chained and watched by the warders and armed soldiers.

One time, when Jem and several others were taken up and detailed to whitewash the decks, he looked out across the cold grey waters of the Sound and, to his surprise, saw a hulk not fifty yards off which appeared to have a large assembly of small boys on deck, all lined up and standing still while they were being addressed by a man from a higher deck.

The warders, seeing his surprise, said, almost with a sigh: 'They are all boys caught stealing mostly, picking pockets, taking linen and the like. A few are orphans who have been taken wandering the roads.

They come from all over, every county, not just London. Some of them are only ten or twelve years of age. Still, some say they are better off here because they are at least fed and taught to read the Bible and to write and they do industrious work ashore during the day, gardening at the big houses or working in the town laundry.'

Jem's stay on the *York* was short: for two weeks he was taken by boat to a fort on the Isle of Wight to load large stones as ballast for ships, rising at five for breakfast at six and all boats away by seven. By the end of the second week, however, more and more men and youths were coming aboard each day, agricultural labourers from Berkshire, from Wiltshire, from Dorset. Finally, on the morning of February the fourth, he and four Berkshire men were called out, taken over the side, put into one of the same small boats as before and rowed again under guard some three-hundred yards farther out in the roads to a waiting ship, the *Eliza*.

Once on board, his convict's indent was recorded as 'widowed, two children, aged forty-three, a Protestant, can read and write': his trade or calling was described as 'ploughs, milks, reaps and mows,' to which were added the information of his previous convictions. His physical description was given as five foot ten-and-a-half inches; ruddy complexion, dark brown hair; hazel eyes, scar across back of left hand, walks with limp, crooked left arm.' He was then given his cooking, eating and drinking utensils, with a small keg for water, and taken below by the first mate to a ward in the middle deck where he was assigned with five others to a mess.

Jem's small party was the last to be taken on board: by that time, the ship had received its full complement of two hundred and twenty-four, a hundred and one of them from Wiltshire alone, put to the bar in batches of twenty at a time at the Special Commissions of Assize in Salisbury and then marched all the way to Portsmouth. So crowded was the ward to which he was assigned that hammocks had to be slung: the other rioters, being farm workers mostly, were not keen to sleep in a hammock and so avoided them, preferring the seven-foot-square bunks in which they slept four together side by side. Thus Jem was able to take one of the hammocks and was thankful for it, having got used to climbing into and out of one during his time in Melchborough Gaol.

Even as he lay in his hammock, listening to the working of the air pumps, Dick Dollery, Enos Diddams, John Romble, William Stubbs and Thomas Judd were themselves being taken from Melchborough Gaol by several 'flys' to London and there put on barges and taken downriver to the new gaol at Milbank, specially built to hold those awaiting transportation. After being held there for two weeks, they were put aboard a boat at Greenwich and taken round to Portsmouth and rowed across to the hulk *Leviathan* along with other rioters. All except John Romble sailed for New South Wales on board the *Eleanor* on February the nineteenth: he had to wait until mid-April before he sailed for Hobart Town on board the *Proteus* with ninety-seven others, the third and smallest contingent.

At that time, Titus Broake wrote a letter to Lord Melbourne: *'Your Grace, I had the good fortune to be the prosecutor of several men who invaded my estate and broke my threshing machines besides doing me a great deal more damage in attemptiong to burn down my barn. Your Grace will I hope appreciate that, what with the expenses of riding out with the yeomanry and the expense of the prosecutions, I shall be in need of a loan of a great deal, more than two hundred pounds to set myself straight. As I was the cause of these men to be convicted, the magistrates of the county inform me I am entitled to the rewards which you were so kind as to offer. I do most humbly and sincerely thank you for your prompt action in dealing with the agriculturalist by order of the King's proclamation. It was the wisest thing that could be done. I can say it was the salvation of the nation.'* In due course, he was paid his five hundred pounds.

Meanwhile, aboard the *Eliza,* Jem wrote his last letter to Jed and Thirza: *'My Dears, I am on a ship which is to take me to Van Diemen's Land right across the other side of the world. Believe me my heart is almost broken to think I must leave you behind. I am greatly distracted by the thoughts of parting from you who I love so dear. I still hold out hope in my heart that I shall see you both again, if not in this life then in the next. Be assured I shall do my utmost to return to you. If I get my freedom, I shall never be happy except I can be with you both again. – From your loving father.'*

Sadly, they did not receive it: that day they were walked by Ephraim Simms to the old, rundown poorhouse at Hamwyte, which now served the surrounding villages as well as the town till the one at Inworth could be rebuilt: the parish had decided it could not pay the keep of 'orphans,' particularly those whose father was being transported.

The next day, Sunday, February the sixth, the *Eliza* sailed for Van Diemen's Land on the morning tide...